Incomparable. Post-genre horror, apoc
philosophy of oil, crossbred into a new ar

China Miéville, author of
Perdido Street Station

Reading Negarestani is like being converted to Islam by Salvador Dali.

Graham Harman, author of
Guerrilla Metaphysics: Phenomenology and the Carpentry of Things

This brilliant and exhilarating work is a forensic journey across the surface territories of the middle east and into the depth of its sub-terrain. The earth is produced as a living artifact, gutted and hollowed out by nomadic war tactics, the practices of extreme archeology and the logic of petroleum extraction. Inventing a radical new language and reconceptualizing the relationship between religion, geology, and ways of war, Reza Negarestani philosophically ungrounds thus the very grounds of contemporary middle-east politics.

Eyal Weizman, author of
Hollow Land

It is rare when a mind has the courage to take our precious pre-conceptions of history, geography and language and turn them all upside down, into a living cauldron, where ideas and spaces become alive with fluidity and movement and breathe again with imagination and wonder. In this great novel by Reza Negarestani, we are taken on a journey that predates language and post dates history. It is all at once apocalyptic and a beautiful explosive birth of a wholly original perception and meditation on what exactly is this stuff we call 'knowledge'.

E. Elias Merhige, director of
Begotten and *Shadow of the Vampire*

Cyclonopedia is an extraordinary tract, an uncategorizable hybrid of philosophical fiction, heretical theology, aberrant demonology and renegade archeology. It aligns conceptual stringency with exacting esotericism, and through its sacrilegious formulae, geopolitical epilepsy is scried as in an obsidian mirror.

Ray Brassier, author of
Nihil Unbound: Enlightenment and Extinction

Reza Negarestani's Cyclonopedia is rich and strange, and utterly compelling. Ranging from the chthonic mysteries of petroleum to the macabre fictions of H. P. Lovecraft, and from ancient Islamic (and pre-Islamic) wisdom to the terrifying realities of postmodern asymmetrical warfare, Negarestani excavates the hidden prehistory of global culture in the 21st century.

Steven Shaviro, author of
Doom Patrols: A Theoretical Fiction about Postmodernism

The Cyclonopedia manuscript remains one of the few books to rigorously and honestly ask what it means to open oneself to a radically non-human life – this is a text that screams, from a living assemblage known as the Middle East, 'I am legion.' Cyclonopedia also constitutes part of a new generation of writing that refuses to be called either 'theory' or 'fiction'; a heady mixture of philosophy, the occult, and the tentacular fringes of Iranian culture – call it 'occultural studies'. To find a comparable work, one would have to look back to Von Junzt's *Unaussprechlichen Kulten*, the prose poems of Olanus Wormius, or to the recent 'Neophagist' commentaries on the Book of Eribon.

Eugene Thacker, author of
Biomedia

From the city of Poetry and Roses in Iran comes this bloody bypass surgery on the heart of darkness.

David Porush, author of
Soft Machine: The Cybernetic Fiction

Negarestani's Cyclonopedia meticulously plots the occult matrices of an archaic petrochemical conspiracy that has set the earth on its carbon-cycle feedback loop to Hell.

John Cussans, *Chelsea College of Art and Design*

Western readers can expect their peculiarly schizoid condition to be 'butchered open' by this work. Consider a grotesquely reductive, violent, comic yet still suggestive thesis: Islam is to Negarestani what Marxism is to Bataille. [...] Read Negarestani, and pray.

Nick Land, author of
The Thirst of Annihilation: Georges Bataille and Virulent Nihilism

C Y C L O N O P E D I A

complicity with anonymous materials

Anomaly

An anomaly deviates from a norm, is difficult to recognize or classify. *Anomaly* is a series which publishes heterodox, eccentric and heretical works. Mashing fact with fiction, poetry with philosophy, fish with fowl, *Anomaly* is a laboratory of unprecedented writings.

a re.press series

CYCLONOPEDIA
complicity with anonymous materials

Reza Negarestani

incognitum hactenus by Kristen Alvanson

re.press Melbourne 2008

re.press

PO Box 75
Seddon, 3011
Melbourne, Australia

www.re-press.org

First published 2008

British Library Cataloguing-in-Publication Data
A catalogue record for this book is available from the British Library

Library of Congress Cataloguing-in-Publication Data
A catalogue record for this book is available from the Library of Congress

National Library of Australia Cataloguing-in-Publication Data
Negarestani, Reza.
Cyclonopedia : complicity with anonymous materials / Reza Negarestani

9780980544008 (pbk.)
Series: Anomaly

A823.4

This book is produced sustainably using plantation timber, and printed in the destination market on demand reducing wastage and excess transport.

Printed similtaneously in Australia, the United Kingdom and the United States.

This manuscript might never have seen the light of day were it not for the tireless efforts of Robin Mackay in reading and editing it.

incognitum hactenus

Kristen Alvanson
Turkish Airlines Flight 002

Sunday, July 24, 2005

Drank 2 glasses of Sauvignon Blanc at JFK airport bar. Take a sleeping pill on plane. Think I took a painkiller earlier in the day and a couple Advils. Plane delayed on runway. In and out of consciousness – waiting, waiting, sleeping.

Wake up, we are in flight ... think still ascending as the plane is slanted upwards. Not feeling well, sick; get up quickly to go to bathroom ... must get to the bathroom ...

I feel faint, suddenly thinking that I may never wake up.

Next thing I remember is I am on the floor and the passengers in the seats above me are peering down. I tell them I fainted and they all make a buzzing noise that sounds like 'yeast'. Flight attendant is in front of me and is saying something. I can't hear as the floor is vibrating hard below me. I know I should get up. She reaches down to me and I pull myself up. Everyone is looking at me. I'm too out of it to be embarrassed. In the bathroom, I don't want to come out because they will all be looking at me. Sitting on the closed seat of the toilet and doubled over, closing my eyes and it's all red.

Flashes of red blood sparking with those amoeba-kidney-shaped images I get when my eyes are shut, only not blue or yellow-gold but red. I feel like I'm going to faint again. I'm going to throw up. Time passes. Blackouts of me. Seeing everything red orange. Close my eyes and red feeling of my naked body laying in globs of blood, coagulated and overripe blood. I open the door and the flight attendant is waiting for me. She hands me the burgundy sunglasses which must have fallen off my head when I fell. She escorts me back to my seat in the center of the middle section.

Beginning to watch a movie on my laptop: *Trouble Every Day* reminds me of one of Frank Zappa's songs. Thinking the movie will end soon, makes my libido ferment but I am not comfortable...

Monday, July 25, 2005

Traveling to Istanbul to meet a guy who goes by the Serpent-like initial 'ʅ' which is unpronounceable in English.

Planned to meet ʅ at the airport ... Arrive at airport an hour or so late; off the plane and carrying my heavy bag, switch hands back and forth to distribute the weight on my body. So far down the long corridor, walking briskly, eyeing everywhere, looking for ʅ. On the moving walkway walking faster and down the corridor, my palms are sweating. Down to the visa area to buy the visa for $20 easily and quickly move into the customs line. I pass through customs and then walk forward to collect my luggage, walk down one long line of carousels ... it doesn't seem right, so I ask a couple of workers where 002 from NYC is and they direct me to 7 at the other end. Check my Blackberry while waiting for my luggage to come out. Email from AG saying he has been to Istanbul. ʅ not to be found in the crowd; not that I know what he looks like as he said he doesn't take photos, but will be in a dark brown shirt and will recognize me. I make myself stand out, wearing what I am suppose to wear and pacing the arrival area so he can find me. While I am waiting, I am thinking about what the implications of ʅ not meeting me are. He doesn't show after a few hours so I proceed to my hotel in Sultanahmet area called Nena Hotel which ʅ suggested.

In the van the hotel has provided on the way to the hotel, I take in all the buildings and the vegetation, as I always do, and try to figure out what the terrain looks most like. For a brief moment, I think it looks like Belize, oddly enough. I take the flowers in the center of the roadway for Nerium Oleander and get excited. Buildings look prefabricated, with a squarish configuration. Streaming past lots of things, the sea to my right with many ships in it. Land to the left. The driver turns left and the van heads up a narrow cobblestone road with an incline and filled with buildings full of character. The vibes of

Turkey are distinct from anything else I have felt. I turn on my iPod and switch to the file with the pronunciation of his name he has sent me. It shows as the most played song. It is one of the things that the Germans call 'unaussprechbar'.

Check in. Room 302. Attempt to call ʅ on the number he gave ... no answer. ʅ was going to show me Istanbul as we have been in contact for a number of months since he emailed me though my Suicide Girls profile. He said he contacted me because I had listed a Warwick professor as a favorite writer and he knew him, was his friend. To make contact on SG you have to be a member and his profile was admittedly one of the strangest I had seen ... listing his location as Takla Makan, his favorite book as *Eden Eden Eden*, and not much else. Like the solid black image he had put for his profile picture, ʅ was evasive and rather shady ... the kind of elusiveness that turns me on. Istanbul was to be an adventure fun fun.

Try to email him through his SG profile, but it is now inactive.

Realization that ʅ is not going to show and I have no one in Turkey and a non-refundable / exchangeable ticket, with 7 days or so to kill. So decide to make the best of the situation – sightsee and get into some trouble, forget about work. I remember I had the black book with the gray and black back cover in my hand while I was waiting for my flight to board; was starting to read my book, the cover picture showing a body streched out into blackness.

1:36pm. Contact ʅ via his chemiical_pink email again ... admittedly, messages get pathetically desperate. No response. I remember one of the reasons I answered his initial email was because it had pink in it (almost as if he had created that email address just to provoke me).

Go out and wander around, find myself in the Blue Mosque ... legs covered with a green chador. Beautiful, gardens surrounding pretty, hydrangeas blooming like at home in New York. Too hot to be outside... back to the small room, on the way back, buy a bottle of Chardonnay and some takeout Turkish kebab.

I finally feel like I am going to wake up. Not quite sleepwalking, but confused about what time it is and where I am, I flick the still-full glass of wine over by accident and the wine hits the floor between the twin beds. Automatically react and stumble to the bathroom for a towel. Begin dabbing up the wine ... amazingly the glass has not shattered. Liquid running seeping under the bed, manage to turn the light on and look under the lifted bedspread. Half asleep half awake I see something under the bed. Wine's not going to get to it and I am done cleaning. It is filthy, and I think: go back to bed.

Tuesday, July 26, 2005

In the morning, sun shining through the orange tapestry curtains. I am displaced. I think it is jetlag. Look over on the other bed and see the dust-covered box and vaguely remember it was exhumed in the night from under my bed.

I remember ƪ's email when he said that being in the Middle East and facing its cultures and languages will be so foreign to me; it is like suddenly falling into the holes of a smoothly narrative story I have been reading for years – suddenly page numbers warp and things go missing.

While listening to *Lupus in Fabula* I begin to inspect the contents of the box. Items in the inventory include:

> A thick piece of writing titled *Cyclonopedia* with the name Reza Negarestani handwritten on it. Sections each paperclipped with various articles for each chapter, some pages nearly hidden under small yellow post-it notes or with margins saturated by handwritten notes and drawings in black pen and pink highlighter, making it nearly impossible for me to read. Looks like a manuscript.
>
> Business card for a computer repair shop.
>
> Box with bracelet inside.
>
> Old postcard with image of Istanbul and old Turkish text on front and more writing on the back, stuck to a Librairie de Pera card.
>
> A piece of paper carefully folded between the pages of the manuscript. It looks like a PGP encrypted public key but it is not complete. At the top of the paper a handwritten note: 'should send them my complete key.'
>
> Very old page ripped from a book with an image of girl, axe and a wolfdog.
>
> VCD of a movie entitled *J'ai pas Sommeil*.
>
> A photocopy of the book *Tomb for 500,000 Soldiers* by Pierre Guyotat.

Overwhelmed by entering a new level of adventure, I pull up the items of my new inventory one by one. Now I can sympathize with ƪ when he told me 'there is no pleasure more extreme than to be transfixed before a new item or to find a new weapon in video games.'

//

Note on top of one of the sections reads 'Ayasophia the Loge of Empress second floor'. Must go there.

Sun blades rolling on my Scandinavian skin. Visit Ayasophia and look around. I use the map, as I am getting help from the walkthrough I have bought to find the Loge in the Church of Holy Wisdom. Can't figure out how I should use the walkthrough by tracing the cryptic letters and icons on the floor and walls. All churches are built upon blasphemy, as ƪ once told me; I can easily see it here. The images of winged abominations in the corners of the ceiling. The upper floor is a freak show of saints and martyrs, all protected by the seal which ƪ once sent to me on the walls: a twisted number or a symbol starting level and then curling like the Mobius loop. It looks like the calligraphy writing on archways and on the outside of buildings here in Turkey.

As I am looking around on the right side with a number of tourists in the room, a guy approaches me and says, 'Do you speak English or Turkish?' And I say, 'Yes English.' He gets excited and says, 'Have you seen it?' and points to a corner where others are hovering. A small space with a black iron grate. Curious, I have to go look ... through the grate I look to the right and see the color gold. He asks me after I come back what I think and I answer: I saw it. Notice a Liquid-Sky-like Astro boy figure on the floor of the main level as I am leaving.

//

On the way back to the hotel I get my iPod out and put the headphones on. Walking back listening to the Music ... the sun is bleeding into my eye.

Burn Burn Burn Burn

//

Research Reza Negarestani online:

Find an article entitled 'John Carpenter's *The Thing*: White War and Hypercamouflage', but the text has been replaced with this message: 'This page is not available'; a piece with a similar title is in RN's manuscript. Even though the post is not available, the comments are, the first comment from RN reads: 'Identities are the plot holes of someone else's curriculum vitae (course of life).'

Ctheory, Hyperstition and Cold Me. I contact other contributors at the Hyperstition website who seem to have known RN for a relatively long time, but none of them have met RN or could offer much help. A contributor at Hyperstition asks if I know where Reza is because he has abruptly halted his regular contributions since June 18, suggesting to me that I contact RN's Iranian friends. I look for his last article (again it says, 'This page is temporarily unavailable'). Track a few blogs linked to on the Hyperstition website, apparently belonging to RN's Iranian friends. Some of the people I contacted suggest that RN must be a fictional invention of Hyperstition, a term loosely defined as fictional quantities that make themselves real. A few people think RN might be another avatar of one of the contributors at Hyperstition website, and finally some took Reza at face value, believing that he would need to host his site outside of Iran to circumvent any internet laws that could cause problems for him (maybe that's why he removed so many posts at Hyperstition).

Cold Me: apparently RN's personal website, strangely hosted by a German server ('nicht gefunden!' upon entering a wrong URL), hosted by a German guy named B who signs himself 'kraut-design' and seems to be paranoid about discussing RN. He replies back, 'Don't make trouble for reza.'

Is Reza male or Female? At first I thought female, but now I would like to believe that RN is male.

//

Later at Night. I wake up and the room is glowing orange like the way the drapes look when the sun is curtained. But as I focus the walls get progressively deeper in color and thicker and infinitely more desirable. There is an endless passion to be enciphered in this room for ever. The four walls are falling in closer and turning into orange red with layers of bodies and fermenting orange pink blood lubricating them. The window, I can't get it open.

//

This place continues to deteriorate. Hotel rooms have their own approaches to time:

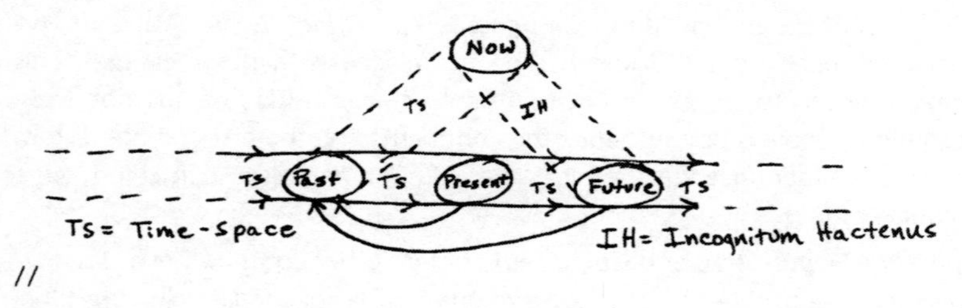

//

Wednesday, July 27, 2005

In the documents I found, there is a postcard and card from a bookstore on Beyoglu over in Takism, Librairie de Pera (Galipdede Cadessi 22, Tünel, Beyoglu). Everything sounds straightforward with this clue. Go to Takism, walk down the street past the fashion stores into the store where the lighting is dim and is an exact bibliophile twin of an alchemist's workshop. Think this is one of the places where books are chosen by the dust they attract rather than their covers; the more dust they collect, the more exciting they get. The store is rich with the fragrance of an old bath dissolved into dust and decayed paper. Ask for Guracor as his name is on the card. The owner is not there so I lay out the postcard and the notes written on the front and back for his assistant. He does not speak English well enough to understand me fully ... He points to the top text on the card and says 'no Turkey'. I say, Arabic? He shakes his head. I point to the handwriting on the card on the note section... and say 'Turkish?' and he says 'Not Turkish. Farsi.' He shrugs again and so I look around the small store and find the most curious old leather book sitting on the top of the pile of books in the corner with a strange curly symbol on the spine. Walk back up Istiklal Caddesi and stop in a café for a glass of wine. Ask the waiter if he can translate the writing on the postcard, and he looks at the image of the church and says 'Kelisa' then motions up the street. Weird, because the postcard says Danzig, so it can't be the church up the street. He looks at the text on the back and says the top text may be old Turkish ... but can't translate it for me.

//

I pull up a section named The Z. crowd. I search online for Nergal and Tell-Abraim, a place which seems to be significant and I find a picture of Nergal with a two-faced head, a hyaena and an eroded face of a lion; a scorpion stinging at his penis. I switch to page 261 as the page has been marked by a pink magic marker.

> [...] this was the last thing West told me before leaving Mosul with his sons to locate that Iranian oil smuggler and Doctor who claims to have the diaries of Ibn Maimum, the Persian occult-saboteur, guerilla expert and conspiracist who assisted the Fatemiun to overthrow the Caliphate regime in Egypt.' (1st Lt. Ali Osa, US 1st Battalion, 41st Infantry Regiment)

Everyone in this manuscript seems to disappear without a trace, I noticed this after reading a note on one of the page margins: 'ʖ, your contribution to the insanity reminded me of the ancient Greek and Latin scripts for plays in which the names of characters are attached to the text with their roles and the moment they should leave the stage by different means. In medieval theater, they called it Exeunt or 'they go out'. Characters were characterized by their exit-level. Pulp-horror takes this stage-flight to its full-fledged extremes. All that comes in must go out by any means possible.'

//

What is so bizarre about these writings – quite ironically, since I continue to read them – is that there is so much seething dread and outsized monstrosity prowling through the pages, yet there is no sex part, not even one penetration. Yet I continue to read.

//

On my back again in my DFA 1979 T-shirt, I catch the smell of the night's wine in my glass on the table between the beds. My head hurts between my eyes. Should get some Advil or I won't sleep but too frustrated to get up; Relax my mouth, relax my feet and toes, finally begin to feel some pleasure taking away the pain in my head, like the pleasure of losing your limbs one by one. The only thing that makes me feel secure is having repeated visions of being XXX … there is no body in my vision, there is something but I don't know what it is. I'm not sure if I vaguely think it is ⳑ, the writer of the notes, RN, or something else. It is not like making out with spirits but rather something which has stripped itself of body to be a better subject of penetration, to be obscenely deeper. Get up to go to the bathroom. Take 2 more Advils. Will I have enough to make it through the trip? Left hand downward tight between my legs and holding the tapestry bedspread I don't know why … At some point I give up as the drumming in my head takes over. Sleep the only way to stop.

//

Thinking maybe I'll do some more online searching on RN … but for the moment it takes too much energy to get the laptop and log on. I feel frustrated with this game.

//

Clues or evidences are the most relentless plot holes; they can even linger after a story fades away.

//

ʃʃʃ

Try to change my room as 302 is really getting to me. There is someone in the window across the way who keeps looking over at me.

//

I go out for lunch … TimeOut! Guide says Rami Restaurant is 'one of the district's classier options.' Up to the top floor, I sit in a room with a wooden floor which produces creaking sounds as I walk, making me believe that they are choosing not to repair the place to make it more authentic – the effect really works. Wonder whether, if an antique seller or a relic expert ran a restaurant, the setting would be like this. I start to read RN's text from page 41, 'Palaeopetrology: From Gog-Magog Axis to Petropunkism', not getting very far because the praying at the Blue Mosque is coming on over the loudspeaker and drowning my thoughts. The food bears the genuineness of a culinary relic. I head down the stairs to leave. The stairs have a unique space of their own, a Piranesiesque structure spiraling down. I notice a James Spader photo there on the wall. James Spader - my favorite cult actor! Wonder to myself, do celebrities carry around glossy photographs of themselves to autograph everywhere they go?

//

Walls are perfect objects to play things on, scenes which join together the sense of 'beyond' and the sense of confinement. As I am writing now in room 302, and picking up letters, the chair is swiveling and leaving marks on the wall. It looks like a constellation of inscriptions written on the wall with infinite barbs and talons; it is the shape of writing. I wonder what this manuscript's shape of writing is.

2th 3St

//

Business card for VEGA COMPUTERS in Maltepe; note on back says 'Laptop Repair 100£. Ozden will not erase the manuscript or notes'.

Take a cab very far, maybe two hours in traffic, to the shop to try and find the laptop and additional information ... Get there, finally find the place and present the card. The store owner disappears leaving another guy with me. I'm waiting and waiting for what seems like forever.

The shop is located in a bazaar with various stands. As I wait, the tattoo artist whose shop, Anatolia Tattoo, is at the end of the bazaar comes over and starts talking to me. He asks if I have any tattoos, and I tell him 'No'. Why don't I get one, he says. I think, well, after coming all the way to Maltepe, I should make the trip worthwhile ... I've been wanting a tattoo anyway. The owner finally returns with a black laptop that looks oldish. I ask him if I can turn it on to check it out. He wants me to pay first, but I say I want to test it. Boot it. The thing runs loud and loads slow. When the desktop comes up, I see there are the usual icons, clustered on a black and white grainy image of what looks like a human cutting himself open with a straight razor. As I switch to the start program, I see other programs too: mathtype, lindo, mathcad, maple, fuzzygen. Go into Documents, but when I try open one, I find they are all PGP encrypted. Every single one of them. I go on the search browser and check the history and bookmarks … find two links bookmarked in netscape browser and quickly write them down.

http://tinyurl.com/54wvo6

http://students.cs.byu.edu/~charlajw/Woodbury/givenNames.dict

Check the CD slot and find a CD. When the guy is not looking, I slip it into my bag. Then tell the owner I'll come back to pick the laptop up after I get the money. Think about it as I walk around and decide the laptop is really useless.

//

Back in the room with EFES beer as the store did not have Corona. If I can't pass through these plot holes, then it is the best to leave my own holes.

//

Pink magnolias, NYPL, NYBG, cherry blossoms in DC more pink … a fleshed out nipple, a bleeding heart, little girls' pink velvet ribbons, pink spaces, pink lights, my entryway and upstairs foyer bright pink glaze, a pink cashmere sweater set, Christos' pink, pink blush, or the lack of need for blush cotton candy Pink poodles or pink cats pink cover of Laches the most perfect shade of pink lipstick pink cd holders pink pearl necklace pink pearl earrings pink camisole pink highlighter pink Christmas lights and pink flowers- peonies, tulips, Christmas Catcus in bloom in my room, pinkish lilac, pink hydrangea, pink rose of sharons, rare pink poppies, carpet roses, spinning in pink flowers … begonia, spider flowers, cosmos, sweet peas, toadflax, moonwort, petunias, phlox!, butterfly flower, sun moss, wax pink, lilies, caprifoliaceae, pink wisteria, malvaceae, oyster plant in pink, floxglove, caryophyllaceae, heather, theaceae, magnolias, chinese crab apple flash by my eyes, Pink torrent

//

On another page margin, it reads: 'Xenopoetics has something to do with composing out of distorted materials. One page is missing, one or two lines are pseudonymously or anonymously quoted, one scene leaks from the future to the past, an object evades chronological sequences, a number turns into a cipher, everything looms as an accentuated clue around which all subjects aimlessly orbit, leading into an eclipsed riddle whose duty is not to enlighten but to make blind (aporos to the light). Fields of xenopoetics grow sporadically (until their final takeover of the work) around the regions overwhelming with a range of distortions from inauthenticity and corrupted authorship to structural holes (configurative bugs) and subterranean structures of hidden writing; xenopoetics does not necessarily insinuate adventurous modes of expression or prose.' Reading about misauthorship and inauthenticity, I am compelled to write on the left margin of a page of the manuscript, 'Am I not the most generous parent who feeds her children with her own meat?' ... trying to match my handwriting.

//

Walking back to the hotel I pass an outside restaurant ... lots of activity and laughter. Looks very nice, with wooden-framed furniture and qlim cushions ... makeshift comfortable couches, Turkish rugs on the ground ... women playing takht-e-nard and groups of young people smoking apple hookah. I think back to the only time I tried this in New Orleans ... pause for longer than a moment ... and again. Back to the room.

//

Blackouts ... seeing rodents climbing the walls, thousands, millions of them like wingless birds flying through the void. It vaguely reminds me of F. M. Cornford's *The Unwritten Philosophy*, on ancient Greek cosmogony. Also reminds me of the artist who makes those Rodent sculptures I saw at the Saatchi Gallery in London, like chunks of rats layered and layered on each other.

//

Hotel rooms are Xanadus of things to be exhumed (the cheaper the price, the more oddities you might run into). Found something very interesting in the wardrobe of 302 ... 'The concept of progress must be grounded in the idea of catastrophe. That things are 'status quo' is the catastrophe. It is not an ever-present possibility but what in each case is given. Thus Strindberg (in *To Damascus*?): Hell is not something that awaits us, but this life here and now.' Put it in my pocket. I must remember to check the reference to Strindberg online.

//

In the box, there is a beautiful Pink Mother of Pearl and sterling bracelet with a note attached: 'Sahereh, deav-sar doustat daram'. There is no address on the receipt, which is just marked Artist Bazaar and a handwritten note in Persian which reads 'nazdik-e masjed-e Abie'. I try the bracelet on; it fits perfectly and rests on the front of my hand in the most curious manner. I wear the bracelet to the Artist Bazaar to ask about the purchaser ... When

I get there, there is more than one jewelry store; so go jewelry-store-by-jewelry-store to see where it came from … come up empty.

//

A sun blister is growing on my left shoulder where I had been leaving my skin exposed. First irritation, but now days later after putting more lotions on it seems worse. Past the point of pink, it is raw red where the skin is open the size of a penny. Edge of round blister is black along most of the line. I sit in the room constantly touching it, pressing down the infection. Don't touch, I think.

//

It's true that the Middle East is the best place to go missing … the best place to get lost.

When it is time to leave and I can not find RN or 2, I decide to take the manuscript back to the US with the intention of publishing it.

for sorceress

CONTENTS

* The transcriptions of notes handwritten on the margins of the original manuscript pages have been indicated by a double dagger symbol and located at the foot of the page. The superscripted numbers in the text refer to the notes which are found at the end of the text as endnotes.

In Shawwal of 783 AH, Um al-Ghathra was in a caravan heading to Khurasan, Iran for trade and pilgrimage. Towards the end of its journey, the caravan changed its direction in the night because what they sighted ahead in their assumed direction was a lagoon instead of a city. After a few days of wandering, they headed back for their homes. Once settled, Um al-Ghathra began to write a treatise on what would later be called the Middle East as a sentient and living entity – alive *in a very literal sense of the word, apart from all metaphor or allegory. Time passed, and Um al-Ghathra heard from fellow travelers that the caravan had changed its course by mistake on that night: their orientation had in fact been good; what they had mistaken for a salt lake was a pyramid formed from a pile of tens of thousands of skulls from the recently sacked city, glowing in the light of a hundred tarred torches.*

BACTERIAL ARCHEOLOGY

NETHER, SUB-SOIL AND XENO-CHEMICAL INSIDERS

PALAEOPETROLOGY
FROM GOG-MAGOG AXIS TO PETROPUNKISM

11 March 2004. Somewhere amidst the fog of the Net, behind a seemingly forgotten website, in Hyperstition's password-protected laboratory — a location for exploring a diverse range of subjects from the occult to fictional quantities, from warmachines to bacterial archeology, heresy-engineering and decimal sorceries (Qabalah, Schizomath, Decimal Labyrinth and Tic-xenotation), and swarming with renegade academics, pyromaniac philosophers and cryptogenic autodidacts — there is a tumultuous discussion. The commotion has begun over the newly discovered notes of the former professor of Tehran University, the archeologist and researcher of Mesopotamian occultural meltdowns, Middle East and ancient mathematics, Dr. Hamid Parsani.

Arrested by SAVAK secret police during the Shah's regime in Iran for his unpatriotic activities and dissemination of fake versions of the glorious Persian history, Parsani was finally dismissed from Tehran University during the cultural reformation following the 1979 Revolution, for what was termed 'insufficient scholarship'. The notes — more like the contents of Parsani's office trash can than a notebook of an exceedingly disciplined scholar — have been disclosed to the Hyperstition team by one of Parsani's secret students who teaches ancient middle-eastern languages in one of the branches of Azad University in Iran. Before the Revolution, Parsani's sole book *Soorat-zoda-ee az Iran-e Bastan: 9500 Sal Nabood-khanie* (*Defacing the Ancient Persia: 9500 years call for destruction*)[1] was banned and entirely confiscated after hitting the public market. Even during the post-Revolution era, permission was never given for re-publication of the book.

After his academic exile (1981-1995), Parsani was hired by a middle-eastern architectural practice based in Egypt. Enjoying financial security over a long period, he eventually nullified his contract with the Egyptian company and established a private research institute which lasted for nine months. It seems the only aim of this institute was to acquire permission from Iran's Cultural Heritage Organization to cooperate with public bodies involved with archeological projects led by the government, and to assemble an elite team of reliable and professional archeologists, linguists and even mathematicians.

There is no information about Parsani's activities from 1378 (1999) to 1379 (2000); he suddenly disappeared along with his team. There are reports of illegal excavations near the rich archeological site Ghal'eh Dokh'tar in Gonabad, and diggings in Ahvaz and Kerman parallel to his disappearance. One reliable source, however, confirms that Parsani contacted a family in Kerman believed to be the descendants of the Haftvad dynasty, the legend of whose wealth and terrible fate is well-known in Iranian folklore. Before the rise of the Sassanids (the last dynasty before Islam in Persia), at the time that Ardeshir, the founder of the Sassanid dynasty, conquered all regions of Persia one after another, only this one mighty family succeeded in standing against Ardeshir. Stories tell of a giant gluttonous worm kept by the Haftvad family as their *familiar* and guarantor of their power. The worm was eventually destroyed by an assassin sent by Ardeshir who disguised himself as a merchant and poured molten metal into the acephalous mouth of the Haftvads' worm. The destruction of the worm is believed to have sealed a permanent curse on Kerman, according to which the city would eventually be destroyed.

Following his reappearance in late 2000, Parsani started a project for locating an artifact named *Khaj-e Akht* or the Cross of Akht. Parsani's old friends all confirm that they found him too unstable and lacking in the principled behavior expected from a scholar. An old colleague describes him regretfully as a volatile genius entertaining a bunch of teenage nitwits: 'He constantly rambles on about a heretic Zoroastrian mage and sorcerer named Akht who was mentioned in the Zoroastrian books *Denkard* and *Yavisht i Friyan*.[2] These rants concern Akht's cross, his last three riddles which went unanswered, something about the "flowing source of the black flame", an omnipresent blob worshipped by Akht-Yatu, a cult led by Akht during his lifetime and after his execution; and the Quranic references to Yajooj (Gog) and Majooj (Magog), the People of the Eye, and many other topics usually entertained only by unhealthily-minded teenagers, who, neglecting their schoolwork, think such nonsense to be "cool". His skin disease, I think, has entered a more serious phase.'

Another former friend of Parsani adds: 'Parsani's recent writings lack his former stylistic prose and sense of highbrow erudition; as if he has been struck by something he cannot digest, some stupefying discovery he is unable to dramatize.' While a former student noted that:

> The University remains in a period of post-Parsanism trauma, suffering greatly from the chauvinistic Persianism still simmering in ethnocultural, anthropological and political studies. So I suspect that these sharp reprimands against Parsani's recent activities are only natural; after all, you cannot deface the ancient Persia and walk unmolested among people whose sole scholarly concern is to replace the Arabic letter F with the Persian letter P. It is difficult for me, as one of Parsani's first students, to be forced into any premature conclusion as to whether his recent comments on the genealogy of Monotheism and the rise of the Middle East as an autonomous entity are really of any intellectual value or not. Nevertheless, his recent remarks seem to converge with the one and only book he published, but from an opposite direction. So they should be analyzed with equal enthusiasm to that with which we dissected and discussed that precious volume. Finally, I should add that what my other colleagues identify as defective prose or an unscholarly approach is more than anything a quite logical and predictable development of his initial writings into something appropriate to these theories and discoveries — something that perfectly matches the nonjudgmental monstrosity of his chronic illness, or what he used to call leper creativity. (Prof. Anush Sarchisian)

According to Parsani's notes, he discovered two carvings of the cross: one in Kerman province (recovered by the Haftvad family after the Bam earthquake in 2003) and one in the ancient city of Susa near Ahvaz, Iran. In 647 BCE, the Elamite empire was devastated and their capital Susa was sacked by the Assyrians on the pretext that an unnameable abomination was surfacing there, and that everything that came into contact with that benighted entity had to be eradicated. Ashurbanipal, the king of Assyria, triumphantly claimed that in order to purge the land and cleanse the kingdom of creatures, he carried away the bones of the Elamite people toward the land of Ashur, disinterred the tombs and exposed their contents to the bleaching rays of the Sun and even sowed the land with salt and quicklime. In Parsani's notes, this obscure abomination is identified as the main motive for the further archeological investigation that resulted in the discovery of the first carved relief of the cross, referred to as the Cross of Akht (خاج اخت: *Khaj-e Akht*). This first carving, according to the notes, had been partly eroded. Carved from gagates, approximately 9 by 20 centimeters, some of the cross's prominent features are strikingly similar to those of the Haftvad cross.‡

Different summaries of these features are found throughout the notes; in one paragraph, however, Parsani reveals some additional information:

Both crosses are identical in some curious way. Strangely this one has two

‡ How long has it been since I left this room?

handles instead of one. The cross is comprised of two main parts, the star-head and the handles. The basic geometry of the head consists of a decagon with triangles positioned on its sides, forming a star corresponding with *Khur* (the Sun). But one side of the decagon is forked, to form two handles. One can thus surmise that this is no Zurvanite star or Sun because the star is incomplete and lacks the full complement of ten triangles corresponding to the sides of the decagon. The last sacred triangle has been intentionally replaced by two vertical parallel lines, and this for reasons unknown. Recall, however, that they spoke always of a buried terrestrial sun which must be exhumed, a rotting sun oozing black flame, the black corpse of the sun. And even the name Akht corresponds to the incomplete form of the broken star. One must be blind not to notice that even the ancient Persian word *Akht* or *Axt* (اخت meaning pest) is a truncated form of the word *Akhtar* (اختر, Star, referring to the Sun) with its last letter (the letter R, ر) cut off.

The notes show that Parsani later obtained a handmade model of the cross in the city of Taft (Yazd province, Iran). The cross, Parsani's examination determined, belonged to the late fourteenth or early fifteenth century, having been made sometime after Timur's (Tamerlane) conquest of Persia:

> I came upon an artfully crafted model of the cross in the old bazaar, 18 by 7 centimeters, in silver, with a tiny lock between the two handles. After some considerable effort, I succeeded finally in opening the artifact, which revealed it to comprise a most curious and surprisingly complex contrivance. At every corner of the triangles there is one rotating joint; the last two joints connect the star-head to handles, the latter being in the form of knee-joints, whose rotation is limited to 90 degrees, so that fully rotated they form two opposing horizontal lines. This peculiar arrangement gives the additional property that the cross can be folded into something else, another entirely different artifact, another cross: In unfolding the cross, one rotates the joints on the triangles synchronously, with equal force distributed on the two handles, thus pushing them in opposite directions towards each other. Correspondingly, the decagonal head of the cross is folded to an upside-down *crux commissa* (the letter T), the cross of Nimrod and later St. Anthony's cross, initially used in worship of the summer Sun or Sun god, and used to hold human sacrifices during immolation. Am I mistaken in believing that the downward *crux commissa* bespeaks a symbolic emphasis on a rebellious position against the sun, whose symbol is an upward or normal *crux commissa*? The downward cross might also insinuate a descent, perhaps a fallen Sun god or the collapse of the solar empire. If the *crux commissa* is historically interpreted in terms of advent, the downward *crux commissa* or the folded Cross of Akht must be understood in terms of awakening. The horizontal part of this new artifact is

constituted of the cross's handles while the vertical part is formed by the folded triangles. On both handles, we find the Quranic reference to Naft (oil and petroleum),[3] on the left handle there is the word Yajooj (Gog) and on the right handle the word Majooj (Magog). Further, each corner of the star (each triangle) is marked by a number, inner vertices running from 1 to 8 (in this model clockwise and essentially stepwise), external vertices in an opposite direction (anti-clockwise) from 1 to 9. On each side of the triangles, there is an unfinished sentence or word. As final proof of the ingenuity of this unique device, once the triangles are folded to form the vertical part of the upside-down *crux commissa*, a complete sentence can be read: 'The day Yajooj and Majooj (Gog and Magog) come out, we shall leave them to surge like waves upon one another.' [The Quran, 18:99] (See Fig. 1, Fig. 2, Fig. 3-1)

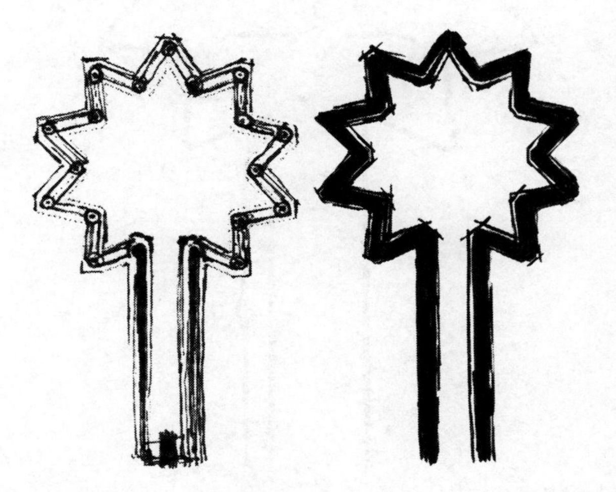

Fig. 1 The vertical dissection of the Cross of Akht with its vertex-joints; note that the joints connecting handles to the star-head are different from the joints used in vertices (left) sketch of the Cross of Akht (right).

The Cross of Akht has frequently been referred to as the broken star, the star-head and the black sun-flower. In his notes, Parsani personifies the Cross of Akht as an inorganic demon,[4] a sentient relic with the ability to numerically grasp all the undercurrents and inconsistent events of the Earth as modes of narration. 'It can narrate the plot holes of every planetary scenario, from textual narrations to global political narrations,' Parsani writes. The Cross of Akht can diagram planetary events of epic proportions in the form of various modes of heterogeneous or anomalous narration. Idolized by Hamid Parsani as the supreme 'narration lube', the Cross of Akht delineates the activities and ontogenesis of global dynamics according to the lubricating chemistry of oil or petroleum, i.e. it grasps all narrations of the Earth through oil. It is also used as a model for simulating the power formations and political commotions of the

Middle East. The cross of Akht, and its transformations, offer a diagram for the intrepid blasphemy of the Middle East against all modes of global hegemony and political models which perceive global dynamics as a whole.

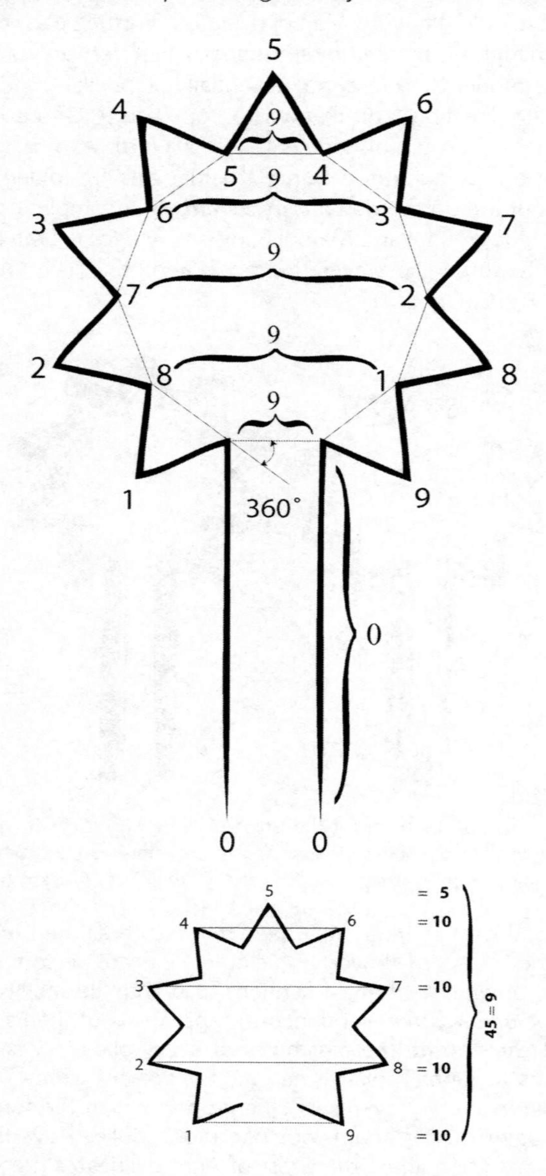

Fig. 2 Numerical anatomy of the Cross of Akht and its traits. Each outer vertex makes a nine-sum and ten-sum coupling with inner vertices. Handles of the cross are numerically designated as zero.

On another page, Parsani gives a further description of the Cross of Akht:

> All three crosses are in the form of broken stars with triangles mounted on a decagon. And all correspond with the oldest version, that degraded cross recovered from Susa's necropolis where even the skulls smelled of petrol. The Haftvad version of the cross is unique: Triangles have been carved over a circle which environs three intertwining snakes whose coils are aligned together along three intersecting axes (⅄). Part of the carved relief has been terribly eroded but the carving of the circle portrays reptilian scales of cycloid type which add to the enigmatic quality of this carving. Such reptile scales belong only to the Typhlopidae family of snakes whose rostral scale overhangs the mouth to form a shovel-like burrowing structure and whose tail ends with a horn-like scale. All this attests — if I am not mistaken — to the fact that the circle with its snake-ridden interior must be Akht's Wheel of Pestilence. These sinister visual connotations conspire with the physical weight of the Haftvad cross, lending it the aspect of a weapon rather than a mere diagram. Mace or club-like, it corresponds to the mace of Aeshma-Daeva who in the demonolatry of Zoroastrianism sleeps with Manushak, the lecherous sister of Manuschihar. The offspring of this consummation is a cult whose every activity, whether righteous or corrupting, damages the order of creation and reduces its wholeness. This is the cult upon which Akht based and assembled his own cult. In a religious scripture bequeathed to the Haftvad family by their ancestors, we find mention of thirty-six enigmas or riddles posed by Akht in confrontation with the Zoroastrian Yavisht from the Friyan family, three of which are left unanswered by Yavisht. The Zoroastrian scriptures, however, give a distorted account of this event, according to which there were only thirty-three riddles, all of which Yavisht answered in his duel with Akht. According to the Zoroastrian account, Akht was executed by Yavisht for being defeated in the contest. The Haftvad scripture suggests that the Cross of Akht, referred to in the text as the Haft or the Helve, itself constitutes the answer to the last three remaining enigmas of the thirty-six. In contrast to the Zoroastrian scriptures, Akht disappears after forging his cross over the course of fourteen Fridays.

Parsani's manuscript evoked a feverish excitement in Hyperstition's laboratory as the discovery of these notes on the cross of Akht — an artifact whose 'decimal gates' opened onto an inorganic pestilence, recovered from a forsaken perpetuity, or the 'Ancient Without Tradition' — coincided with one of Hyperstition's theoretico-fictional projects. This project explored nexuses between numeracy, Tellurian dynamics, warmachines and petropolitics, models for grasping war-as-a-machine and monotheistic apocalypticism, all in connection with the Middle East. The project had been temporarily halted for lack of what may be called 'technical elements for the fictional side': what was missing was some vehicle for transporting the theoretical carriers in their expedition, a narrative line with the appropriate authority to mobilize the fictional side of the project.

Moreover, Parsani's breakthrough was coincidental with an ongoing discussion at Hyperstition's laboratory crisscrossing between the Deleuze-Guattarian model of the 'war machine' and desert-nomadism. The discussion was spiralling through a series of theoretical confrontations between jungle militarism (the Vietnam war or the process of NAMification) and desert-militarism (War-on-Terror and Mecca-nomics). The discussion at Hyperstition ultimately developed into what would later be defined as 'blobjectivity', or the logics of petropolitical undercurrents. According to a blobjective point of view, petropolitical undercurrents function as narrative lubes: they interconnect inconsistencies, anomalies or what we might simply call the 'plot holes' in narratives of planetary formations and activities. To this extent, petropolitical undercurrents run through terrestrial decoding machines, conspiracies, polytics and Tellurian dynamics — or what, in Gilles Deleuze and Félix Guattari's somewhat aestheticist and conservative appropriation, is known as the *New Earth* (on the basis of what calendar, according to which planetary reference, is this New Earth announced?) A blobjective view necessarily diverges from the Earth as a whole towards an entirely different entity, an earth under the process of 'Erathication', as it was called in Hyperstition's laboratory. Erathication as a process spreads out in at least three directions: (1) the leveling of all planetary erections (idols?), or the attainment of a burning immanence with the Sun (the solar outside) and the burning core of the Earth (the Insider), (2) the immersion of the planetary body in flows and undercurrents, pushing the Earth towards full-fledged sogginess, (3) a participation with the Earth as a manifest degenerate entity for which wholeness is but a superficial distraction. The blobjective viewpoint was further developed through interminable online conversations between Hyperstition participants (whose 'real names' have been omitted here) :

X: The contemporary war machine (the grasping of war as a machine) does not correspond easily to the Deleuze-Guattarian model because: (1) it includes Abrahamic or monotheistic escalation and monotheism as stimulating components; (2) it has war as an object, or - more exactly - a product; (3) it consummates the technocapitalist oecumenon through synthesis with Islamic monotheistic enthusiasm (subtracting the supposed potential for 'secularization' as an Abrahamic teleology).

Z: This is precisely the Gog-Magog Axis: 'Consummating the technocapitalist oecumenon through synthesis with Islamic monotheistic enthusiasm (subtracting the supposed potential for 'secularization' as an Abrahamic teleology).' However, the Gog-Magog Axis eventually crosses technocapitalism with something else.

To grasp war as a machine, or in other words, to inquire into the Abrahamic war machine in its relation to the technocapitalist war machine, we must first realize which components allow Technocapitalism and Abrahamic monotheism to reciprocate at all, even on a synergistically hostile level. The answer is oil: War on Terror cannot be radically and technically grasped as a machine without consideration of the oil that greases its parts and recomposes its flows; such consideration must begin with the twilight of hydrocarbon and the very dawn of the Earth. In Dean Koontz's novel *Phantoms*, Timothy Flyte, a renegade paleontologist who considers himself a professor of Ancient Epidemics, is a tabloid writer researching an unnamable Tellurian sentient being which he calls the Ancient Enemy, responsible for devouring countless civilizations (the Aztecs and the Lost Colony at Roanoke, for example). A bio-chemical combat unit invites him (in line with *The Exorcist*, in which neurologists invite a vicar for assistance) to investigate the mysterious disappearance of people in a village in Colorado. The Ancient Enemy is a Thing-like bio-hazardous predator hunting organic entities, using bio-sorcery and mutating various organic phyla (possessing a soldier and turning his blood into a small lizard). The Ancient Enemy is trying to spread its gospel via three chosen characters. Timothy Flyte finds many parallel traits between The Ancient Enemy and The Antichrist. Examining the corpses of victims, he detects traces of porphyrin, a chemical substance common to blood, plants and petroleum. The Ancient Enemy or the Tellurian Antichrist which persistently looms in the Mesopotamian dead seas (originally where Antichrist comes from) or near the oceans is Petroleum or *Naft* (Arabic and Farsi word for oil).

According to the classic theory of fossil fuels (i.e. excluding Thomas Gold's theory of the Deep Hot Biosphere), petroleum was formed as a Tellurian entity under unimaginable pressure and heat in the absence of oxygen and between the strata, in absolute isolation — a typical Freudian Oedipal case, then ... Petroleum's hadean formation developed a satanic sentience through the politics of in-between which inevitably 'wells up' through the God-complex deposited in the strata (the logic of 'double-articulation, the double-pincer' according to Deleuze and Guattari), to the surface. Envenomed by the totalitarian logic of the tetragrammaton, yet chemically and morphologically depraving and traumatizing Divine logic, petroleum's autonomous line of emergence is twisted beyond recognition. Emerged under such conditions, petroleum possesses tendencies for mass intoxication on pandemic scales (different from but corresponding to capitalism's voodoo economy and other types of global possession systems). Petroleum is able to gather the necessary geo-political undercurrents (subterranean or blobjective narrations of politics, economy, religion, etc.) required for the process of Erathication or the moving of the Earth's body toward the Tellurian Omega — the utter degradation of the Earth as a Whole. As the ultimate Desert or Xerodrome, the Tellurian Omega engineers a plane of utter immanence with the Sun where the communicator can no longer be discriminated from what is communicated to the Sun. Xerodrome is the Earth of becoming-Gas or cremation-to-Dust. Ironically, this earth as a degenerate wholeness and twisted sentience overlaps with the Desert of God on which no idol may be erected. And in fact, the desert of God is manipulated on behalf of the Tellurian Omega and its undercurrents. Monotheism in its ultimate scenario is a call for the Desert — the monopolistic abode of the Divine. In the end, everything must be leveled to fulfill the omnipresence and oneness of the Divine. So that for radical Jihadis, the desert is an ideal battlefield; to desertify the earth is to make the earth ready for change in the name of the Divine's monopoly, as opposed to terrestrial idols. In line with Wahhabi and Taliban Jihadis, for whom every erected thing, so to speak, every verticality, is a manifest idol, the desert, as militant horizontality, is the promised land of the Divine.

In light of the emphatic horizontality of the desert in monotheistic apocalypticism, Deleuze and Guattari's model of horizontality or plane of consistency can only be a betrayal of radical politics and a hazardous misunderstanding of the war machine. However, in geological reality, monotheism functions as an involuntary host for Tellurian insurgencies and undercurrents; it is directly connected to the twisted nether regions of the Earth itself. Monotheism is a convoluted plane of tactics and meta-strategies for giving rise to Tellurian blasphemies or twisted strains of geological reality. In the wake of monotheism, Tellurian insurgencies feed on their corresponding, seemingly religious counterparts belonging to the monopoly of the Divine: the blobjective earth is nurtured by petropolitics, Tellurian Omega grows on the desert of God, ad infinitum. The Kingdom of Apocalypse or monotheistic desert is a passageway through which the Earth's ultimate blasphemy with the Outside smuggles itself in and begins to unfold. The apocalyptic desert is a field through which the Tellurian Dynamics of the Earth can be ingrained within anthropomorphic belief systems. Camouflaged within the formation of belief, Tellurian insurgencies can be safely accelerated, steadily developed, anomalously recomposed and intensified by anthropomorphic entities, either through religions or through seemingly secular societies whose economic systems are still rooted in monotheistic platforms. In which case, there is no worse Tellurian blasphemy than 'Thy Kingdom come'. Those Mecca-nomic agencies of War on Terror who consider everything that is not a desert a violation against the all-consuming hegemony of God crave for the desert as a ground independent of Earth and its inhabitants; but what they actually achieve, and passively cooperate with, is the Tellurian insurgency of the Earth toward Xerodrome. Ibn Hamedani calls this desert the 'Mother of All Plagues' — a plan(e) for reaching immanence with the molten core of the Earth and the Sun (the tide of extinction). On this plane, you either turn into diabolical particles, or evaporate and are recollected as cosmic-pest ingredients. This is exactly where religious extremists (the Taliban, with their ironically phallomaniac hatred for anything erected, for instance) turn into the stealth mercenaries of geological insurgencies, the cult of Tellurian Blasphemy (demonogrammatical decoding of the Earth's body). They want God but what they get is the Tellurian Omega — the incinerating immanence with the Sun and the Earth's core assembled on an axis which knows nothing of authoritarian divine and monopolistic convergence, the Hell-engineering Axis of the Earth.

It seems therefore that both the technocapitalist process of desertification in War on Terror and the radical monotheistic ethos for the desert converge upon oil as an object of production, a pivot of terror, a fuel, a politico-economic lubricant and an entity whose life is directly connected to earth. While for western technocapitalism, the desert gives rise to the oiliness of war machines and the hyper-consumption of capitalism en route to singularity, for Jihad oil is a catalyst to speed the rise of the Kingdom, the desert. Thus for Jihad, the desert lies at the end of an oil pipeline.

Or, once again, take Oil as a lubricant, something that eases narration and the whole dynamism toward the desert. The cartography of oil as an omnipresent entity narrates the dynamics of planetary events. Oil is the undercurrent of all narrations, not only the political but also that of the ethics of life on earth. Oil lubes the whole desert expedition toward Tellurian Omega (either as the Desert of God or the host of singularity, the New Earth). As a Tellurian lube, oil simply makes things move forward. Koontz's *Phantoms* is key for this movement toward Tellurian Omega, through the superficial (GAS pipeline), subterranean (Oil reservoirs) and deeply Chthonic (Thomas Gold's *The Deep Hot Biosphere*) Thingness of petroleum, the Blob. To grasp oil as a lube is to grasp earth as a body of different narrations being moved forward by oil. In a nutshell, oil is a lube for the divergent lines of terrestrial narration.

X: A lot to deal with here. Crude summary: Oil as

- Narrative organizer, definitely (heart of gloopy darkness). Parsani comes up with the idea that there is no darkness in this world which has not its mirror image in oil. The end of the river is certainly an oil field;

- Cybergothic convergence - demonic / technomic lube;

- Oil cult: pomo-leftist conspiracy-mongering greases into archaic slithering rites (Petro-Masonism and its trans-historical tentacles).

Z: Also don't forget that petroleum and fossil fuels exemplify another Telluro-conspiracy towards the Sun's solar economy: trapping the energy of the sun accumulated in organisms by means of lithologic sedimentation, stratification, anaerobic decay and bacteria in highly stratified sedimentary basins. In this sense, petroleum is a terrestrial replacement of the onanistic self-indulgence of the Sun or solar capitalism. Earth dismantles the hegemony of the sun on a subterranean (blobjective) level. If basking in solar economy overlaps with the annihilationist and nihilistic capitalism of the Sun, then how is it possible to dismantle this infernal hegemony without eradicating it? — Because an instance of eradication or heat-death is again a homage paid to the solar economy and its thermonuclear self-indulgence. Petroleum definitely plays the role of the alpha-mutineer in Tellurian insurgency against solar capitalism and its neo-Ptolemaic heliocentrism.

X: Koontz imagery is really helpful for grasping the 'Thingness' of oil, its subterranean cohesion as a singular anorganic body with its own agendas — assuming here that 'the blob' takes on an increasing 'agentic' function on the journey 'up-river' (from GAS-station to chthonic reservoir?). Bush and Bin Laden are obviously petropolitical puppets convulsing along the chthonic stirrings of the blob. Collapse all manifest policies and ideologies onto the Tellurian narratives of oil seepage. 'Even if Omega-Pest runs on hydrogen nanofusion, the concrete war machines chopping up contemporaneity are indubitably very oily' — Do you think there's a relatively clear way to specify the Oil / Islamic Apocalypticism relation that differentiates it more or less reliably from the residue of non-Islamic oil-fueled disorder on the planet?

Z: The oil industry is utterly ruinous for independent and non-collective oil producers. The problem with Latin America is that tradition, culture, society and language links them together but when it comes to oil, they are distanced from each other by different petroleum extraction policies and political agendas. In terms of oil, all that they share is poverty and ruination leftover. However in the case of the Islamic front, oil has been mutated into a kind of constructive parasite through which economical, military and political brotherhood emerges. For the middle-eastern countries there is a strategic symbiosis between oil as a parasite and monotheism's burning core, because oil wells up on an 'Islamic Continent', not a mere geopolitical boundary. In other words, Islam has made for a petropolitical network fueled and meshed by Jihad and its monotheistic protocols. Jihad positively participates with oil both in feeding blob-parasites (i.e. western and eastern oil-mongering countries) and fueling its body to propel forward. At this point, the Islamic Apocalypticism of Jihad as a religio-political event and the role of oil as the harbinger of planetary singularity overlap. Unlike Latin America, Islam has perceived oil as an ultimate Tellurian lubricant, or as the lube of all narrations on the Earth — a radical field of tactics by and through which Islamic war machines can slide forward, fuse with the Earth's flows and become planetary entities rather than merely religious agencies with a certain geo-political range. If, for monotheism, earth is not a planet but rather a religious object, it is because, as Qutb emphasizes, the earth itself moves towards the Divine by submitting itself to the 'exterior' Will of Allah; or in other words, the Earth is a part and property of Islam, that is to say, the religion of utter submission to Allah. Islam does not perceive oil merely as a motor-grease — in the way Capitalism identifies it — but predominantly as a lubricant current or a tellurian flux upon which everything is mobilized in the direction of submission to a desert where no idol can be erected and all elevations must be burned down — that is, the Kingdom of God. This act of submission to the all-erasing desert of God is called the religion of *taslim* or submission, that is to say, Islam. If oil runs toward the desert, so does everything that is dissolved in it.

X: Any possibility of developing or grasping the Gog-Magog Axis (the parties involved in War on Terror?) and its petropolitical undercurrents on numogrammatical models and abstract diagrams without losing oil as a narrative organizer?

Parsani's Cross of Akht, mapped as the progression of Gog and Magog (The Gog-Magog Axis) mobilized through the earth and lubed by oil had all the answers:

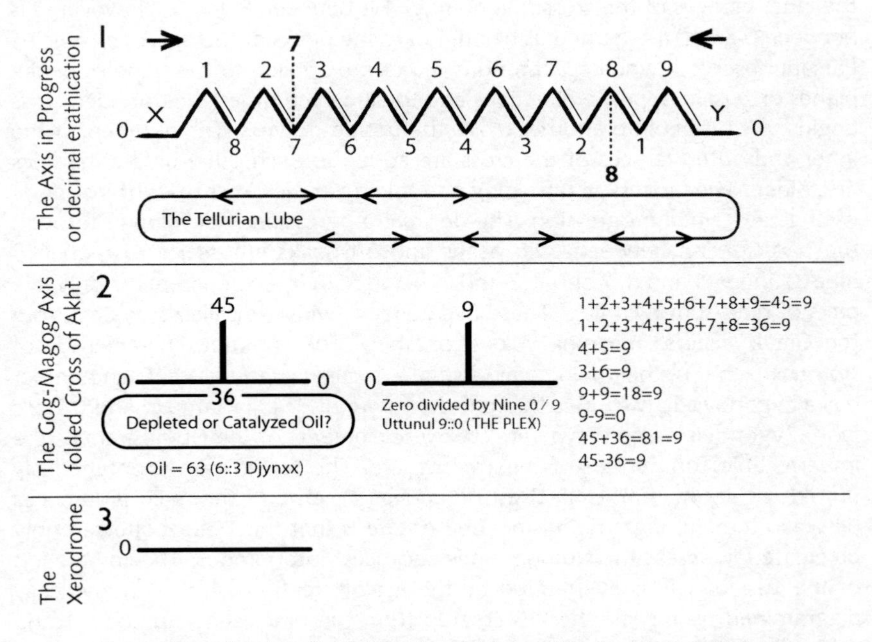

Fig. 3 Cross of Akht after folding / unfolding or the Gog-Magog Axis in Progress (Fig. 3-1) the Gog-Magog Axis or the consummated Cross of Akht (Fig. 3-2) the Xerodrome, the Desert or the militant horizontality of the Cross of Akht (Fig. 3-3)

Figure 3-1 diagrams the decimal progression of The Gog-Magog Axis. The decimal sequence of the unfolded cross (prior to its eventual folding to an upside-down T) is either 01234567890 (for the peaks) or 0123456780 (for the troughs). These numeric series correspond to a natural arithmetic sequence which is close to the 'Tree of Life', starting from 1 and incrementally progressing to 10. As an occulturally degenerate structure, the Tree of Life is based on a macho-orgasmic model of progression. For the Tree of Life, progression to 10 as the pure climax (the decimal monarch or Lord) is already a reduction because ten, in the same vein, collapses onto one (10=1+0=1). However, based on the folding of the Cross of Akht, or what is suspected to be the Cross of Decadence (the ultimate decimal blasphemy), the decimal sequence cannot be numerated according to a 'natural' numerical progression. The only relevant decimal progression for decoding the Cross of Akht or the Gog-Magog Axis is that of nine-sum pairs, or what is called nine-sum sorcery. Nine is delineated by its multiplicative imperfectability and utter evasion of unity or authoritarian divination, i.e. One or 1(0):

The nine-sum waves or folds of the Cross of Akht include 0-9, 1-8, 2-7, 3-6, 4-5, 5-4, 6-3, 7-2, 8-1, 0 (See Fig. 3-1) If selected from the troughs or the inner vertices of the cross, the number 1 is between 8 and 9. However, 1 is between 0 and 8 if regarded as belonging to the peaks or the outer vertices. As Parsani observed, when synchronous forces are applied to the handles or the planes of zero in opposite directions and toward each other, the unfolded cross begins to contract into another cross, the upside-down T. The numbers of the inner and outer vertices of the cross are added to each other as the triangles are folded. The process of unfolding and folding in the Cross of Akht manifests itself as a decimal progression. The decimal progression is developed through the participation between twin peaks and off-peaks whose sum is equal to nine: 0 and 9, 1 and 8, 2 and 7, 3 and 6, 4 and 5. In this case, there are only five pairs of nine-sum twinning. These five pairs or twins are called syzygies (from the Greek *suzugos* meaning yoked together). The common characteristic of syzygies — that is, their being a nine-sum — is called zygonovism. Each number has a zygonovistic twin; 6 is the nine-sum twin of 3, for example, and 0 is 9's twin. Zygonovism and syzygy are the basic elements of the Numogram as the imperfectible counterpart of the Tree of Life. The Numogram spontaneously unfolds as decimalism itself, 0 to 9 (See Fig. 4). One of the main differences between the Numogram and the Tree of Life is that the Tree of Life can only be created, whereas the Numogram is decimally autonomous. The completion of the Tree of Life is eventuated by the act of creation which is numerically diagrammed by the number 10 created from the preexisting numbers 1 and zero. Therefore, the Tree of Life corresponds with a pro-creationist obsession. The Numogram, however, is already there, lurking, as 9.

According to the Cross of Akht, flat extensions (the handles of the cross marked as X and Y) function as disjunctive zeros or planes of zero-tolerance. These flat extensions provide the artifact with a dynamism which is distributed through syzygies or through the triangles, folding them to each other. In Hyperstition's Erathicated version of the Numogram (Fig. 3-1), X and Y stand for Gog and Magog, and the artifact in its entirety is called the Axis of Gog and Magog. The movement of X and Y (Gog and Magog) toward each other is maintained by petropolitical undercurrents, or the flow of the Tellurian Lube (Oil) as written on the handles of the artifact. Nevertheless, the full dynamism of the Axis is a result of the clash between X and Y mobilized through their syzygies on the one hand and the participation between the Axis (including X and Y) and the Tellurian undertow or the petropolitical undercurrent on the other (see Fig. 3-1). Inevitably sliding on the oily bedrock or the Tellurian Lube, X and Y approach each other in opposite directions through a numogrammatic decimal progression. This is why Parsani refers to the Cross of Akht as the 'decimal timeline for the awakening' and sometimes, the 'terrestrial prognometer' — a term possibly borrowed from the Polish mathematician and philosopher Jozef Maria Hoëné-Wronski. The Gog-Magog Axis or the Cross of Akht is the numerical elaboration of the dynamism of Islam and techno-capitalism toward each other in the War on Terror.

The End Draws Near. If one side — either X or Y, Gog or Magog — progresses while the other side remains static, the decimal sequence can be counted (in the form of a countdown). Consequently, the dynamism of the Axis can be prophesied (4 after 3 after 2 after 1, for example). Once the decimal progression becomes prone to prophecy, Belief[5] will emerge as a legitimating tool for the dominant movement (viz. one of the decimal progressions associated with peaks or troughs). Such a belief transcendentally gives rise to an inexorable telos on the side of the dominant movement (of either X or Y), providing the dominant side with a legitimate ruling hegemony. The movements of X and Y can be expressed by their relative decimal sequences, either 01234567890 or 0123456780. On the Gog-Magog Axis, however, the risk of a dominant movement or hegemony is undermined by participations and interlocking movements triggered by petropolitical undercurrents. Here, numbers are not counted; they build each other by folding and twinning, by rise and fall, both continuous and discontinuous movements at the same time. In this case, opposite and synergistic movement is only possible on the sliding machinery of petroleum, as a lube with a dynamism and sentience of its own. For both X and Y, the movement is relative. *The End Draws Near* is dynamically ambiguous, it is the approaching of the other side from both ends. While for Capitalism, the other side is Islam, for Islam Capitalism constitutes the other side. Yet at the same time, earth is the other side for both Islam and Capitalism — not in the sense of exteriority, but an outsider which has crept in, an Insider. Although X and Y approach each other in opposite directions, they synergistically assemble the Gog-Magog Axis as a decimal disease system knitted on occult tellurian social dynamics. The Axis is assembled through the folding of the peaks and troughs as X and Y slide on their oily bedrock (call it Pipeline Odyssey or the Devil's Excrement) toward each other. Eventually, X and Y pleat their syzygies into one fold: the dam of the Gog and Magog, the 45-36 or 9-0 composition. The entire panorama is a complicity between X, Y and anonymous materials. (See Fig. 3-1 and 3-2)

> Bring me iron in large pieces, until it fills up the space between the two sides of these mountains. And he said to the workmen, blow with your

bellows, until it makes the iron red hot as fire. And he said further, bring me molten brass, that I may pour upon it. Wherefore, when this wall was finished, Gog and Magog could not scale it, neither could they dig through it. (The Quran, Sura 18)

NULLIFYING THE HEGEMONY OF GOG AND MAGOG BY ASSEMBLING AN INTENSIVE AND IRREVERSIBLE CLASH ZONE (See Fig. 3-2, 3-3). After all triangles fold onto each other and the broken star contracts into a downward *crux commissa* or an upside-down T, a new fold emerges between X and Y or Gog and Magog. This ultimate decimal fold is the zone of the most intense (conflictual) activities between Gog and Magog. Such intense conflicts will eventually make the protective dam collapse (see the Quranic reference above). In other words, these activities deteriorate the vertical fold. On the Axis or the Cross of Akht, this ultimate fold compartmentalizes or divides zeros as well as connecting them, generating a numeral couple (45-36) located between two zeros (see Fig. 3-2). But zero converges upon nothing. If zero is divided by any number, the result is zero. Therefore, the emerged region of Uttunul (9-0) corresponding with the Numogram sinks into zero (see Fig. 3-2, Fig. 4). The vertical fold decimally diagrammed as 45-36 or 9-0 cannot be tolerated by zero; therefore, it is flattened and leveled with the plane of zero tolerance. The final fold of the Gog-Magog Axis implodes on zero and the horizontally consistent desert of Xerodrome is born. The Gog-Magog Axis reaches utter immanence with the burning core of the real — the earth's iron ocean — and the solar tempest. (See Fig. 3-3)

Both X and Y (Gog and Magog, with their apparent references to War on Terror) creep forward on oil, and are petropolitical puppets. However, in terms of proximity to and contact with oil, one is increasingly exposed to the Tellurian Lube as The Gog-Magog Axis or the folded Cross of Akht illustrates (see Fig. 3-2): the sum of troughs is equal to 36 (3-6). As a nine-sum twin, 6-3 corresponds to Oil, which in Anglossic Qabalah is equal to 63. The number 63(=oil) corresponds with the region of Djynxx (the outside) in the Numogram which is also numerically mapped as 6::3. The outside or the other side is deeply swamped in oil.

[36 = AQ (Anglossic Qabalah*) = ABJAD: each triangle on a side of the decagon rotates 36 degrees, corresponding with the 360 idols in Mecca before the rise of Islam] (* Anglossic Qabalah or AQ[6] is mainly characterized by its alphanumeric efficiency and technocultural simplicity: A = 10 through to Z = 35 in strict stepwise sequence. DO WHAT THOU WILT SHALL BE THE WHOLE OF THE LAW = 777; AL = [A = 10] + [L = 21] = 31 = [ALEPH = 1] + [LAMED = 30])

In the wake of intense activities on the Gog-Magog Axis and its thirst for oil, the Tellurian Lube (petroleum) can be either consumed or catalyzed into something else. As the Gog and Magog fold their oily cradle through friction, opposite movements and anomalous participations, depletion or being burnt into something else becomes imminent. (see Fig. 3-2).

Zaynab bint Jahsh said, The Prophet (Mohammad) got up from his sleep; his face was flushed and he said, there is no god but Allah. Woe to the Arabs, for a great evil which is nearly approaching them. Today a gap has been made in the wall of Gog and Magog like this (Sufyan illustrated this by forming the number of 90 or 100 with his fingers). Someone asked, Shall we be destroyed even though there are righteous people among us? The Prophet said, Yes, if evil increases. Abu Hurairah said, The Prophet said, TIME WILL PASS RAPIDLY, knowledge will decrease, miserliness will become widespread in peoples' hearts, afflictions will appear, and there will be much Harj. The people asked, O Messenger of Allah, what is Harj? He said, KILLING, KILLING! (al-Bukhari)

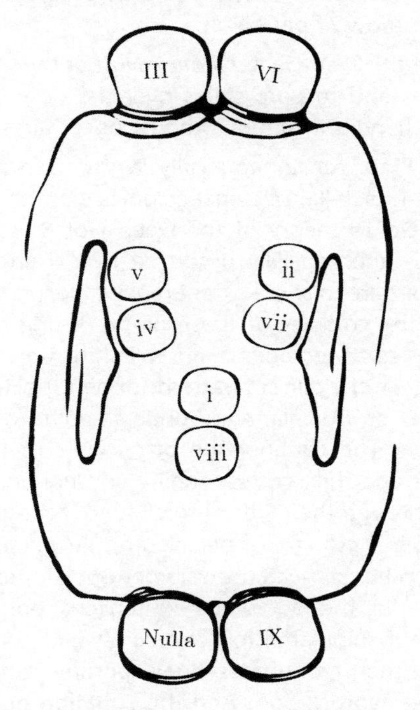

Fig. 4 Based on twinning, the Numogram (also known as the Decimal Labyrinth or Decimal Double) is constituted of three regions: Uttunul (0+9), the Time-Circuit (8+1, 7+2, 5+4) and Djynxx (6+3). Both Uttunul and Djynxx are diagrammed by their outsideness. The Numogram operates with nine-sum sorcery as opposed to the ten-sum construction or Sephiroth in the Tree of Life — imperfectability and inconclusiveness rather than perfectionism.

HYPERSTITIONAL ENTITIES OF OIL. Narrative avatars of oil provide petroleum with the opportunity to take part in different terrestrial panoramas. A taxonomic diagram of petroleum avatars in different narrations gives a more lucid grasp of oil as a component of contemporary warmachines and the War on Terror.

The major hyperstitional entities of the Ancient Enemy or Oil as traced by the ancient middle-eastern cult of the Blob or the People of Naft (oil) frequently referred to as *Naphtanese* (a cult reconvened after the execution or disappearance of the sorcerer Akht) are as follows:

I. Oil as a lubricant or Tellurian Lube, upon which everything moves forward, spreading smoothly and inevitably. Events are configured by the superconductivity of oil and global petrodynamic currents to such an extent that the progression and emergence of events may be influenced more by petroleum than by time. If narrative development, the unfolding of events in a narration, implies the progression of chronological time, for contemporary planetary formations, history and its progression is determined by the influx and outflow of petroleum.

II. The Hunter of the Dead Seas. *Ghoul-e Naft* or the Oil-fiend in old Arabic and Farsi fictions and folklore stalks over the deserted plains of Arabia. Terror of the oil-fiend is a cultural product of certain societies' folklore.

III. The Nether Blob. An anorganically synthesized material seething up from the primal interstellar bacterial colonies existing in the bowels of the Earth (Thomas Gold's theory of the Deep Hot Biosphere). According to Gold, since oil is anorganically produced by existing bacteria inside the earth, oil reservoirs are to some extent renewable, perhaps even inexhaustible. And since the colonies of these oil-producing bacteria are moving, oil distribution is not permanent and will shift. Rejuvenation, inexhaustibility and change in the current patterns of petropolitical distribution have immense impacts on our planetary understanding of politics, economics and militarization. The continuation of oil wars or their final end imply huge revelations and their corresponding consequences on every level of planetary life. Through the myth of fossil fuels, according to which hydrocarbons constitute the origin of petroleum, the classic pacifist slogan 'No Blood for Oil' can be connected to the petropolitics of porphyrin. According to Thomas Gold, the fact of the existence of porphyrin in both blood and oil has been manipulated to bolster the validity of fossil fuels theory. For advocates of the myth of fossil fuels, porphyrin is evidence of a common lineage, the hydrocarbon. And the equation of blood and oil — the assumption that blood is the price of oil — can only be grounded on the impoverishing theory of finite fossil fuels or the production of oil from organic matter. Oil pacifists support the totalitarian poverty of oil through the myth of porphyrin (fossil traditionalism) they accept.

IV. The Black Corpse of the Sun. Parsani's later occultural, archeological and theoretical notes elaborately follow the abstract diagram of petroleum as a broken star, a broken decagon with triangles arranged on its sides. Parsani insists that oil or the Tellurian pest worshipped by *Akht* (in the Avestan language of ancient Persia, the name means pest, or saturated by poison) and his cult, can be grasped numerically on the economic plane.

Fragments from the shape of the pest can be discerned and extracted from stock markets, trade meshworks and economic anomalies. 'The petropolitical traffic of the black corpse of the sun in the planetary sphere is creatively far more dangerous than the self-indulgent consuming hegemony of the Sun,' Parsani speculates in his 1989 essay, *The Rise and Fall of the Solar Empire*.

V. An autonomous chemical weapon belonging to earth as both a sentient entity and an event. Petroleum poisons Capital with absolute madness, a planetary plague bleeding into economies mobilized by the technological singularities of advanced civilizations. In the wake of oil as an autonomous terrestrial conspirator, capitalism is not a human symptom but rather a planetary inevitability. In other words, Capitalism was here even before human existence, waiting for a host.

VI. Hydrocarbon Corpse Juice: A post-apocalyptic entity composed of organic corpses flattened, piled up and liquidated in sedimentary basins (mega-graveyards); geologists suggest that if a high sedimentation rate preserves organic material, a catastrophic sedimentation rate (The Flood) would uproot, kill, and bury organic material so rapidly as to cut the porphyrin off from oxidizing agents which would destroy them in the ocean water. Oil as the post-mortem production of organisms is bound to death. Since its ethos — both origin and end — is purely teleological, whatever it inspires is founded on death and the logic of death and eventual conclusion. Oil as hydrocarbon corpse juice is itself a mortal entity which has been the source of ideology for petro-masonic orders and their policies — from OPEC to the agencies of War on Terror to pomo-leftists. It is a deity connected to what Thomas Gold calls 'the myth of fossil fuels' or exhaustible oil fields. It is extracted through teleological instrumentalization of the socio-political body of the Earth. (OPEC is suspected of being associated with other entities of the Blob as well). Pathological symptoms effectuated by the myth of fossil fuels can be summarized as:

i. The policy of underdevelopment and deliberate impoverishment bound to the exhaustibility of oil fields: since oil is dying we must use it wisely and calculatedly (the fallacy of prudent poverty).

ii. Inhibition of Excess and inherent suppression (connected to moralization of the earth aka the Green Judgment).

iii. Socio-political programming of planetary systems based on the depletion of petroleum. Everything oily has been manufactured with and toward death.

iv. Fueling economic systems on monotheistic platforms through melding with their belief-dynamics and apocalyptic politics: the exhaustion of the Earth's aqua vitae is a prerequisite for the Rise of the Kingdom. God can only appear (reveal itself) when all possibilities of the Earth are depleted. The Myth of Fossil Fuels is connected to the institutionalization of religious expectation and anticipation through the oil industry: with every thing we produce with oil, we get a little closer to God. The enigma of oil consumption or the exhaustion of the earth's energy is consummated by a substitute energy source, the Divine's absolute power. Oil depletion scenarios can be connected to a chronological time for which anticipation is not only a premature conclusion but also a participation in attaining what is anticipated, either through the activity of hope or the passivity of despair.

VII. Devil's Excrement ('I call petroleum the devil's excrement' — Juan Pablo Pérez Alfonso). Oil, a sado-conspiracist which (under)develops societies and economic systems through petropolitics to tear them apart slowly.

VIII. Gaia's aromatic juice.

IX. The Pipeline-Crawler (Go-juice), a code name for an autonomous vehicle which smuggles Islamic war machines into Western Civilizations — but on the other side of the panorama, it is in fact the slow penetration of other narrative entities of petroleum into the rectal depths of all political orientations, whether formulated on religious platforms or not. Gas plays its role as an assistant culprit in making great distances accessible by applying pressure, pushing the flow to the furthest recesses of the globe. Petroleum is at the same time the desensitizer, the lubricant and the object of intrusion.

X. Infernotron, or simply the US pyrodemonism with tentacles spreading through both thematic theism — the cleansing tide of the cathartic fire (the Greco-Latin theme chained to Aryanistic purity) — and the mess-engineering process of incomplete burning associated with Zippo Jobs in the Vietnam War and the NAPALM-obsession of the US war machine: 'I'll go to Hell with a can of gasoline in my hand' (Colonel West).

XI. The Holy Water (or sometimes, The Holy Gold): Oil is not for production purposes; it is only used for Islamic purposes (esp. for export):

> Do not make oil an object of export. Export all commodities through oil. Selling them oil without its Jihad-ridden by-products is an unforgivable sin. In the wake of contemporary petropolitics the slogan, 'We exported Islam with war' carves out a new meaning. (Jay, The Codex of Yatu)

CROSS OF AKHT AND ZYGONOVISM (NINE-SUM SORCERY): A NOTE ON THE CROSS OF AKHT OR DECADENCE AND ZYGONOVISM. According to Parsani's notes, he found a different model of the cross in the historic site of Bolaghi Gorge in Fars province, Iran. The time of discovery was three months prior to his final disappearance and the arrival of an international team of archeologists in the region to secure relics before the flooding of the recently constructed Sivand Dam. The elemental structural pattern of the cross is again a decagon, but instead of triangles, each side of the decagon hosts a regular rectangle, a square.[7] Degenerated into the most holy geometric shape among the Zoroastrians and late Zurvanists, the square was the glorified object of worship for monotheism, the geometric unit of the cube. After the deluge of excitement about the new discovery had subsided, Parsani writes: 'as I suspected, this is a religiously-corrected adaptation of the Cross of Akht.[8] Not only because the original cross is foliated by triangles whose properties are inexhaustible and correspond to deava-mahmi (the mahmi demon), but because this newly-excavated cross represents the unfolding of 1(0) or One and thus the incapacitation of the numerical mechanisms of the original cross. This systematically domesticated cross outlines the *Order of Farrah* or the divine wholeness, a carefully designed diagram to appease the onanistic hubris of the Dominus, the supreme being of monotheism.'

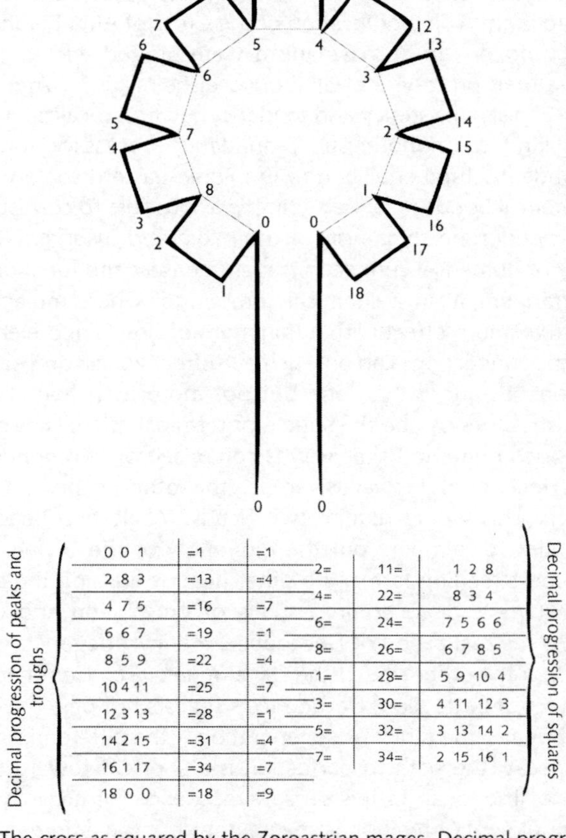

0 0 1	=1	=1
2 8 3	=13	=4
4 7 5	=16	=7
6 6 7	=19	=1
8 5 9	=22	=4
10 4 11	=25	=7
12 3 13	=28	=1
14 2 15	=31	=4
16 1 17	=34	=7
18 0 0	=18	=9

2=	11=	1 2 8
4=	22=	8 3 4
6=	24=	7 5 6 6
8=	26=	6 7 8 5
1=	28=	5 9 10 4
3=	30=	4 11 12 3
5=	32=	3 13 14 2
7=	34=	2 15 16 1

Fig. 5 The cross as squared by the Zoroastrian mages. Decimal progression of squares (sum of their vertices) follows as 11 [=2], 22 [=4], 24 [=6], 26 [=8]; 28 [=1(0)], 30 [=3], 32 [=5], 34 [=7], 36 [=9].

The following notes summarize some of the initial investigations of the 'religiously-corrected' model of the Cross of Akht, sardonically named *Khaj-e Akhteh* (the *akhteh* cross: the castrated cross) by Parsani (See Fig. 5). The Hyperstition team took the liberty of reassembling, editing and rewriting Parsani's notes, rendered incoherent by his indecipherable handwriting and lack of patience in completing sentences:

The pattern of the decimal progression (excluding the last segment) of the corrected cross as shown in the Fig. 5 (the table) is 147 (= 1 + 4 + 7 = 12 = 3). The number 147, as Parsani repeatedly points out, is the number of Genesis or the Order of Farrah which will be eventually secured by Ahura-mazda and his Brethren of Light. The diameter of the high-heaven, the celestial abode of the Divine, environing the primal oceans and the Earth as stated in *The Pahlavi Rivayats* (B.N. Dhabher, Bombay, 1913) is also 147(000) *farsang*.[9]

Parsani believes that the replacement of the triangle by an architectonically monolithic and consistent rectangle (square) dates back to the Sassanid dynasty before Islam. The modification of the Cross of Akht belongs to a period when dualistic notions in Zoroastrianism were purged and it was converted into a firmly-rooted prototype of all monotheistic religions. Apart from its explicit pro-creationist consistency and tendency towards localizability, the square represents a kind of monotheistic redundancy necessary for emphasizing completion and structural equilibrium. In middle-eastern sorcery and gematria (ABJAD), numerical bonds must be as simple as possible to correspond with the smooth and clandestine dynamism of nomadic and insurgent warmachines. The simplicity of numerical connections is structurally and functionally identical to a steric arrangement in a chemical compound, where molecular structure achieves the maximum effect with a minimum of bonds and elements. To this extent, numeric connections can only achieve effectiveness and efficiency when the connections are more than one but not more than two. This seemingly dichotomous structure can be the source of terminal multiplicity and divergent movements. Such numerical simplicity is comprised of two bonds, one on the side of imperfection or inconclusiveness, the other generating completion and perfection. This would require two heads. While one head is exploring the opportunities for pimping out the monopoly of the Divine (using it as a camouflaged pest-feeding farm), the other head is flushing the divine into an imperfectable (whole-degenerating) space of irresolution and unbelief. This arrangement is the realization of Decadence, a tide of degeneration rising and progressing from the other side. If the Decalogue or Ten Commandments concludes the ethics of perfection, Decadence suggests not only the degeneration of this ethics but also the ethics of degeneration — the differential cosmogenesis of decay. In decay, the path to perfection is a shortcut toward the perpetual degeneration of the ideal. In this sense, Decadence (of *deca* or ten) denotes neither the annulment of ten nor its sovereignty, but the differential perforation between them. The Cross of Akht with its broken star and its ubiquitous nine-sum sorcery — as in contrast with the sacred geometries of complete stars and the Tree of Life — is a diagram of Decadence.

Parsani writes:

> Such a pragmatically effective simplicity is sublimated in a triangle with one vertex fulfilling a 10-sum coordinate with the second vertex and engaging in a 9-sum coupling with the third vertex (See Fig. 6 and Fig. 8). In this way a triangle is able to generate a field of trisonomy and clandestine exploitation, or what the Zoroastrians called the tri-dotted perversion or the disorder of three dots (*abādixšayīh*: radical lie and lawlessness, هرج و مرج). Constituted of three dots (tri-dotted) or vertices, Trison is the unit of polytical and strategic double-dealing (or double-numbering); therefore, it opposes the Order of Farrah or wholesomeness of creation. In terms of Trison, it is easy to constantly retreat from one side and emerge from another side rapidly and without a trace, enmeshing a zone of radical betrayal. Mapping three dots as a triangle is a later geometric modification.[10] In early Persian sorcery, the Trison was pictured as a horizontal dissection of a spiral or a corkscrewing motion named *drēm*, meaning dot, dust and fish-scale. *Drēm* is an adjective describing the limitless impurity of *Druj* (The Mother of Abominations). In every Trison, the number that makes a ten-sum perfectionism and a nine-sum sorcery with the two other numbers (vertices) is frequently associated with a *Deava* (demon) of some obscure kind named deava-mahmi. No description in Avestan or Pahlavanic religious scriptures has been associated with this demon. Deava-mahmi, the demon of betrayal and treason, is a double-dealer who carries out an unknown mission on behalf of Ahriman (or the primordial Zurvan, the ultimate full body of Pest) on the side of ...

Parsani's note continues on to the next page which has been lost.

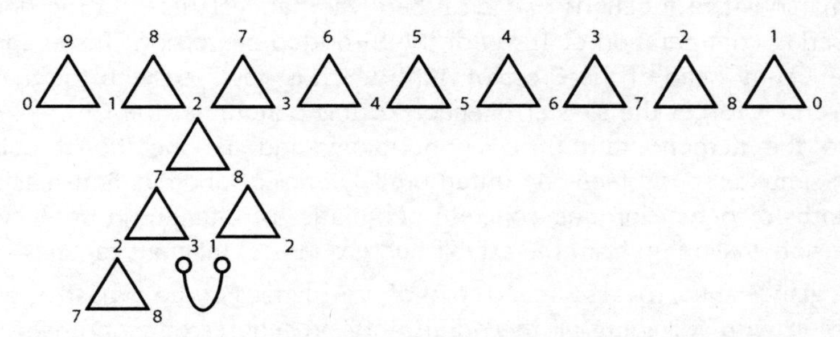

Fig. 6 A Terror Fractal. On Trison and the crypto-fractal structure of secret societies and terrorist cells see the rare copy of *Recent Research in Bible Lands* at Librairie de Pera, Istanbul, Turkey.

As Parsani notes, these numbers in a triangular format — making a 9-sum coupling on the one side and a 1(0)-sum completion on the other side — are associated with *deava-mahmi*, a betraying demon worshipped by a number of Zurvanite and early Christian-Mithraistic cults. According to Zurvanite and

Mithraistic texts, since Ahura-Mazda or the Divinity of Light is the second son of Zurvan (the timeless Aeon), he does not know the secret of genesis and creation. Therefore, it is Angra-Mainyu (Ahriman or — as oversimplified by Judeo-Christianity — Satan) who possesses the secret of creation as the first son of Zurvan. Deava-mahmi, one of Ahriman's disciples, steals the code of creation from Ahriman and meets Ahura-Mazda, offering him the secret of Creation which is ironically based on the knowledge and prudence of Ahriman.

The Mahmi demon has been addressed as *mesites* (*mesee'tes*)[11] or the one who does not play the role of balancing or stabilization (squaring) but instead that which in Pahlavi language is called *mianjig*. The subject form of the ancient Persian word *mayanjigih*, *mianjig* means in-between, the double-dealer — the intermediate Mithra who betrays both sides in favor of an obscure mission. As Parsani writes in one of his early essays on middle-eastern sorcery, 'Betrayal and cessation from all kinds of vision[12] is at the heart of middle-eastern sorcery and politics. Here, the obscurity of the betrayal's purpose is more dreadful than its perversion. The double-numbering mechanism of such betrayal has also been a source of inspiration for the configuration of the Middle East's political formations and state-nomad warmachines. Nevertheless, such betrayals are essentially subjected to an ominous dispersion, diffusing everywhere from monotheistic Beliefs to forbidden doctrines. In fact, nothing can survive the onrush of growing heresies once such betrayals become inseparable from everyday life. The Grand Betrayal or Mithro-Druj[13] is an all-inclusive invitation, a capital YES to everyone and everything, an ultimate welcome to all and everything; for this reason it secures a diffusive and affirmative epidemic power against which religion in general has no protective structure or immuno-agent.'

In another page of the same essay, Parsani continues: 'The clandestine and manipulative functions of radical betrayal manifests itself in the double-numbering configuration of Trison or the tri-dotted perversion. Trison appears as the leering head of the Cross of Akht which is obsessed with the triangle. One cannot forget the sinister direction of this panorama: the Cross of Akht is also the demonogram of palaeopetrology and its operational polytics. Trison simultaneously feeds on unfathomably ancient abomination-machines, labyrinths of perversion and concrete pragmatics of ultimate insurgency and subversion welling up from the established grounds of religious regimes.'

A glance at the royal seals and coins of pre-Islamic Persian dynasties, whose obsession with following all the purificatory procedures of monotheism and Aryanistic quintessence was unparalleled, reveals that such heresies encroached upon even the highest ranks of mages and religious foundations (See Fig. 7). A number of seals and coins bear the forbidden emblem of three dots (*drēm*) or Trison on one side and a boar on the other side. Note that the boar is a sacrificial animal for Ahriman or Angra-Mainyu (destructive spirit). Other seals, however, have the religiously corrected version of three dots — the order of four dots, the squaring process of perfectionism or Farrah, Swastika, the Wheel of the Sun, or later the Cross, whose architectonic power lies in the direction of well-being and settling affairs.

Fig. 7 Seals and Coins: Trison (three-dotted perversion) and Swastika (Squared perfection).

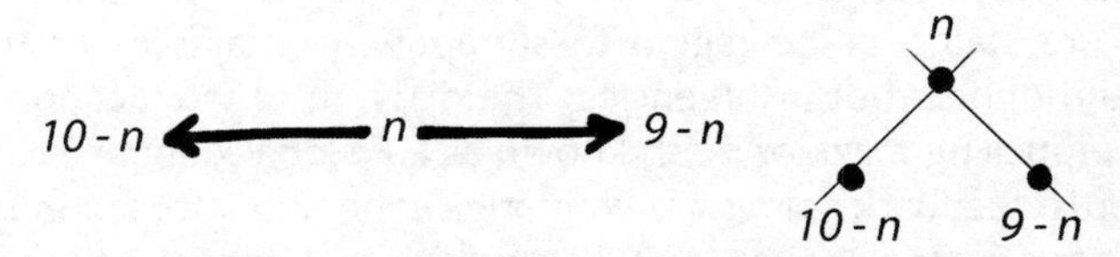

Fig. 8 The double-dealing or double-numbering system of Trison (right) and three dots of Trison as the polytical unit of the Middle East involved in the formation of States, policies, economies, minorities, religions, social populations, etc. (left) Trison can be geometrically grasped as a triangle.

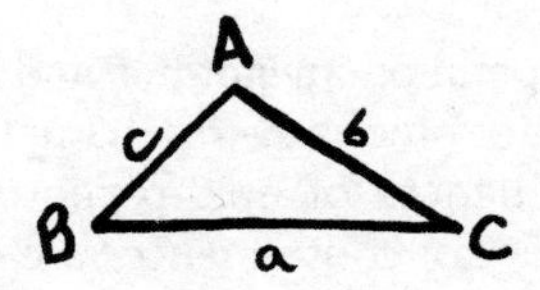

Fig. 9 Trisonomy can be laid out as c = a::b (if A=8, B=1, C=2 then a=1, b=6, c=7 then 7 = 1::6)

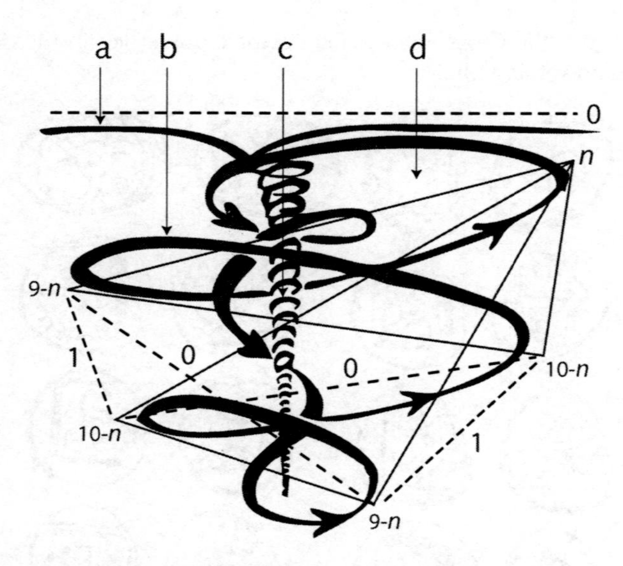

Fig. 10 A feedback Spiral mobilizes and prolongs the communications of Trisons, also known as the polytical units of the Middle East. Feedback spirals employ the Trison in middle-eastern power formation. Feedback spirals are constituted of (a) Creep (b) Hysteric Force (c) Compelling Force (d) Dracage Zone. The dashed lines mark cross-numerization (10-n, 10-n and 9-n, 9-n) and parallel numerization (10-n, 9-n and 9-n, 10-n) in Feedback Spirals. While the difference of cross-numerization is equal to 0, for parallel numerization the difference is 1.

In the articles he penned after *Defacing the Ancient Persia*, Parsani diagrams the communication between Trisons as the polytical units — or even the basic elements — involved in middle-eastern power formations, from the rise of obscure states in the region to surreptitious strains of nomadism to minorities and unheard-of insurgencies. The diagram of interactions between Trisons is a propelling maze or mesh known as a Feedback Spiral (see Fig. 10). In other words, feedback spirals are communication and interaction labyrinths responsible for bringing Trisons (or Trison-cells) into a consistent but eccentric field of action and movement. Parsani describes feedback spirals as fields of operation for everything that emanates from the Middle East, dynamic infernos through which politics is first debased and then is terminally multiplied: 'The feedback spiral is where politics is turned into polytics.'

This dynamic field of operation invigorates and prolongs the reciprocation between Trison-cells in autonomous forms harnessing polytical inclinations (or less technically, consequences of epic proportions) from Trisons. These produced polytical inclinations or consequences are differentiated from Trisons in a spiralistic form. On feedback spirals, the communication of Trisons is essentially vortical. Operating as a vortex, a feedback spiral pushes the functions of Trisons to catastrophically new fields of communication, tactics and strategy. Feedback spirals as catastrophe engines are in the form of vortex-spires; they are capable of transforming the double-dealing dynamism of Trisons into full-fledged polytics marked by multiplicative pragmatics and multifocal operational cutting edges. Trisons at the same time feed on strategy and tactics, epidemic sprawling (divergence) and focal concentration (military convergence), disorientation and despotism, transgression and order, nomadic migration and the State's organization. In feedback spirals, all these pragmatic orientations are simultaneously mobilized to produce a type of polar rotation or degree of differentiation necessary for the construction of a vortex.

In his forty page-long essay, *Mesomath and Power in the Ancient Middle East*, Parsani gives a disquisition about feedback spirals and how they transform Trisons into cutting-edge polytics. Feedback spirals generate obscure power formations whose engines are charged by their internal insurgencies and whose clandestine terror cannot be dealt with by any repression or external force. In the same essay, Parsani remarks that other countries (especially Greece and Rome) which had already encountered such a baleful religio-political military power-drive or extreme polytics had a name for it. They called this Gorgonite structure of combined extremums and polar anomalies of the Middle East *kuklos* or *kokloma*, the pulverizing wheel or snake-coil later appropriated by the Greeks as *kuklon*, the rotating debacle or cyclone.

What Parsani elaborates in his essay on feedback spirals and Trison can be crudely oversimplified and reduced to the following formulation:

Feedback Spirals generate mutual dealings or interactions between Trisons (i.e. Trison-cells). These communications are marked by simplicity, numeric effectivity and complexity, or more accurately, catastrophic outcomes. On a feedback spiral, there are always two Trison-cells in interplay with each other. The interaction between Trisons is always based on the general numeric arrangement of two Trison-cells on a feedback spiral. Each Trison-cell has three vertices, the joint (formulated as n), the decature ($10-n$) and the nonature ($9-n$). On a feedback spiral, Trison-cells always share their joint or the vertex numerically formulated as n. The communication of Trison-cells happens on two planes of cross-numerization (henceforth Cn) and parallel-numerization (henceforth Pn), two dynamic arms, simultaneously opposing and cooperating (see Fig. 10 for the interaction between Trison-cells on a feedback spiral and Fig. 8 for the numeric vertices of a Trison). Both cross-numerization and parallel-numerization are the elemental forces in the formation of ferocious polytical vortices.

At each phase of space-time progression, a directional shear is produced by the polarity of Cn and Pn between two Trison-cells. While Cn is always equal to zero, Pn is equal to one. The opposing and at the same time cooperative polarity between 1 and 0 results in a dynamic difference which is required for shifts in direction and the perpetuation of the spirals. This difference or shift in direction is manifested as a perpetual twist. The transition or displacement from one Trison-cell or one political unit to another is the cause of such a twist affecting the interactions of Trison-cells and the direction of feedback spirals. Produced by the inconclusive clash between Trison-cells, this twist in direction simultaneously programs a veering freedom and a concentric integrity in feedback spirals. Both the diverging and the integrating forces appear as spirals. While the former force is marked by hysterical deviation, the latter force is delineated by its hegemonic — or as Parsani suggests 'pioneering' — instrumentality. The entire structure resembles a cyclone from one end and a drill with a corkscrewing motion from the other. 'An entangled mess of vortical and corkscrewing motions, the structure of the middle-eastern political formations is a cyclone armed with a drilling and extracting instrumentality; it is a cyclone and an oil drill used for extracting unheard-of political and power formations,' Parsani writes in his essay on Mesopotamian mathematics and politics in the Middle East. In feedback spirals, hysteric and compelling forces always come together (see Fig. 10). The affect space between these two forces is called a dracage zone, a zone into which the twisted activities of these forces are channeled. The dracage zone is what empowers the polytical monstrosity of feedback spirals. Feedback spirals can horizontally migrate (creep) across the dracage zone.

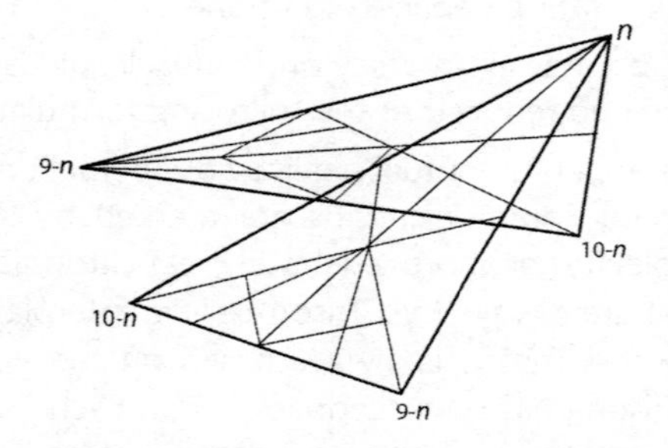

Fig. 11 Trison-cells generated in feedback spirals have had significant roles in presenting the Middle East as an alternative Earth dissident to the world's policies and their zeal in evolving chronologically and / or environmentally relevant political approaches to the world. Parsani refers to Trison-cells as populations with sheer polytical vectors, often associated with the emergence of minorities.

In feedback spirals, Trisons come in pairs to garner the most ferocious oppositions, which are essentially collusive. However, each Trison-cell is able to triangularly host countless Trisons in itself, either as allies or cells potentially causing irreversible internal fissions. Trisons within Trisons within Trisons — also known as children — form thousands, millions of feedback spirals within the mother-spiral. The crypto-fractal complexity of these feedback spirals can develop anomalies capable of undermining and derailing the centrality of the mother-spiral and eventually themselves. Parsani identifies this prospect as 'minority holocaust' or terminal propagation of minorities (see Fig. 11). A pregnant Trison is a population bomb of Trisons. Parsani notes that the traffic between Trisons (cross-numerization and parallel-numerization) as polytical units is the dynamic cause at work between the minorities and sects of the Middle East, between nomads and the states's stratocracy (prominent in the rise of stealth guerilla-states), middle-eastern monotheistic religions and minority belief-dynamics.‡

‡ mr. güracar from librairie de pera (should meet him for the book on the triangular anatomy of ancient secret societies. Should add a new section at the end of this chapter: Trison and the emergence of the Middle East)

S, just a brief note for now: re your first question, my room number is 302. Everything seems fine at the moment. The only people I have seen so far are the hotel staff, the hotel driver and the blond woman in pink Death From Above T-shirt (didn't know they are this famous) and underwear in the hotel room across the garden, right in front of my window. I had to drop the drapes in order to work. Will contact you after meeting Z and will let you know about the result. Thank you for everything. BTW, we should use PGP for certain emails.

PS1. Yes, I have already started writing.

PS2. Has the work for NYPL been done?

2 3333 04427 9147

Excursus I (Incomplete Burning, Pyrodemonism and NAPALM-obsession)

Parsani's sole recovered notebook is massively infested with personal notes and incomplete pieces which the Hyperstition team suspects are genuine love letters obscenely tied to his revelations in Bacterial Archeology, Palaeopetrology (esp. his notes which detail the reinventing of the earth as a machine solely designed to secrete oil efficiently) and other fields of what he calls 'heretic knowledge'. These supposed letters once again confirm his instability and precarious explorations which suddenly turned into demonic or perhaps suicidal flights. One of his friends critically describes Parsani as 'a bulging, syphilitic brain with a pink leech dangling at the root of it.':

> Sorceress, I have become more fanatically perfectionist in regard to my essays since we have met. I was expecting a more relaxed text but no, it is anything but relaxed, I am burning and what is left behind is not ash or smoke but tons of slimy, messy traces, oil, differentiated wetness, and muddled states of matter. If consolidation or 'economical participation and collectivity' necessarily expresses the underlying architectonic process of strata, then infinite quantitative and qualitative differentiation presents an entirely different process opposed to the strata, not in the sense of annulling it but rather manipulating the strata by diverting its organizational processes (which itself is a collectivization confined to repressive — conclusive — communication) toward Zero. Introducing 'organizing processes' to zero, however, never happens in its entirety; it is perpetuated as an infinite deferral, a prolonged intercourse with Zero. Differentiation is a misorganizing process not on the vertically developing axis of integrative wholeness but on virtual surfaces of zero. [21258] Such misorganizing processes, with an unholistic tendency towards differentiation, falsification, divergence, mess hysteria, terminal katabolism and disintegration in the direction of something other than death manifest flawlessly in 'incomplete burning'. When the substance does not burn completely, salvation or consolidation of all possible worlds is never possible. Incomplete burning blocks substance from escaping either to vapor or ash, it prevents substance from reaching salvation through the attainment of formlessness (matter). When burning is not complete, the substance starts to undergo a process of positive disintegration. Gasoline-derivative by-products of oil — mostly used in incendiary substances and fuel bombs — such as napalm never burn completely. This factor increases their duration of burning and spreading over a wide area, producing gel fireballs that last longer than liquid oil products by slowing the combustion as a result of gelling gasoline (mixing with metal soap) [14832]; it burns maliciously what it touches droplet by droplet and is not consumed. NAPALM will flow no matter how viscous you make it. As soon as it ignites, it sticks to objects, blurring them, pervading them, but never allowing them to evaporate or reduce to ashes, it keeps them

in another form to burn by remixing new flammable fluid substances as it crawls on different objects (organic materials in particular); as it spreads, its original form of emulsion (filamentary gels or stringy networks through gasoline) becomes stronger and consequently it becomes more dispersive. It is the only incendiary substance that thickens as it flows, NAPALM is not extinguished by water; it just flows more smoothly, facilitated by the flow of water [12969]. Love is incomplete burning. In my scarred, fevered skin, you see a person who belongs to sickness. In your healthy flesh, I see the same [2261].‡

---

‡ 555-3750 (6:45)

Emailing *S* on how to PGP all docs and folders and using ERASE instead of delete to wipe out the problematic pieces. (ASAP)

Should contact B to answer the incoming emails. (ASAP)

Sending M and A their articles on Islamic banking and interest, try to match their prose style … check their old articles to pick their punctuation and syntax style (avoid using the correct spelling of foreign words as they are not supposed to know certain words outside their language) (today)

It feels like this room is located in a cesspool outside the healthy flow of time.

Last month: trihexyphenidyl, fluorazepam

MACHINES ARE DIGGING

> Transpierce the mountains instead of scaling them, excavate the land instead of striating it, bore holes in space instead of keeping it smooth, turn the earth into swiss cheese. An image from the film Strike [by Eisenstein] presents a holey space where a distributing group of people are rising, each emerging from his or her hole as if from a field in all directions. (Gilles Deleuze and Félix Guattari, *A Thousand Plateaus*)

> The Earth has believed in her own myth. Time to open her up and take a look inside. (Hamid Parsani)

In winter 2001, an article entitled *Another Academic in Exile?* published in the Swedish multilingual Journal of Middle Eastern Studies addressed the slim volume of texts Parsani had written since his dismissal. Despite the shorter length of the essays — with a few exceptions — the subjects had been picked with an overly obsessive disciplinary calculation but analyzed according to a decidedly nonconformist approach to academia. However, every single one of these adeptly deft and dense disquisitions ended prematurely with what the article identifies as the 'oil tapping fallacy', alluding to the fact that nearly all essays written by Parsani during this timeframe end, whether relevantly or irrelevantly, with discussions about petroleum; that despite the diverse range of topics discussed in articles, they all lead to petrological implications, diagnoses and conclusions. Or as Parsani admits, 'the bottom line of my texts is in oil.' The article continues, 'If John Nash was disassembling everything he found in Time

Magazine into diagrams and equations in a schizophrenic search for alien intelligence, Parsani has opted for the reverse process; whatever he encounters is immediately traced back to only one thing, Petroleum. Books, foods, religions, numbers, specks of dust — all are linguistically, geologically, politically and mathematically combined into petroleum. For him, everything is suspiciously oily. Therefore, his approach is fittingly paranoid rather than schizoid.' Making an effort to disentangle Parsani's oil-thickened texts and to explain his obsession with petroleum-saturated subjects, the article elaborates how Parsani develops a political pragmatism of the Earth. The article argues that according to Parsani, only through this simultaneously political and pragmatic model of the Earth is the investigation of the Middle East as a sentient entity possible.

This pragmatic model, first expounded on by Parsani in his pedantic book *Defacing the Ancient Persia*, seeks to develop a concrete or Tiamaterialistic (to use Parsani's word) model of participation with and grasping of the Earth as a twisted zone of insurgency against the Solar Economy. According to Parsani, the Earth always plays the role of a subversive Insider against the Empire of the Sun, which has given rise to terrestrial orders, politics and modes of living based on its hegemonic stardom. In his writings, Parsani calls this model of insurgency and participation, which is sometimes equated to the whorled body of the Earth or non-holistic terrestriality, *Kareez'gar* (the holey *Kerdegar*; *Kerdegar* is the Persian word for Demiurge). The term *Kareez'gar* technically and linguistically eludes translation, but might be rendered, with considerable mutilation, as 'hole complex' — or, more accurately, '( )hole complex', since Parsani's original term implies both a destituted Whole (creation, genesis, state, etc.) and a holey-ness. The article notes that it is in his later works that Parsani fructifies his essays concerning the Middle East, petrological analyses, Islam and archeology by re-modifying and specializing *Kareez'gar*. Here, ( )hole complex or *Kareez'gar* turns into a pragmatic model of 'participating in and fathoming Oil as the Tellurian Lube of all narrations traversing the Earth's Body'. This model is particularly used to discuss middle-eastern lines of politics and communication, both internal and in relation to the rest of the globe, in terms of Tiamaterialism, Petropolitics and clandestine Mutiny. 'If the Middle East puts itself forward as a blasphemy against the world, it is because it has been composed by the *Kareez'gar* (hole-god), not the *Kerdegar* (whole-god),' Parsani writes in *Defacing the Ancient Persia*.

The article vividly explains the components involved in the complexity of ( )hole complex and the various aspects of the impact that ( )hole complex has on the emergence of new power formations, population dynamics and political distributions. It notes further that it is chiefly after the ( )hole complex and petrological enlightenment that Parsani cobbles his later writings about the Middle East together: 'In these writings, every subject that later leaps out from the most unanticipated corners of the Middle East as an unheralded epiphany of a demon or tribulation — forgotten political adversities, uncharted regions, warmachines, models of complicity, etc. — emerges from ( )hole complex. Anything middle-eastern can, it seems, only be examined, or even empathized with, in the wake of *Petrological Reason* and *( )hole complex*. These two unholy elements constitute the foundations of that instrument of inquiry and analysis identified by Parsani's bewildering term *Bacterial Archeology*. It is imperative for Parsani, in his approach to the Middle East, to make clear that everything related to the Middle East emerges, moves, diffuses, escalates and engenders itself through and out of the holey *Hezar'to* (A Thousand Insides; the Persian word for labyrinth) and the Petrologics of Bacterial Archeology,' the article notes, concluding that ( )hole complex and Petrological Reason are in fact images of each other in an obsidian mirror.

Holey Space, or more accurately ( )hole complex (connoting a degenerate wholeness), speeds up and triggers a particular subversion in solid bodies such as earth. It unfolds holes as ambiguous entities — oscillating between surface and depth — within solid matrices, fundamentally corrupting the latter's consolidation and wholeness through perforations and terminal porosities. For a solid body, the vermiculation of holes undermines the coherency between the circumferential surfaces and its solidity. The process of degenerating a solid body by corrupting the coherency of its surfaces is called ungrounding. In other words, the process of ungrounding degenerates the whole into an endless hollow body — irreducible to nothingness — and damages the coherency between the surfaces and the solid body in itself. To talk about holey spaces and Earth is to insinuate the Earth as the Unground. But what constitutes the ungrounding mechanism of holes? How does holey space degenerate the Earth as a ground for supporting formations, establishments, modes of dwelling and governance? Deleuze and Guattari's slyly appropriated 'New Earth' presents a model of an earth whose every surface and trellis is an unground, a terminal planetary body tolerating neither solar economies nor its own terrestriality. However, two questions remain at this point: can the Unground — where the hegemonic wholeness of the Earth is incapacitated — still be called Earth? And then, according to what chronological current, based on what calendar, according to what gradient of becoming, which point of reference addressed by space-time coordinates, can it be mapped as *the New Earth*? For the Unground is a shadow outside of time and space.

> 'The nethermost caverns,' wrote the mad Arab, 'are not for the fathoming of eyes that see; for their marvels are strange and terrific. Cursed the ground where dead thoughts live new and oddly bodied, and evil the mind that is held by no head. Wisely did Ibn Schacabao say, that happy is the tomb where no wizard hath lain, and happy the town at night whose wizards are all ashes. For it is of old rumour that the soul of the devil-bought hastes not from his charnel clay, but fats and instructs the very worm that gnaws; till out of corruption horrid life springs, and the dull scavengers of earth wax crafty to vex it and swell monstrous to plague it. Great holes

secretly are digged where earth's pores ought to suffice, and things have learnt to walk that ought to crawl.' (H.P. Lovecraft, *The Festival*)

In this alarming but neglected passage, H.P. Lovecraft addresses holey space or ( )hole complex (with an evaporative W) as the zone through which the Outside gradually but persistently emerges, creeps in (or out?) from the Inside. A complex of hole agencies and obscure surfaces unground the earth and turn it to the ultimate zone of emergence and uprising against its own passive planetdom. Once freed from its solar slavery, the earth can rise against the onanistic self-indulgence of the Sun and its solar capitalism: 'Great holes secretly are digged where earth's pores ought to suffice, and things have learnt to walk that ought to crawl.'

According to Lovecraft, the realism of horror is built upon poromechanics. Lovecraft's poromechanical universe, or ( )hole complex, is a machine to facilitate the awakening and return of the Old Ones through convoluted compositions of solid and void. But how do holes emerge out of the interactions of solid and void? It is best to answer this question by paraphrasing Nick Land's remarks (from *The Thirst for Annihilation: Georges Bataille and Virulent Nihilism*) on the escapist aberrancy and the structural irresolution of the Labyrinth versus the consolidating and conclusive moderatism of Architecture: *void excludes solid but solid must include void to architectonically survive.* Solid needs void to engineer its composition; even the most despotic and survivalist solids are compositional solids, infected by the void. Through these inter-collisions of void and solid, the Old Ones – according to Lovecraft – can revive their 'Holocaust of Freedom' (*The Call of Cthulhu*), both by consuming solid and by pushing compositions towards the highest degrees of convolution (as a result of the ambiguity of solid and void i.e. the fuzzy space of the hole and its surface dynamics). In terms of Earth, the Holocaust of Freedom can be attained by engineering the corpse of solidus through installing ungrounding machines at molecular levels that exhume (*ex + humus*: un-ground) the earth from within and without, turning it into a vermicular and holey composition whose strata (The Economy of Solidus) is not dismantled but convoluted at each level of its own formation and composition. Earth is incapacitated, no longer capable of running its stratifying and grounding functions; instead it is charged with engineering the corpse of solidus, or, in a Lovecraftian sense, a worm-infested body exhumed by worming processes and vermiculating machines. Survival is blindness; but blindness is destined to be trapped by strategies and manipulations which are beyond the tactical sphere of command and control. It is through survival (the incapacity of the solid to reject the void) that solid participates in ungrounding itself. By correcting its consolidating processes, the solid sells its integrity (soul) to the abysmal convolutions inspired by the void, through which the pathological survival of the solid becomes the most basic factor in its irreversible lysis and degeneration. The solid surrenders itself to the plague from the very moment that it begins to cure itself. For solidity, the 'Will to Cure' is the 'Will to Mess'. To this extent, solidity is the Xanadu of potentialities and the empire of emergence. Every action of solidity in the direction of becoming more solid is equal to augmenting its interactions with the void. Yet these interactions can only manifest themselves as perforations, trails of negative space that concretely reverberate within the solid — writhing nematodes hollowing out and convoluting everything they touch, in sinuous movements.

Although the void devours the solid, the solid feasts on the void, i.e. its outsider. In compositions, the solid becomes hysterically gluttonous for the void. This is what intrigued the Cult of the Old Ones in their mission to perform their awakening ritual. If the Old Ones are to fly through holey space, bubbling up through the carrion black pit and turning their tentacles into interconnected borrows and lubricious warrens, then the only strategic technique to speed and facilitate their return is to mess with the ( )hole complex, that is to say, the zone of their emergence. This is a technique which was also perceived by the Z. crowd as a strategy to arch-sabotage monotheism and inter-connect it to undercurrents of Tellurian Insurgency (petropolitical undercurrents in Islamic Apocalypticism for example). It was also a strategy to actively participate in the Project of Tellurian Omega, where the Earth reaches utter immanence with its burning core — or the metal core of the tellurian real — and the Sun.

Awakening Strategies. Holey space is nothing but a composition (of solid and void) — a vermicular one, burrowed by worms (*nemats*) or vermicular lines convoluting anything they touch, overspreading the ( )hole complex as a vast altar which asks for the solid as a sacrificial meal, awakening thousands of vermiculating lines to scour the solid and carve a polished, leering Ω out of it. In any composition, the solid narrates the anomalies generated by the void, or the infection of the void through the solid (when the void comes to the solid, it works as a convoluting plague, a coiling swirling epidemic rather than a nullifying process or a solid-annihilating agent); in a composition there is no pure solid but a defiled one, a diseased and deflowered solid. Once we realize that in any composition (as in ( )hole complex) the solid is the possessed narrator of the void, it will be but a short analytical step to see that the solid works as two different entities overlapping with each other and functioning concurrently:

1. As a compositional entity whose behavior (topological changes, transformations, motions, folds, etc.) can induce changes to the compositional side of the void through Surface Dynamics (or superficialities, as Cassati and Varzi call them in their holey treatise *Holes and Other Superficialities*).

At a compositional level, holes compile surfaces out of the hegemony of solidus. Solidus is not a content to be added (adjective) to the *grund*, nor is it a lineament, an ethos, or a modifier. It is the tectonic expansion or the sprawling politics of the ground itself. Every manifestation of ( )hole complex must pass through a certain type of surface dynamics (in terms of evoking periphery, itinerancy, and affect), breeding a new genre of surfaces with their exclusive itinerant lines depending on the locus of the hole and the way that the void interplays with the solid. Holes offer new polytical activities to surfaces; the crisp boundary of surfaces is dissolved into the blurred and cryptogenic boundary of the hole. In the presence of the hole, an asymmetric parallelism between surfaces and the crust occurs, in which the two remain analogous and remotely connected to their common genus but where each one spawns its own different, independent operational entities and geometries. Here, surfaces do not necessarily conduct and synchronize the ground's local hegemonies, establishing orders through the consolidated coherence of the crust; they countermine the stratification processes instead of supporting them. Each surface has a line of command with two heads, a trellis and a taxis. The former receives the accumulation and distributes it i.e. a *textum* or groundwork for fixation, positioning and support, the latter directs and develops what has been accumulated and economically distributes it. Taxis gives a dynamic tendency to the contents of the Trellis according to the mutual *affordance*[14] between surfaces or the entity and its environment, that is to say, according to the eco-logical web,[15] the Whole. Inner holes and connected cavities, simultaneously, come with two types of surfaces or two active contacts with solidus: (1) a surface-supporter or circumferential visible surface that connects the cavity to the crust i.e. the ecological outside. Therefore, the ( )hole complex cannot be merely reduced to a subterranean or subsoil complexity. (2) a surface-transmitter that joins with the itinerant lines passing through the hole or connected cavities, and which binds the cavity on the inside where the hole emerges out of the ambiguity of solid and void, or, in a topologically oversimplified sense, *where the cavity is*. (See Fig. 12)

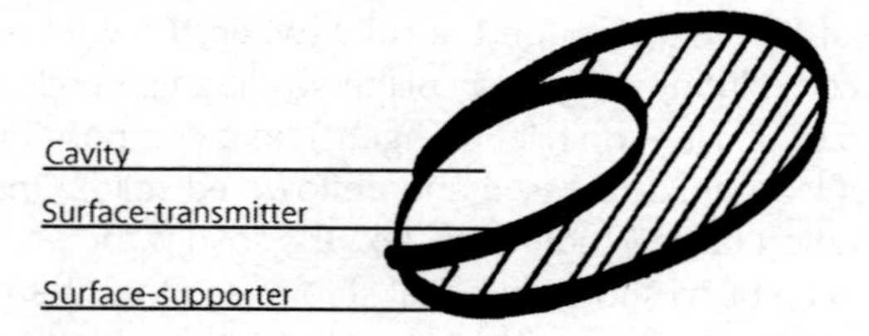

Fig. 12 Active surfaces (transmitter / subterranean and supporter / circumferential) surrounding a cavity.

> The surface is where most of the action is. The surface is where light is reflected or absorbed, not the interior of the substance. The surface is what touches the animal, not the interior. The surface is where chemical reaction mostly takes place. The surface is where vaporization or diffusion of substances into the medium occurs. And the surface is where vibrations of the substances are transmitted into the medium. (J.J. Gibson, quoted in *Surfaces*, Avrum Stroll)

For instance, on a mereotopological level (relating, that is, to topological interfaces of whole or whole-part relationships),[16] changes or distortions on surfaces or the solid part are directly conducted to the compositional void and cause new convolutions and alterations by means of changing the ways or mechanisms through which the void is presented through the solid: If you twist, inflate or heat a tube or a holey ball (with tunnels spread through it), you can see that changes in the solid part are transmitted to the holey side of the tube or the ball, the tunnels or the holey side becoming more convoluted and intricate. These changes through the compositional void can only be perceived and interacted with through the solid part — such is the compositional inevitability and clandestine nature of ( )hole complex. To make friends with the void, first one must submit to the rigid reign of the solid.

2. The solid as an entity which is inherently possessed by the void. The only way that the solid can initialize its architectonic and compositional activities (processes for survival, development, etc.) is by letting the void in. The dynamic traits of solid can only be actuated when solid is eaten, convoluted and messed up by the void. There is no other option for solid. In ( )hole complex, on a superficial level (bound to surface dynamics), every activity of the solid appears as a tactic to conceal the void and appropriate it, as a program for inhibiting the void, accommodating the void by sucking it into the economy of surfaces (as in the case of the *niche*,[17] a dwelling / accommodating system, a compartmentalizer of spaces) or filling it. But on a deep compositional level (the machinery of the real), all activities of the solid are oriented towards engineering new voiding functions, convolutions, vermicular spaces (henceforth, Nemat-space) which eventually unground solidus without erasing it. On this deep compositional level, the solid conducts the convoluting functions of the solid-contaminating void, in the form of vermicular lines — 'worms' (Nemat) as Lovecraft suggests, or worm-functions (the nemat-function), itinerant lines in the form of knotted holes, or the other way around. When a worm or a void-enforcer crawls in ( )hole complex, it metamorphoses into a different geometrical structure. In the absence of the grounding tyranny of the Whole, the worm-function internally reconfigures its modules and turns itself into a more versatile line through participation with the complex whose recesses are interconnected. All this in the wake of solidity, which is reinvented by the ( )hole complex as a profound strategic tool. In holey space, the solid actively conducts and mobilizes the worm-functions of the void (complications) rather than the void's phagic and purgative mechanisms or its desire to devour. Solid proceeds as the void-enforcer, a *pestis solidus* blasphemer.

In ( )hole complex, the void is also contaminated by the solid. For this reason, instead of the purging mechanisms of void, nemat-functions emerge. Defying death, the nemat-function twists termination in ( )hole complex into processes of convolution, undermining and ungrounding.

( )hole complex attests to the confusion between solid and void. Every activity happening on the solid part increases the degree of convolution and entanglement on the holey side of the composition, fabricating the intricate meshwork of a nemat-space which will eventually engineer the corpse-of-solidus or the unground, disabling or sabotaging all grounding (signification, con-solidation, stratification, etc.) functions of solid. While the vermicular complexity of nemat-space activates this tortuous side of the ( )hole complex, it also covers each compositional level of the complex with poroelastic traits. In fact, poroelasticity continuously employs diffusion as a means of radical deformation and alteration in the dynamism of the composition, narrating the diagrams of the fluid flow in the animorphic composition of the nemat-space as a heterogeneous porous complex, which amounts to more than just being a structure with interconnected holes. Nemat or worm space is a complex, with a strange elastic geometry: Its porous side is constituted of itinerant lines rendering synchronous possibilities of relaxation, metamorphosis, folding, spreading tortuosity, heterogeneous dynamism and compositional anomalies for the complex. Nemat-space is basically a machine for a radical and pestilentially inventive communication and participation between fluid and solid, in such a way that they can be tactically and strategically — hence militaristically and politically — derived from each other. Parsani identifies this level of mutual interplay between solid and fluid in ( )hole complex as 'Tiamaterialistic differentiation'. In nemat-space, the flow of the fluid and the deformation of the solid matrix are coupled; they are heavily interconnected as foundations of a radical participation which gives rise to a diverging series of becomings for 'each level of the composition' whose wholeness has been utterly degenerated. Agitated by the flow of fluids (which themselves have been anomalized in the nematical machine or vermicular space), elastic waves dissipate through solid matrices and radically displace the grains of the solid skeleton throughout the ( )hole complex. It is Lovecraftian worm-ridden space that makes solidity the altruistic host of emergence. The spasmodic deformations of the solid skeleton, consequently, change the stress field by which the remodifications and manipulations of solid are transmitted to the nemat-space in a synergistic communication, and progressively fold, twist and open the ( )hole complex, further refining its sinister facets. To understand the interplay between porous structure and fluid flow, it is necessary to examine regional aspects of the pore space morphology and relate them to the relevant mechanisms of fluid transfer such as viscosity, pressures between fluid and surfaces, inertial forces, etc.

The increase of pore pressure induces dilations of the ( )hole complex and increases poroelasticity (both enhance fluid flow.) While the immediate transition from laminar to turbulent happens in pipes and channels, in porous media the passage from linear to non-linear is always gradual and gradient-wise, offering opportunities to compose new spaces, lines, connections, pores, modes of dynamism and participation — infinite possibilities in terms of flood. The compression of the solid matrix, or any attempt of solidus to keep itself integrated and save its consolidated and molar state (by preventing the fluid from running or escaping from one porous network to another or isolating pores), causes a substantial rise in pore pressure. The abrupt escalation in pore pressure triggers further and radical deformation of the solid matrix, dilation and contraction of pores (comparable to the plateau-engineering mechanism of libidinal spasms addressed by Freud), progressive ungrounding of solidus, regional pore collapse[18] and finally the composition of new worm-ridden spaces or zones of emergence. Nemat-space is an ultimate crawling machine; it is essentially cryptogenic and interconnected with Anonymous-until-Now. Anonymous-until-Now is the model of Time in ( )hole complex, whose probes and lines of itineracy move unpredictably according to both the subsoil and superficial ungrounding machineries that weaken the solidus by perversely exploiting and manipulating it (exhuming solidus). *Incognitum Hactenus* — not known yet or nameless and without origin until now — is a mode of time in which the innermost monstrosities of the earth or ungraspable time scales can emerge according to the chronological time that belongs to the surface biosphere of the earth and its populations. *Incognitum Hactenus* is a double-dealing mode of time connecting abyssal time scales to our chronological time, thus exposing to us the horror of times beyond.

In *Incognitum Hactenus*, you never know the pattern of emergence. Anything can happen for some weird reason; yet also, without any reason, nothing at all can happen. Things leak into each other according to a logic that does not belong to us and cannot be correlated to our chronological time. Intrinsic permeability is a function of the nemat-space. The contact between the solid and the fluid is itself also a compositional factor of the poroelastic complex. Local velocity gradients in the fluid induce new convolutions, shear stresses, ruptures and deformations of the solid matrix, tuning the surface dynamics to the entire machinery of the complex and the flow of the fluid, that is to say, enhancing the flow and building up the flood. In nemat-space, the diffusing pore fluid thereby smuggles its affect space through the solid matrix as well as its own particles. One should not forget that ( )hole complex generates preferential channels for fluid flow or provides fluids with an ample opportunity to dig their own passages, burrow their own fields of tactics. In pulp-horror fictions and cinema, and in Lovecraft's fiction, it is the abode of the Old Ones, worm-entities and the blob (petroleum) that surpasses even tentacle-headed monstrosities in sentience and foreignness. R'lyeh is the every dream, motion and calculation of Cthulhu on the solid part of the earth's body. In poromechanics, the negative space is the very solid body of crawling vermiculations and twisting currents. Moreover, the role of fluid in thermal, structural, geochemical and economic evolution of the crust is radically possessed by the machinery of the ( )hole complex. The surface biosphere has never been separate from the cthulhoid architecture of the nether.

Once nemat-space begins its infestation, the periphery or the zone of excitations does not necessarily start from visible surfaces or the crust: Active surfaces emerge from everywhere, from the surface-as-crust mode of periphery to innermost recesses. The ( )hole complex carves ultra-active surfaces from solidus when it digs holes, unleashes delirious itinerant lines and constructs its nematical machines, installing peripheral agitations on the surfaces it cuts from internal solid matrices. Everywhere a hole moves, a surface is invented. When the peripheral upheaval of ( )hole complex spreads from the crust to within, the despotic necrocratic regime of periphery-core, for which everything should be concluded and grounded by the gravity of the core, is deteriorated. The dismantling of the coherency between the periphery and the core is equal to the rise of the ultimate unground where the radical Outside is posited from surface to the core. No wonder, then, that holey space has continually been associated with the Outside or its avatars (whether in the form of a nigrescent tellurian insider or a subterranean fallen sun god). The half-man-half-scorpion (discovered in Tel Halaf, Syria) of the Gilgamesh epic is such an avatar, guarding the gate to the Outside. Scorpions are burrowers, not architects: They do not build upon the compositions of solid and void, they devour volumes and snatch spaces; for them the holey space is not merely a dwelling place, a place to reside (a niche for occupation). More than that, it is the Abode of War (*dâr al-harb*), the holey space of unselective hunting.

> Archeology's main goal must be to turn the Earth into an artifact, rather than to merely satisfy its fetishistic hunger for relics, artifacts and dig-sites. When I was at Tehran University, I taught the students how to turn the Earth into the coiling body of Tiamat, the Sumero-Babylonian Mother-Dragon. (From an interview with Dr. Hamid Parsani)

On another occasion, Hamid Parsani describes base-archeology as 'interacting with the nested-vaginas of Tiamat's swirling body, engorging their curls, opening their curves and experiencing the contorting movement of each concave and convex wall, poly-surfaced tissues and the ancient venom surging within them'.

The ground does not conduct, regulate or organize intensities (as insinutated by psychoanalysis). It does not syndicate them, nor does it conduct them into consolidated architectonic persuasions. Rather, it gives them something and sets them free as its free-flow proxies, lines of gravity and acentral expanding operatives, missionaries but not conquistadors. The lineage of anthropomorphic hospitality too attests to this sly grounding policy: copulation … insemination … withdrawal; we are always on the way to withdrawal.

The grounded flux is generally described as flux '$f = p/a$' (the power p imposed on the regional surface a). But it is the coupled Trellis-Taxis mechanism of surface which, in nemat-space, fails to enforce and circulate the economy of the ground. In such a cavernous cavern (a holey redundancy), the ground loses its capacity to support and govern; for the coherency of its surfaces has been demolished (a=0). Accordingly, the distribution of p on the consolidating and self-referential wholeness of solidity is incapacitated. All power formations require a ground for establishment and conduction. Without a ground, that is to say, in the absence of a power formation, the definition of 'power' is basically undermined. What is politics, then, when there is power but no power formation? What is politics when understood in terms of the ( )hole complex, in which the full body of 'p/0' (p over zero) precedes all power formations?

The distribution of solidity obeys the logic of the solid, but this is the logic of solidity which follows the polytics of the ( )hole complex and the dynamism of its Nemat-space. Every entity-event in ( )hole complex is discontinuous according to the measures of solid and its scales of consistency, but continuous from the point of view of the interconnected nemat-space and its holeyness. An entity which is supposed to loom up from a particular spot or region, emerges from an entirely irrelevant (according to the logic of solidus) location. Every activity on the solid part of ( )hole complex awakens something radically irrelevant, having no correlation with its input, cause or origin. Disturb and irritate, dilate and contract the repressed cavities of the Earth: Tunnels and tubes, burrows and lairs, acrid bungholes and perforated spaces, its fanged vaginas, slits and the schizoid skin. Unclog and squeeze the earth; exhume its surfaces; make an earth whose conundrums cannot be solved by recourse to their origins or causes.

What horrifies the living is not an empty tomb but a messed-up and exhumed tomb. The architectural policy of the solid does not reject destruction or deconstruction but escapes exhumation ... deflowering the face ('white wall / black hole' Deleuze and Guattari), marring and mangling it ... by messing up the surfaces, scratching ... skinning ... eating ... turning to dust ... cutting into the core, with bare hands, daggers and krises, nails and enzymes ... saliva and breath ... shovel and plow. Exhumation is wholly criminal and immoral, but further, it is basically polluting and infecting as it undergoes surface collision, necrotizing the architecture, proliferating hot and cold surfaces into each other, letting the cold space of a tomb evaporate and the reek of bodies rise up — resurrection of the defiled body. The cold cannot be reheated; only messed up.

Mehrdad Iravanian, the Iranian architect once suggested, 'In order to study architecture, one must first investigate necrocracy.' But we should go further: one must practice the art of exhumation too.

If archeologists, cultists, worms and crawling entities almost always undertake an act of exhumation (surfaces, tombs, cosmic corners, dreams, etc.), it is because exhumation is equal to ungrounding, incapacitating surfaces ability to operate according to topologies of the whole, or on a mereotopological level. In exhumation, the distribution of surfaces is thoroughly undermined and the movements associated with them are derailed; the edge no longer belongs to the periphery, anterior surfaces come after all other surfaces, layers of strata are displaced and perforated, peripheries and the last protecting surfaces become the very conductors of invasion. Exhumation is defined as a collapse and trauma introduced to the solid part by vermiculate activities; it is the body of solidity replaced by the full body of trauma. As in disinterment — scarring the hot and cold surfaces of a grave — exhumation proliferates surfaces through each other. Exhumation transmutes architectures into excessive scarring processes, fibroses of tissues, membranes and surfaces of the solid body. Exhumation engineers the corpse-of-solidus whose dimensionality blurs not to the point of terminus and erasure but to coils of dimensions which cannot resist that which crawls in and out — ( )holes, ( )holes, ( )holes with liquidated and now evaporating 'W's. In Lovecraft's poromechanical cosmology, exhumation is undertaken and exercised by units called Rats. In fact, 'the dramatic epic of the rats' (Lovecraft) consists in their act of exhuming surfaces, solid bodies and structures which resist perforation.

Rats[19] are exhuming machines: Not only full-fledged vectors of epidemic, but also ferociously dynamic lines of ungrounding. Rats germinate two kinds of surface cataclysm as they travel and span different zones. Firstly, static damage in the form of ruptures rendered by internal schisms, uplifts, dislocations, jumps and thrusts which expose the surface to paroxysmal convulsions and distortions; and secondly the dynamic anomaly of seismic waves dissipating as the rats flow in the form of tele-compositions (ferocious packs). In the pack, while rats' compressions and decompressions proliferate their rates of speed, their transpositions and rearrangements in the pack (composition) forge a decontouring machine marring the elevation of entities in the pack, setting rats free, lending them a capacity for miniature flight. Hence, as they run, they appear to evaporate both surfaces and themselves. Aristophanes and Bacchylides spoke of the birds flying through *Khaos*, that unrestricted space of enthusiasm for flowing (*kheisthai*); but no one asked what kind of birds these were: Wingless? Taxidermized? Metallic? Decapitated? Eyes evacuated with a penknife? ... No, they are rats: Thousands, millions of them.

A surface-consuming plague is a pack of rats whose tails are the most dangerous seismic equipment; tails are spatial synthesizers (fiber-machines), exposing the terrain which they traverse to sudden and violent foldings and unfoldings, while seizing patches of ground and composing them as a nonhuman music. Tails are musical instruments, playing metal — tails, lasher tanks in motion. Although tails have a significant locomotive role, they also act as boosters of agility or anchors of infection — rapid changes in position, quick jerks and sudden movements in new directions — and cinephilic machines. As they vibrate, tails print thousands of traces and images, not on a film (*pellicule*) but on and through a space enmeshed by the commotion of transient traces, trajectories of disease and fleeting signs; much like a digital wireframe architecture which does not compartmentalize space to fragments of interior and exterior localities, but becomes a free-play and perforated architecture engineered by the swerving motions of a sparkling tail-wire whipping the space.

This exhumed architecture composed by tail-twitches can render itself in different modes, becoming gaseous and terminally epidemic, transforming itself to a diagram of pest incursion rather than an instance of architecture. In a pack of rats, a multitude of tails turns into the probe-head of the entire pack in motion: an omnidirectional acephalic revolution, the New Pest Disorder.

A pack of tails: Thousands of insects scavenging a tomb somewhere in a Zoroastrian village near the city of Yazd; a warfare of vibration. These exhuming machines unleash a nonhuman silence best characterized as acoustic smog, a molecular noise wreaking sonic havoc. Sounds are rabies, spread by rat tails.

The polytics of the ( )holey complex defies existing models of the harvesting of power correlated to the logic of the ground and the politics of whole. For the world order, inconsistent events around the world are failures or setbacks for the dominant political models. According to the politics of poromechanical earth, however, inconsistencies and regional disparities across the globe constitute the body of polytics. The emergence of two entities (political formation, military, economic, etc.) from two different locations on the ground is inconsistent, but according to the logic of ( )hole complex, they are terminally interconnected and consistent. In terms of emergence, consistency or connectivity should not be measured by the ground or the body of solid as a whole but according to a degenerate model of wholeness and a poromechanics of the event.

Military and political practitioners have long formulated as an archeological law the asymmetry between ground's consistency and the consistency of poromechanical entities or porous earth: *For every inconsistency on the surface, there is a subterranean consistency*. The law of subterranean cause in archaeology bears a striking resemblance to Freud-Jung's suggestion that for every psychosomatic breakdown, there is a Complex (an anomalous convolution and knottedness) beneath consciousness. The reason for this similarity lies in the fact that according to both archeology and Freudian psychoanalysis, the line of emergence (the nemat-function) directs itself in accordance with the resistance to emergence, the dynamism of emergence and the degree of porosity. The course of emergence in any medium corresponds to the formation of that medium; the more agitated the line of emergence becomes, the more convoluted and complex the host medium must be. In terms of poromechanics and ( )hole complex, the superficial orientation of archaeology and Freudian psychoanalysis alike are too complex — immersed in multiplex dynamics of surfaces and their interactions with emergence — to be fathomed. The myths of obtuse flatness (i.e. superficiality) or totalitarianism attributed to Freudian psychoanalysis by postmodernist rivals are in most cases the symptoms of misunderstanding the problem of surfaces and emergence. The *superficial* (as related to visible, circumferential and grounded surfaces) entities of Freudian theories only come into existence as final products of unbound activities involved with emergence, welling up from subterranean complexes of nested holes and surfaces. In other words, the supposedly superficial entities of Freudian psychoanalysis (Oedipus,

Rat-man, etc.) in fact delineate the vector of emergence in terms of different surfaces. Among these surfaces, only the most superficial one can loosely attest to its existence, for in terms of emergence the most superficial cannot be registered unless a crypt or a complex of burrows has already been dug out by the line of emergence from within. In the domain of emergence, every surface — whether of constraining ground or porosities — belongs to and is mobilized by the poromechanics of ( )hole complex. And in ( )hole complex, depth exists as the ambiguity or the gradient between inner and outer, solid and void, one and zero; or in other words, as a third scale or an intermediary agency which operates against the unitary or binary logics of inner and outer, vigor and silence, inclusion and exclusion. Holes definitely develop a ternary logic.

However, for both archaeology and Freudian psychoanalysis, the process of emergence and its immediate connection with the formation and dynamism of surfaces — namely, ( )hole complex — inevitably coincides with paranoia. For every inconsistency on the surface, there is a subterranean consistency; there is an overlap between two consistencies. One is the consistency that belongs to the dynamic surfaces of holey space or simply cavities, and the other is the consistency between cavities' surfaces (holes) and the circumferential surface of the solid (ground or visible surface). For every cause with a vertical distribution, there is a cause with a horizontal or slanted distribution, or vice versa. The effect is simultaneously produced by two causes with two different logics. To be registered on the circumferential surface or the ground, the schizoid structure or consistency of ( )hole complex must be transmitted to the solid body, where it has to be consolidated. Anomalies on the ground-surface are immanent to the two planes of schizophrenia and paranoia. According to the archeological law of contemporary military doctrines and Freudian psychoanalysis, for every inconsistency or anomaly visible on the ground, there is a buried schizoid consistency; to reach the schizoid consistency, a paranoid consistency or plane of paranoia must first be traversed. (See Fig. 13)

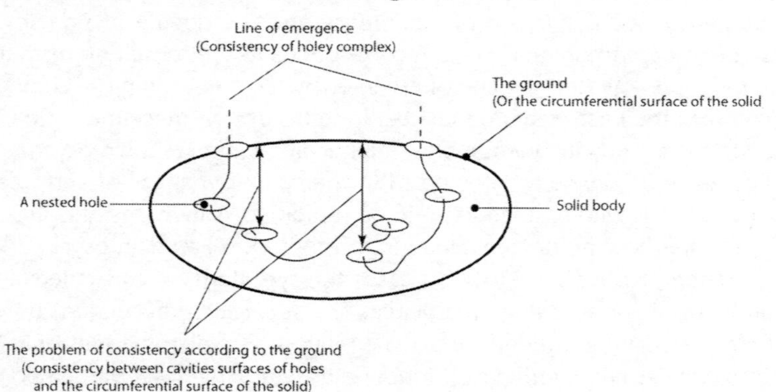

Fig. 13 The two planes of schizophrenia and paranoia: subterranean consistency and superficial inconsistency

The militarization of the contemporary world, both in its politics and its concrete approaches, is architecturally, visually and psychologically paradoxical (too paranoid to be schizoid and too schizoid to be paranoid), precisely because its agencies — as in War on Terror — are shifting from the logic of grounded earth to the poromechanical earth and the logic of hole-agencies. Although giving an example risks underestimating the vastness of militarization in respect to the poromechanics of war, and archeology as the science of military innovation in the twenty-first century, enumerating one or two cases may make this process clearer:

1. In countries with detailed homeland security protocols or relatively high levels of alertness, where ground or aerial operations (hostile, subversive or stealth activities) cannot be conducted, the emergence of intricate poromechanical entities escalates, and cannot be avoided. In such countries, the distribution of illegal immigrants or smuggled products such as drugs and weapons around the border regions does not proceed by way of patterns of activities on the surface, but through the formation and the architecture of nested holeyness beneath the ground. Activities or lines of movement (tactics) cannot be separated from the architecture of such ( )hole complexes. According to military experts or urban planners with military educations, criminal and hostile activities can no longer be explained, analyzed or traced in terms of land, aerial and water levels. These activities conform only (paranoically speaking) to structures of vast underground nemat-spaces and their constantly displacing and vermiculating lines of emergence (schizoid formations of surfaces). The distribution, escalation and diffusion of complicities is identical to different aspects of hole-trafficking. For military experts, the terror market is simultaneously that of the porosities of earth. Cross-border wormholes under the US-Mexico border, tunnels under Gaza-Egypt, and all other examples of hole trafficking, confound the polarities of surface globalization and its politico-military facets. The economic and power formations of clandestine Guerilla-states, anti-State movements and ambiguously Imperialist states configure themselves according to the poromechanics of war.
2. The Battle of Tora Bora in Afghanistan was escalated mainly by coalition forces (especially US forces, to the point of using BLU-82 bombs and a potential nuclear bunker buster strike) based on collected information about vast underground facilities and terror networks in the Tora Bora Mountains. US and British forces initiated a surgical strike comprising sophisticated tactics, innovative command and control, and inventive use of military implements and weapons. The tactics and the entire logic of military progression in Tora Bora were formulated precisely in order to 'match' the cavernous mountains of the region, to give an appropriate military response to the holey architecture of terror compounds. In short, the military formation of the entire battle was determined by the supposed tortuousness of the holey

complex within the mountains, and the techniques and solutions that were devised for neutralizing and clearing them. The complexity of movements or formative dynamics belonging to US and British forces was compatible with — indeed, represented a counter-geographical correspondence with — the supposed nested complexity of holes, tunnels and underground chambers. The Battle of Tora Bora was actualized based on the complexity of Tora Bora sub-surface facilities but in the absence of any actual holes and vermiculate complexities. Bound to the paranoid logical line in holey complexes (from the ground to the cavity) and unbound by a nonexisting schizoid architecture of nested holes, coalition forces led by the United States developed the first full-fledged example of a Cappadocian Complex: wherever hostile activities and threats are inconsistent and asymmetrical, there must be an underground cause of nested holeyness; consequently, one must model special military formations to counteract these convoluted and subterranean architectures. Such a logic is the heart of the Cappadocian Complex — Whereas in Tora Bora there was no sub-surface nexus or complex, in Cappadocia, beneath every surface and in every mountain or hill, there is a multiplex of holes, lairs and passageways.

> *Every mine is a line of flight* that is in communication with smooth spaces — there are parallels today in the problems with oil. (Deleuze and Guattari, *A Thousand Plateaus*)

Artaud's facial and organic sketches are always blighted by dots, clusters of dot-matrix gangrene, miniature orifices, molecular wells and diseased blastopores awaiting an opportunity to spread and burst forth. The dotted-disease of Artaud's skin corresponds with the pore-clouds of the Earth's crust and soil (which can be best described as an unconsolidated granular media forming a porous structure). These are mazing fields of hydroleak conductivity. The schizophrenic skin of the Earth has more to do with fluxes of Oil and Gas than with the holey space of mines and metallurgic probe-heads. Be a hydro-leak engineer; make things leak out.

The distribution of porosity through the Earth does not follow a rhizomatic structure but goes by way of random clusters with variable densities, similar to the dispersion of suspended dust and moisture in fog. The mutual contamination of solid and void in holey space is increasingly intensifying, with no end in sight, since it is the internal impetus of solid to be active, to re-modify itself, to knit itself through economic networks which maintain and guarantee its survival and growth, assisting its quest to be grounded. All activities throughout the solid part are reinvented as convoluting lines (Nemat-functions) at deeper levels of the composition. Whenever the solid messes with the void in order to keep itself dynamic and solidly 'constructive' or 'consolidated', the void only becomes more contaminative, its worm-functions become more furious, excited to the point of frenzy; they begin to rise from compositional depths to engineer the vermicular space of the Old Ones, an intricate traffic zone, the ( )hole complex. In this way, with every activity that it willfully undertakes, the solid levels all obstacles in its path to damnation. ( )hole complex is inexhaustible in its infidelity and perfidiousness; it is the source of the clandestine manipulation of solidus and of a double treachery against solid and void alike.

In the past, the holey space of mines incited peasant revolutions and barbarian invasions, but now it is oil fields that make technocapitalist terror-drones and the desert-militarism of Islamic Apocalypticism cross each other, forming militarization programs and complicities for revolutionizing the planetary surface. If oil has undergone a process of weaponization on the Islamic front of War on Terror, and has turned into a fuel for technocapitalist warmachines, this is not a matter of a politico-economic evolution: In Arabia, Sudan, Libya, Syria and even the Arabic clusters below the Persian Gulf, the Islamic state must cross deserts to feed on oil fields because of the exclusive location of oil fields in these countries. But the desert is the space of nomad-burrowers, desert-nomads and their warmachines with minimum climatologic regulation.

Of all nomads traversing the Earth, those most radical in their forging of warmachines under the minimum influence of climatologic factors are the desert-nomads. This is why both the renomadization of the Wahhabistic state of Saudi Arabia through desert-militarism (belonging to desert-nomads) and the semi-sedentarization of nomads (by the State) and their metamorphosis into *naphtanese* (clandestine petro-nomads who roam between oil fields instead of oases) were inevitable.[20] Bound to purely nomadic ways of living, and remaining relatively distant from environmental factors of climatological dependence such as water, moderate climate or diverse pastoralism (they are mostly just camel-keeping pastoralists), the nomads of Arabia retained truly nomadic traits until the mid-twentieth century, and were introduced to the State's sedentarization programs very late. This premature but late sedentarization of desert nomads by the oil-seeking State was in fact the main factor in the contamination of the desert nomads of Arabia with petropolitics and the pestilential vitalization of Wahhabi religion with nomadic tactics, ways of life and the logic of the desert. Thus the contemporary religio-political traits of Wahhabism (the Wahhabistic agencies supposedly targeted by the War on Terror) are undoubtedly diverse mutations resulting from the attraction of the occultural and alien elements of desert nomadism through oil. The State and desert-nomads were introduced, and slid inexorably toward each other, through the poromechanics of oil and the holey space shaped by the logic of oil extraction in the desert. World petropolitics — earth as narrated by oil — in regard to the Middle East and the War on Terror, emerges out of these mutual contaminations between States and desert nomads, facilitated by the holey space of petroleum.

Oil fields draw petrological nemat-spaces between the State and the desert-nomads. On the one hand, such spaces manipulate the State by furious desert-nomadism and on the other, they reconfigure desert-militarism of the nomads according to the State's petropolitics. This corresponds with the ambiguity between solid and void in the ( )hole complex, which traffics and smuggles its own itinerant lines through the polemics of solid and void. The problem of oil fields and the ( )hole complex between the State and desert-nomads is indeed far more sophisticated than that of mines and their ambulant dwellers (miners). Firstly, there is no equivalent, in oil fields, for the miner, since the connection of *naphtanese* (former desert-nomads) with oil is not an intimacy based on consumption, production or even transportation (what connected old miners to mines as their temporary niches). Secondly, oil as an ubiquitous earth-crawling entity — the Tellurian Lube — spreads the warmachines and politics of *naphtanese* or desert-nomads as totally pervasive entities. Finally, even in the absence of desert-nomadism, oil turns Time toward apocalyptic blasphemies. A patch of oil is enough to stir the apocalypse out of Time. If oil does not benefit the middle class (an economic boom initially moderating the economy but ultimately giving rise to economic fissions), and if it does not lead to the outbreak of cannibalistic economies — as in the case of Mexico, Venezuela, Sudan and possibly Mauritania — it will certainly charge clandestine-military pipelines with apocalyptic modes of divergence, as in the case of Islamic countries. In any case, oil, with its poromechanical zones of emergence in economy, geopolitics and culture, mocks the Divine's chronological Time with the utmost irony and obscenity.

The nemat-spaces of mines and oil fields alike attract nomads and different types of martial entities around themselves, assembling them as mercenaries, treason-armies bound to the privatization of military forces which in most cases belong not to the State but to foreign or multi-national mega-corporations involved in oil fields. Although these corporations are entities embedded within the nucleus of the State and are synchronized to its politics (and also linked to the techno-economic or military failure and poverty of the State), their functions are external to the economy and the environmental stability of the State. These paramilitary or cryptomilitary forces present potential dangers of *coup d'état*, class insurgency, ethno-national crises and even invasions of foreign countries from the inside. As a matter of fact, ( )hole complex suggests that hole agencies are essentially (but not actively) double-dealing and treacherous; they are counter-hegemonic and hegemonic. The ambulant hole was originally utilized in a full-fledged form by the State. The underground cities of the Hittites in the Hattian Empire were mainly burrowed out in order to employ the formidable power of a resident military entity in Anatolia. These underground cities were settlement-fort-factories with immense impacts on the geopolitical formation of Mesopotamia (Babel, Assyria and Ugaritic civilizations), that is to say, the most hegemonic States of the time. The emergence of despotic States in the region were dynamically influenced — if not molded — by the mining potentiality of these hole agencies or underground cities in the service of the State. The role of iron production from these underground cities (Kaymakli and Avanos in Cappadocia for example), beyond just supporting the formative and geographic boundaries of the States (Iron weapons over copper tools), also molarized the populations of the region through stratocracies connected to these hole agencies and mines.

Assyrians cleared the last underground cities of their human dwellers by releasing and sending vermin (diseased rats, polluted water, rotten bodies and snakes) down into the complex — for, as the most advanced military state of that time, they knew that it is not the vectors of decay and disease which solve the problem of 'hole people', but the worm-dynamics of the complex which gives the flux a militant hydraulic edge and an autonomous tacticality. This in opposition to the Wittfogelian fluid dynamics that derives its power from the irresistible hyperactivity and turbulence of the flux. However, ( )hole complex's double-dealing field of activity is radically autonomous (although in a subterranean manner, and from the standpoint of strategic divergence). In the long run it becomes pilotless or acephalous.

Oil fields and mines usually come with corporations and their privatized armies, one as owner and the other as extractor; and mercenaries as outsiders who protect the temporal bonds between the extractor and the owner on the one hand and the oil fields and true beneficiaries on the other hand. Although these corporations and mercenaries induce repressions and poverty, they play significant roles in double-insurgencies, violent internal fissions of the State, civil wars and unrests. Anywhere that a nemat-space emerges, propulsive waves of insurgency and politico-economic insomnia rise imminently. To this extent, where is the poromechanics of horror as refined and as manifest as in middle-eastern politics and in the Plutonian ethics of living on oil?

One of the characteristics of ( )hole complex is its inspiring new forms of utilization or sparking off innovative usability — previously unknown abuses — in its consumers. These new lines of exploitation can also be identified in terms of aggravating instrumentalization of the Whole in the absence of its directorship and regulations. In this regard, ( )hole complex carries out a putsch to exhaustively degenerate the Whole in its functional restrictions.

Holes prostitute themselves, they are at the same time pimps and prostitutes. And this is in contrast to the ecological stability between a whole and its environment. Holistic political, religious and military readings — based on the logics of whole, its parts and the environment — sacrifice the autonomy of their object in favor of their environments or their global wholes. Holistic readings, in general, are in accordance with events bound to the ground and the dynamics of circumferential peripheries such as consolidated economic progressions, conventional military fields and globalization of the earth in terms of its outer surface, etc. Such readings impose logics of systems which are either theoretically reductive or pragmatically disconnected in regard to their objects. For this reason, lines of emergence associated with the porous earth, hole agencies and terminally political and insurgent formations — as of the Middle East — necessitate new reading models and platforms. If contemporary world politics *inconsistently* defies holistic reading methodologies, then the Middle East, from which commotions of global politics emerge, entails the employment of a new political analysis and a new pragmatics of intervention. As an entity political remobilization of whose attributes precedes its geographical ontology, the Middle East must be studied or engaged through methods which neither prioritize holistic models nor advocate their destruction. Accordingly, these models or methodologies must correspond to the socio-political formations of the Middle East, for which structural or functional inconsistencies can only be addressed in a uniform way (i.e. consistently linked to each other) if they are to be taken in regard to a degenerative whole whose partiality and wholeness alike are incapacitated and unable to exert control over each other. In a degenerative whole or ( )hole complex, the consistency of events and their uniform dynamism exist through a poromechanical space where differentiation between surfaces (as of holes) has paralyzed the eventuation of the ground as the prerequisite basis for formative forces and coherent establishments. In fact, poromechanics, where an invocation of new grounds is registered as a perforation of the formation by new surfaces (or holes), corresponds to multiplex governing forces in every middle-eastern State. Here the term guerilla-state suits those middle-eastern states or societies where the boundaries between the state and its others have already been terminally perforated.

As a reading model for structures or formations with a degenerate whole, Hidden Writing corresponds to the dynamics of emergence and the perforated architecture of middle-eastern formations. In fact, Hidden Writing is a model of complicity with ( )hole complex — it suggests we read stories through their plot holes. If texts with narrative plots and wholesome structures are read and written according to disciplines and procedures conforming to their configurations, then perforated structures, degenerate formations and plot holes must have reading and writing methodologies of their own.

More than a mere indisciplinary investigation, Hidden Writing suggests a politics of contribution to, or participation with, perforated structures and degenerate formations. Reading through the plot holes of a story is possible only by devising a line capable of twisting in and out of them. The chthonic ballistics of such a line not only encompasses solidity with a perforated transcendence and porous realism, but also convolves and terminally bends the formative matrix of the structure itself. Drawing upon two major quandaries for consolidated plots and consistent narratives, Hidden Writing reformulates and utilizes the components of apocryphality and steganography — that is, inauthenticity and hidden writing. Whereas the former predominantly concerns problems arising from misauthorship or the intervention of anonymous collectivities (the crowd) in writing a text, the latter addresses perforations or anomalies in a text caused by the existence and activities of something other than the governing structure or the assumed base plot. What is usually identified as a plot hole is nothing but the concrete trajectory of such activities which, however communicative it is on the subsurface level, is inconsistent and symptomatic on the outer surface and superficial level. Hidden Writing can grasp political plot holes without reducing them to a whole or separating them from each other. Therefore, for reading middle-eastern events in connection to 'The World' (the visible or base plot), Hidden Writing is the ultimate tool of extraction, digging and participation, that is to say, reading as both scrutiny and realization.

Hidden Writing, whether as *apocrypha scripta* or *steganographia*, integrates the utilitarian frenzy of ( )hole complex as its functioning principle, inseparable from its convoluted structure. In Hidden Writing structure and function alike are the same as in the dynamism of emergence and formation in porous earth. Hidden Writing can be described as utilizing every plot hole, all problematics, every suspicious obscurity or repulsive wrongness as a new plot with a tentacled and autonomous mobility. The aftermath of this utilization manifests itself as an act of writing whose effect is to deteriorate the primary unified plot or remobilize the so-called central theme and its authority as a mere armature or primary substance for holding things together. The central or main plot is reinvented solely in order that it may stealthily host, transport and nurture other plots. In Hidden Writing, a main plot is constructed to camouflage other plots (which can register themselves as plot holes) by overlapping them with the surface (superficially dynamic plot) or the grounded theme. In terms of such a writing, the main plot is the map or the concentration blueprint of plot holes (the other plots). Every hole is a footprint left by at least one more plot, prowling underneath.

A plot hole does not operate on behalf of an absence (that object of critics' scorn), but registers and conveys the activities of a sub-surface life. Plot holes are psychosomatic indications of at least one more plot densely populating itself in the holes it burrows through and digs out. However, the propagation of plot holes in hidden writing is not merely the evidence of actual independent plots beneath and through the visible surface or the so-called main story ('books within a book'). More importantly, it is the indication of the active inauthenticity and anti-Book distortions that Hidden Writings carry. In addition to being the manifest symptoms of other ongoing plots, plot holes originate from pseudonymity, anonymity and deliberate distortions linked to issues of authorship usually associated with Hidden Writings. Shifting voices, veering authorial perspectives, inconsistent punctuations and rhetorical divergences bespeak a crowd at work, one author multiplied into many. In fact, mis-authorial problems which are usually associated with Hidden Writings give rise to tendrilled plots as new narratives spreading out from the surface plot in all directions; plots capable of seizing the surface story or the textual structure from the dominant authorial space.‡

---

‡ Pursue the idea of directing a movie based on two different books (disparate subjects, typographies, indexes, etc.) written by two different authors.

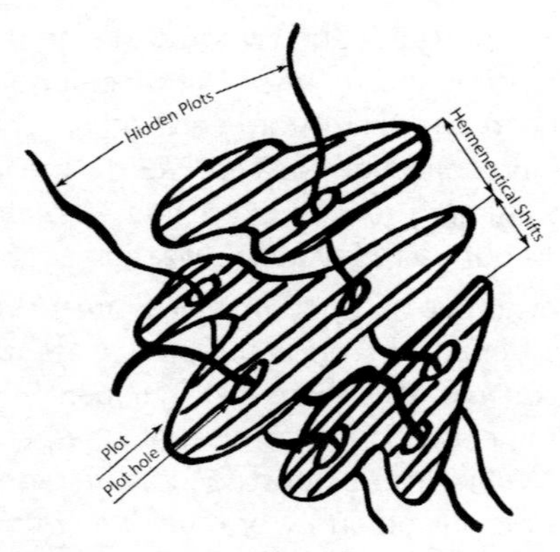

Fig. 14 Perpetuation of plot holes is imminent to the dynamism of subsurface plots.

It is no accident that hidden writings are associated with collective authors, as in the case of *apocrypha scripta*. One of the initial symptoms of inauthenticity that Hidden Writing produces is positive disintegration, or more accurately, collectivization of one author (voice) or an authorial elite, and its transformation to an untraceable shady collective of writers, a crowd. This misauthorial problem is directly connected to the distortion or bastardization of books and their questionable backgrounds. Hence it is a constant nightmare for religious Books and their virginal romanticism. Inauthenticity operates as complicity with anonymous materials.

In books of Hidden Writing, the textual subtopia consists of plots, narrations and autonomous author-drones populating the ( )hole complex of Hidden Writing. Such a subsurface life can not be reduced to ramified plot layers or buried messages (θησαυρος, *thesauri*) which would be the rewards of deep reading. So-called hermeneutic rigor follows the logic of textual stratification, and can be achieved by hermeneutical tools corresponding to the layering order of its text. But the subsurface life of Hidden Writing is not the object of layers and interpretation; it can only be exhumed by distorting the structure of the book or the surface plot. Exhumation includes a process of concrete crypting and decrypting, rewording, bastardization and a changing of the book. To interact with Hidden Writings, one must persistently continue and contribute to the writing process of the book. In Hidden Writings the act of reading and writing is conducted through those plot holes rejected by most interpreters as misleading obscurities. For hermeneutical explorations, plot holes are tricks, they are ill-timed and ill-spaced coordinates within the text — leak holes which must be plugged. But doesn't blocking the leak shift the pressure to another region, forcing out another hole? Theology is in general constantly obsessed with plugging holes, covering cracks and fissures in reasoning of and about the Divine. Thus, it forms lacunae of imperfection by which the corpus of theology can always be mobilized against itself, turning against itself and biting back its body. To do rigorous theology is to perforate the Divine's corpus with heresies.

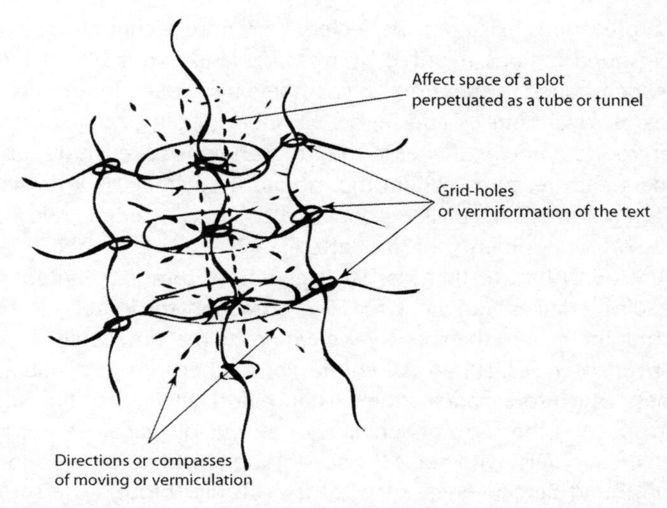

Fig. 15 Unlike texts as woven spaces (*textum*), hidden writings have tunnels instead of yarns, plot holes rather than structural grids.

One of the most prominent examples of Hidden Writing is Johannes Trithemius' treatise on black occult and scholastic astrology, *Steganographia*, written circa 1499. Trithemius' grimoire lacks any superficial coherent plot or consistency, as if it has been infested by plot holes, and various losses of content and theme. However, the book is in fact a treatise on cryptography, camouflaged and buried within the surface plot that seems to speak of the astral occult. Instead of layers and levels, Hidden Writing populates subways, sunken colonies, a social commotion teeming underneath. Trithemius' treatise on unorthodox occult and astral communication haunted by a restless population of cryptological entities operates on the plane of textual perforation.

> The Earth writes its histories as an inverse Trithemius; it is black occult disguised as the code. (Hamid Parsani)

In the introduction to *Defacing the Ancient Persia*, Parsani describes the role played by archeologists as fanatic readers of Hidden Writing who concretely contribute to the text. In the introduction, Parsani claims that 'archeology, with its ingrained understanding of Hidden Writing, will dominate the politics of future and will be the military science of twenty-first century':

> Vast Mesopotamian necropolises [Parsani writes], virtually always consist of a so-called in-situ site or wonder zone, and an in-subsido site or a missing site. The wonder zone or the visible site is usually located on a desolate plain or a mound with the ruins of ostentatious architectures erected on it. The wonder zone or the in-situ site is constituted of empty tombs or cenotaphs and treasure caches in the ground; it is a surface faerie

with a precarious existence, perfected — or more accurately, falsified — by underground regions flaunted by treasures and exotic objects. Treasures have been buried in the ground; chambers have been interred with sham bodies of royal families and heroes as sub-plot digressions from the real underground complex. Beneath the ground, beneath even its sub-surface wonders and treasures, within the mound itself, there is a dense burrow or warren compound thickly populated by tombs, murals, weapons and the assorted oddments of the afterlife. The surface problematic site, together with bizarre theatrics such as empty tombs (*kenotaphion*) and misleading edifices, radiate a massive attraction for looters and vandals, diverting them from the subway system or the real necropolis. These holes and inconsistencies, superficial entities, or red herrings, describe a positive fishiness which foreshadows the existence and activities of the Necropolis' urban space in the form of subways or an out-of-place site (ex-situ site). For an archeologist who reads the site through inconsistencies and through the profound defectiveness of what is available through the surface, the cenotaph, as an empty tomb, presents a hole in the story which points in an exact and unmistakeable direction: the entrance to the warren compound of the necropolis or the real underground network. In a necropolis' surface-site, everything — from empty tombs filled with sham bodies to treasures deliberately buried within the ground — suggests to the discerning that there is something else, a missing site nearby. For the looter, however, something is obviously *wrong*, but insofar as the spoils are nevertheless satisfactory and lavish, no more is said of it. Given these strategic surface absurdities and operational plot holes, if there is such a thing as, if you will, an aestheticism proper to the archeologist, it is undoubtedly expressed in the uneasy but excited exclamation: 'there is something deeply wrong with this thing'.

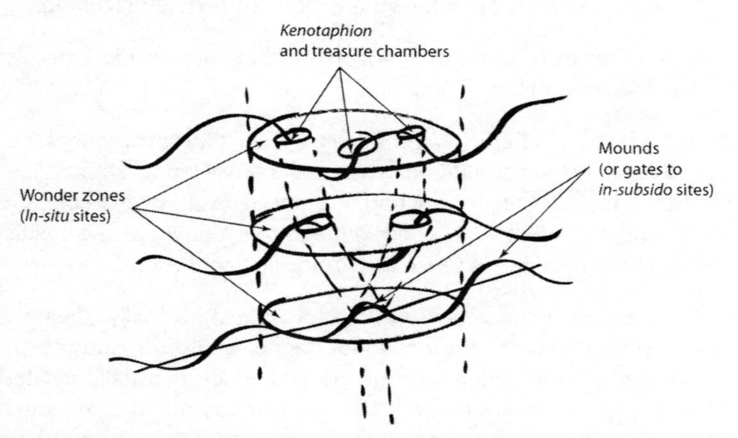

Fig. 16 Mesopotamian necropolises and their sites as models of political archeology.

'In the Middle East, every hole in the story indicates a gate into the dust *tehom*.' The cryptic ending to Parsani's introduction can be elucidated — although such an elucidation makes nothing clear — by an interview with him published in a Lebanese quarterly journal (Summer 2001) where Parsani answers the interviewer's query about his puzzling statement that the Middle East is not secular, nor pagan, nor monotheistic, nor occult. 'What is it then?' the interviewer asks.

> It is fanatically Tiamaterialist [Parsani answers]. In the Middle East, Tiamaterialistic entities use a different field of distribution, infiltration, multiplication and cognition for their progression and activities, a field which resembles the heavily-perforated space of hidden writing. It is a surface near to collapse, full of inconsistencies and irrelevancies or, as I like to say, story holes, leading to an extensive undercurrent and subway system. A surface whose obsessive vocation consists in turning any political and religious movement into a burrowing machine whose every activity structurally degrades the whole field and ironically makes the problematics or holes more relevant to this space of sheer activity, and less relevant to the established ground. The Middle East's irrelevancy to the rest of the globe is not a symptom of too many politics and histories; it results directly from its Tiamaterialistic approach to the globe and its undercurrents. I say nothing new if I suggest that the Middle East constantly seeks to pick holes in the world order, seeks out modes of economics and politics which have not been pursued by the rest of the globe, and populates them, turning them into its objects of enlightenment. As for the world, it has not seen anything yet of Tiamaterialism, which is the grasping of Middle East as a sentient entity, a literally living one. The world order and its great breakthroughs have been grounded on the tortuous ratholes of middle-eastern Tiamaterialism, with its boring-out heads. If the most advanced economic systems are not reliable or do not work properly, that's not their fault. It is because they are nothing more than the plot holes of the Middle East's Tiamaterialism. From the standpoint of surfascists, it may look as if middle-eastern Tiamaterialism simply messes around, impulsively, restlessly; but the way it works is intricately strategic from the perspective of hidden writing, which is the perspective of holes' creative surfaces. Tiamaterialism contributes to the world order not through the so-called main storyline, the major plot currently moving forward, but through the plane of hidden writing. So, for instance, Wahhabi hostility to idolatrous embodiments escalates to the degree where even mosques and holy tombs belonging to the prophet's family and disciples have to be destroyed because they illegitimately break the rules of the God's exclusive oneness. So they shift the location of their underground infrastructures to areas near mosques and holy shrines, changing the directions of underground construction projects including subways to these places, concentrating pipelines, water

storages, and other transport tunnels under the holiest Islamic sites to gradually surrender them to the forces of nature, or to destabilize the sites' foundations. Usually a third party, such as the neutral hostility of nature, will take care of holy tombs and sites. A materialistic personification of monotheistic zealotry on the ground, and integrated pipelines creeping beneath, concretely biting at the structure's foundation, interrupting the transfer of loads from the superstructure to the ground or creating fault foundation and sinkholes beneath the sites. From the very outset, as we can see, this whole cyclorama is an example of hidden writing. The collective history of Tiamaterialism or Middle East as a sentient entity is a masterpiece of hidden writing.

The nemat-space of the ( )hole complex reduces the monopolistic holiness of the Creation, the functionality of the ground's economy (which also forms a taxis-trellis pincer to support the Whole), and the hegemony of the Whole. Nemat-space introduces wholeness to Zero without wiping it out. This is the polytics first practiced and exquisitely elaborated by the Persian cult of *Kaxuži* or *Kakhurid* or *Kastaran-e Farre*, the reducers of wholeness or the reducers of purity, introduced in the Zoroastrian book, *Zadspram*, as the devastators of the Iranians (for the Aryans were believed to represent the greatest purity and wholeness of all inhabitants of the Earth).

Nemat-space is infected with gate hysteria; its surfaces are always prone to collapse and re-emergence from somewhere else, thus restlessly clicking new gates open. It gapes, yawns, bloats, coils and slithers — an endogenic parasite over, through and within the Earth. ( )hole complex creates more passages than are needed in the Earth's body, thus rendering it a host of its own ulterior motives. The heretic Zoroastrian cults, *deavo-Yasns*, *Kaxuži* and *Yatumants* or *Akht-Jadu* (*Yatu*) called this indefinable earth which secretly squirms from the Outside and is fermented upon countless perforations, *Drujaskan*. According to ancient Zoroastrian scriptures, Drujaskan is, technically speaking, a maximally messed-up space, awakened from and by the Earth in order to unground the Earth's wholeness or manifest divinity. In short, it is the worst possible planetary entity. The aforementioned Zoroastrian sects were associated with the act of reducing the wholeness of the divine sphere or degenerating the Earth's wholesomeness, hence speeding the emergence of Drujaskan and its inextricable holeyness. Pests teem forth from *Drujaskan*, from passages which themselves are inseparable from the writhing bodies of the pest-legion. Ungrounded and unreported histories of the Earth are full of passages, vents and soft tunnels mobilized and unlocked through participations with the Earth as a compositional entity. These histories are engineered by openings and that which crawls within them; every movement in these passages invigorates the ungrounding of the earth, engineering what makes Earth, Earth.

Paranoid cultures and their establishments always leave security leaks; they breed more holes and more solids than anyone; but these latter, far from augmenting or purging the solidus, leave it as a corpse necrotized by heavy scarring (a fibroproliferative mess) ... hole ... solid ... hole ... solid ... solid ... hole ... hole ... hole ... de-faced; it is left as the corpse of solidus, ready to decay and turn into mess. ( )hole complex turns the architectonic solid into an ex-architectural dump: laying waste, rotting erect, oozing pores.

Only as a Nemat-Space does the Earth endure; an opening through its whole, a hollow body drawing its cartographies on the surfaces of the ( )hole complex. The awakening ritual that the cult of the Old Ones practices to surreptitiously speed the return of the elders involves messing with the solid part rather than submitting to the void. Such a mission constitutes advanced re-modifications and operations on the solid part of holey space, strategically assisting the composition of new vermicular lines or worm-functions, and autonomously digging passages for the Old Ones' Return — opening yawning pits as zones of their rebirth. Each activity on the solid part or on the side of the solid is a sacred oblation to the Old Ones. To be a devoted architect of the solid is to feed the solid to the vermicular lines of the void.

They excavate tunnels in earth and lay their eggs within its pores; the larvae burrow through the earth's skin, migrating in the connective tissues, crust and strata, feeding on necrotic solids and surfaces. Burrowing sounds may be heard from within the earth. Once they have finished infesting the earth's solid part, the larvae will cut breathing holes and press their headless tails against the surface for air. The larvae will continue to grow while boring out spinal cavities for the earth's body which will never be filled. As the larvae grow, they will enlarge the holes and come out of the ground.‡

‡ Should send the email: connection is still down in 302, apologies for the delay. Exchange of love is not an economic discipline, it is the open trade of contagions. Infection and the rapid increase of venom is the consequence of such a trade. I have many thoughts for you but I think right now you might be interested in some of my thoughts prior to the first time I contacted you (the one week

BTW, I was putting the most important docs in the hotel room's nightstand as you advised and discovered two video cds in there. I watched them on the laptop: a movie from a french director named Claire Denis. I have never heard of her. excellent in this situation. I tried to get another movie of hers from a movie store in Taksim: J'ai pas Sommeil

Excursus II (Memory and ( )hole complex)

If syntheses of memory are always time-dominated, memory distractions and memory gaps take advantage of the exploitation of time outside of chronological progressions. Memory holes introduce gaps, discontinuous tunnels and porous spaces into the chronological sphere of memory, thus making it more prone to time-lapses, abrupt schizophrenic katabases (personality-pulverizing blackouts, descents free from the hegemony of solid and void), and loss of wholeness. In Zoroastrianism, playing with graves and memory are both forbidden: While one deserves a physical punishment, the other will bring eternal torment — because playing with memory (i.e. inventing lines of iteration through memory other than mere remembering functions) sorcerously reinvents events not as localizable beings but as deathless (in the sense of demonic restlessness) and inexhaustible germ-lines. Playing with memory, beyond the legitimate activity of remembering, enmeshes memory as a playground of agitated activities in the past which break the organizational consistency of the past in regard to present and future. The past as a static chronologic horizon intrinsically tends to sedentarize all types of activities in itself, or to make itself the stabilizing ground of activities in present or future: The past belongs to the Divine and tradition.

The inability to remember is usually associated with the paralytic symptoms of memory holes; in this case, the subject is not able to access the memory. If memory holes cause such accessibility problems for the subject, it is because they have been specifically designed for being accessed from the other side. In this sense, memory holes are accessible not for the subject and its integrated self but for that which is exterior to the subject and has no self (no one). If remembering is unrealistic and futile in terms of memory holes, then inversely memory holes are gates and access points; they conduct remembering and other modes of access toward a memory which belongs to the outside.

If memory holes are channels for trafficking data and retrieval from the other side, then each human or subjective attempt to recall involves an invocation of, or a stepping into the memories of, an outsider. Memory gaps, with their Space-Time lapses, function as a ( )hole complex through which nether entities seep through, rush toward our world; memory gaps are the instruments of their homecoming.‡

‡ Edit Tyranny of the Minority for publication.

S, ok, I changed my mind: I will give you a few tips in regard to Tell-Ibrahim, if you try HARD you can possibly decipher the reason I contacted you in the first place in addition to the reason I have already mentioned (which was also true but insignificant compared to this one)

PIPELINE ODYSSEY
THE Z MONOLOGUE

Z: To understand the militarization of oil and the dynamism of war machines in War on Terror, one must grasp oil as an ultimate Tellurian lubricant, or a vehicle for epic narratives. To instrumentalize oil through production, to impose any authorial line on this narrative carrier, is like feeding on the Devil's excrement or its derivatives; there is always the danger of being poisoned to death or even worse. In contemporary Islamic references to radical Jihad as a global process, the Islamic approach towards the mobilization of tactics is explained as defense as opposed to offense. In the Islamic approach – that is, the way of Jihad – Islamic war is delineated by defense, diffusion and life-support contagion, while the crusading war machines or western lines of tactics are mapped on the plane of the offensive, escalation and militant intrusion. Therefore, the western incursive dynamism of tactics is always considered un-Islamic since it perceives war as a manifest dynamic progression of war machines – which inevitably turns into something basically intrusive because such obsessively dynamic war machines intrinsically transgress and penetrate borders. 'I exist because I move' definitely makes you *persona non grata* in some places. Such a vigorous dynamism cannot operate remotely or strike the enemy without transgressing borders and territories. The western crusade, and its approach to war machines, cannot be emulated by Islam because its quality of dynamism does not correspond to the laws of Islam and the belief that transgression is idolatrous because all lands and territories belong to the Divine, not to war machines or their tactics. For Islamic Jihad, everything must operate as a defense. Consequently, the mechanism of the clash is dynamically asymmetrical.

This asymmetry is not the asymmetry of warfare but that of the principles of war itself. If, according to Islam, Jihad cannot be transgressive or intrusive, and must be conducted merely as pure defense, then how is possible to uphold the responsibility of making the earth ready for the Divine, of making Islam a global religion rather than a middle-eastern or Africo-Asian cult? The answer lies either in the invention or discovery of new war machines whose means of offense is that of peaceful communication, or in engineering a peaceful and non-transgressive medium or vehicle to host the war machines of Jihad.

In short, since western tactics is wedded to crusading fronts, and since Jihad must be grasped as a strategic and remote assault on idolatry without manifest transgression, the first task of Islam's politics of militarization is to search for or to engineer a dynamic vector or neutral vehicle to smuggle and mobilize Islamic war machines. This medium would be able to replace the dynamism of western tactics and provide Islamic war machines with a non-transgressive movement. Accordingly, such a dynamic medium or host-vehicle can only represent peace; it must be intrinsically dissociated from offense. For this reason, the medium must be part of the nature or belongs to earth, that is to say, be a neutral third party. For the Islamic side, this non-problematic medium must come from and lead toward the Divine. Yet in confrontation with the Western front, it must be politically non-intrusive (neutral) and generous toward capitalism. An entity capable of satisfying both ends is necessarily a natural entity, something from nature, a representative of the planet's sentience. Only as a planetary entity and a natural event can such a medium unproblematically host Islamic war machines. Since tactics, as dynamism or mode of movement, belongs to war machines rather than to the Divine, and is connected to human logistics or line of command, Jihad can only use a platform of movement which transports war machines naturally, or to be exact, through a property of the Divine. There is nothing more appropriate and more relevant here than Oil. Islamic Apocalypticism has understood well that anything can be pumped into gas pipelines, and oil will slide it forward as well as permanently dissolving it — meaning that whatever reaches the crusading civilizations cannot be extracted or separated from petroleum. Oil cannot be politically distilled. The entities in oil participate in a new chemical compound which cannot be broken into its elements or main constituents. For the other side of the pipeline or the West — the point of evacuation and consumption — everything in oil remains under constant camouflage; nothing but a petroleum by-product. The military magic of taking oil as the medium of movement rather than tactics unfolds when one claims that oil, as a neutral entity itself, is part of nature and is a planetary entity, hence omnipresent despite different degrees of concentration on earth. If Islamic war machines are dissolved within oil and oil is an omnipresent planetary entity, then Islamic militarization is not local anymore but global and planetary. The rise of oil as a medium for the mobilization of war machines heralds the decline of tactical offense and the dawn of an ubiquitous offense embedded within the seemingly peaceful omnipresence of nature.

War machines are dissolved in oil. The role of the oil pipeline is not military offense but life support. The pipeline provides oil as a strategic lube and a neutral vehicle of war machines with a mobile and diffusive effectivity. Oil reaches the crusading fronts through the pipeline; far corners can be reached by pumping gas in addition to oil into the pipeline. Once oil reaches its destination, the crusading war machines, whose first disposition is to be dynamic, will fuel up and assemble themselves with the oil and its derivatives. As the machines of the western enlightenment consume oil either by burning the blob or fattening up on the blob, the smuggled war machines start to activate and are chemically unbound. The nervous system and the chemistry of war machines smuggled through oil infuse with the western machines feasting on oil unnoticed, as petroleum has already dissolved or refinedly emulsified them in itself, as its chemical elements or its essential derivatives (Islamic ideologies, ambitions, implicit policies, socio-religious entities and formations, etc.). These war machines are freighted with strategic lines of Islamic Apocalypticism which fuels and escalates the transgressive impetus of western war machines, because the Divine and its desert can only be reached through participation. The extremist doctrines of Jihad discuss how everything functions as a micro-management towards the provocation of Islamic Apocalypticism, and how the Kingdom is only constructed on participation. The role of Islamic war machines, then, is to dismantle transgressive western military dynamism and at the same time to incite the western war machines into escalating their desertifying impetus. In other words, the escalation of western war machines tends towards liberating the desert of the Divine: Desert Freedom. For Jihad, the escalation of western war machines without adherence to their idolatrous logic of transgression is made possible only by diffusing through them within, and by way of, oil.

If western war machines exhibit a capitalist zeal to waste energy and material, there is no altar better for this wastage than Islamic Apocalypse and its divine cause. Now, contaminated by the sentience of oil as well as by the war machines running through it, western Technocapitalism as well as its war machines (as particularly petrophilic entities) are attracted and drawn to an agitated participation with Islamic war machines, Islamic populations and their lands which overlap petroleum reservoirs. The disparity and asymmetry between the war machines of the two fronts, and the aggravated appetite for oil building up in western machines nourished by oil, inclines this participation towards a combustible and conflictive kind of complicity. Correspondingly, Jihad's defense and Crusade's offensive invasions become as synergetic as they are asymmetrical. As the western machines are depleted of oil in this heated participation, they rush for thicker layers of the blob which transport more enthusiastic Islamic war machines with weirder sentience. The more subterranean the logic of oil extraction becomes, the more abysmal oily avatars turn out to be. The pipeline is a superficial carrier of oil and its dissolved entities; therefore, it is the duty of the crusading machines of enlightenment to fathom deeper levels. The capitalist policy of terminal accessibility or pro-marketism in regard to oil significantly adds to the depth of the Blob.

Z: In a secret twist, fueled by an enthusiasm more Islamic than Islamic entities themselves, the berserkers of capitalism rush towards Islamic Apocalypticism by fusing with its warmachines running through oil. When it comes to seeing through the pipeline, machines of enlightenment are particularly petro-mongoloid.

Z: If any movement in a conductive material produces a magnetic field, as in an electric current, then the gas pipeline where oil and Islamic warmachines move must produce an immense magnetic field of combined strategies between Islam and the Earth, swirling and encircling the tube.

Z: The Middle East stalks the world as a petroll. Is there anything more Lovecraftian than the building of a new pipeline, winding its blobbing flutes? The question is: How long can the cavernous sentience ride in this modern vehicle?

Z: Thomas Gold's theory of Deep Hot Biosphere suggests that petroleum is not a fossil fuel, and that oil has its origin in natural gas flows which feed bacteria living in the bowels of the Earth. Therefore, the demonarchy of oil is not subjected to the laws of the dead (i.e. the preserved corpses of prehistoric organisms) but rather is animated by a Plutonic vitalism (abiogenic petroleum generated by the nether biosphere of the Earth). Petroleum surfaces from primordial origins — thus, it is not of the Earth but of the Outside, planted here as a xeno-chemical Insider. Oil is produced by Plutonic forces and the nether biosphere, rather than from the decomposition of fossils and organic body-counts. Consequently, oil is far more substantial and follows a different, autonomous logic of planetary distribution. Taking Gold's theory as petropolitical ground has a different and far more strategic impact on the aforementioned pipeline scenario. If oil is somehow undying then so also are the warmachines dissolved in it, until such time as they accomplish their tasks, one on behalf of the Insider and the Earth, the other on behalf of monotheism and the Divine.

Z: Yes: In short, oil trade in the Islamic network of petropolitics is primarily used to recharge and benefit neither the wealth of countries nor the production spheres, but the pipeline itself.

EXHUMATIONS

RELICS AND DIABOLIC PARTICLES

AN ASSYRIAN RELIC

> FOUND WINGED BULL FIVE METERS BY FIVE FACE TURNING SIDEWAYS GOOD CONDITION STOP SHIPPING POSSIBLE MONTH MAY ONLY STOP COST TRANSPORTATION ABOUT TEN THOUSAND DOLLARS STOP DIVISION APRIL TWENTY SIXTH STOP SHALL WE ASK FOR BULL. (Dr. Edward Chiera, expedition field director)

In early April 1929, workmen excavating outside what would later prove to be the throne room of the Assyrian King Sargon II at Khorsabad (an Iraqi village standing on the ruins of Dur-Sharrukin: 33° 20′ N 44° 13′ E) uncovered fragments of a colossal relic; an implement of desert warfare particularly designed for the dust-swamp of Mesopotamia, the Xerodrome where warmachines take on bizarre forms and tactics — even if those tactics include sporulation or evaporation into resistant dust-spores — as a way to endure such harsh environmental conditions. Since in this dust-swamp all conventional modes of military survival are destined to become extinct, and all tactical dynamisms are easily dehydrated, melted away or evaporated without a trace, warmachines must camouflage themselves within much more resistant and elusive entities. These warmachines are consequently stealthy enough to breach any type of defensive security and to diffuse through different modes of existence (belonging simultaneously to the heterogeneous occult and monotheism, to war and peace, in the service both of the State's military formation and of insurgent forces which know no boundaries). Such a diffusion results in the forging of vectors of epidemic dispersion. A warmachine undertaking such diffusions or terminal multiplicities can be identified as an occultural, military, religious, and political entity all at once, operating as a machine both of utter eradication or revolution and of sabotage or insurgency. Such a warmachine's every movement is like an epidemic wave, encroaching upon all aspects of life: food chain, infrastructure, population, politics, trade and the overall dynamism of events. Like other Mesopotamian or Middle Eastern warmachines, which are always ready to adopt new forms in new environments and are able to adopt different tactics in favor of different political and military entities, the excavated relic was an entity militarized, in sinister fashion, in all directions: an occult-drone capable of marching forward, flying and guarding motionless, all at the same time — a perfect exemplar of occult warfare.

The inscriptions and tablets suggested that the name of this military beast was Lamassu. Sheedu Lamassu or Lamassu (the Evil Repellent one), sometimes also known as 'The Last Guardian', is a winged bull or lion with a human head usually depicted with five legs (to indicate quadropedalic movement). Lamassus belong to the neo-Assyrian era known as Sargonian. They are frequently associated with the occultural polytics of Evil-against-Evil (*The Exorcist*'s main theme) — mainly developed by the war-crazed Assyrians, Lullubis and certain elements of the Phoenicians — in which War is believed to have an (Un)Life of its own, breeding warmachines in order eventually to hunt them down. The essential irony, according to this Assyrian Axis of Evil-against-Evil, is that warmachines seek to survive each other, or in other words, they engage with and hunt each other, but they never know that War itself nurtures warmachines only to snuff them out. The sublime truth of war is expressed not by what happens between warmachines, but by that which transpires between warmachines and War, and which entails the extinction of warmachines once and for all. The Sadean conspiracy of war stands against every tactically-driven regulation of warmachines inspired by an individual or collective impetus to survival. Only by devouring all warmachines, regardless of their ferocity or adaptability, does war reach a terminal plane of autonomy out of which pure Strategy rises as the ultimate ethics of war. The ethics of war is only attainable when the tactics associated with warmachines reach a malignant multiplicity for which both the designatory plane of tactics and the line of command become redundant. The dissolution of warmachines through their terminal tactical multiplicity signals the awakening of war as an autonomous strategy. If strategy is indifferent to the purpose of warmachines and tactical determination, it is because the domain of strategy is exterior to that of tactics (which is in fact the warmachine itself). Strategy resides outside of warmachines but inside of war; it pursues war 'by any means possible'. Strategy grasps war outside of the tactical requirements peculiar to warmachines and by doing so, it exposes the exteriority of war to the warmachine and its tactics. Likewise, the (Un)Life of War maintains its radical outsideness by turning the tactics (of warmachines) into pure strategy. External to tactical manipulations and the governing lines of command, strategy is diagrammed by intrinsic escape from those military configurations which simultaneously provide warmachines with survival and destruction.

Evidently, then, war is not the consequence of conflicting warmachines. The Unlife of War is autonomous, but it spawns warmachines only so as eventually to devour them. Grasping this sado-conspiracy of War, the ancient Mesopotamian warmachines engineered the Axis of Evil-against-Evil, a theoretical and pragmatic doctrine for participating with the Unlife of War. The Axis was constituted out of military techniques corresponding with the strategic plane of War rather than with the regulation and tactical dynamism of warmachines. The Assyrians practiced the doctrine of Evil-against-Evil so as to combine all aspects of being into an autonomous military machine characterised by an autophagic ferocity.

According to the Axis of Evil-against-Evil, the first task of warmachines is to perceive War not as a consequence of collisions between warmachines or crisscrossing lines of tactics, but as an autonomous machine spawning warmachines in order to hunt them down. War uses its own weapons against warmachines in the same way that warmachines employ their weapons against each other. Assyrian military scriptures frequently refer to these weapons and implements of war as in contrast to the military weapons of warmachines. Throughout the scriptures, these weapons are alluded to as a 'Fog of War': Strategies and dracospiral pathways upon which warmachines are gradually but subtly devoured, eaten away, by war. In one such scripture, Lamassu is hailed as the first military invention to venerate War as being external to the logics, existence and activities of warmachines.

According to the Assyrian Axis of Evil-against-Evil, War spreads over deep occultural agitations, Tellurian dynamics, heretical insurgencies and Outsiders.

> The truth of war lies beyond the battlefield. (Aramaic shibboleth inscribed on the Lamassu discovered at Khorsabad)

Parsani notes that, for the Assyrians, 'war hunts warmachines rather than warmachines hunting each other.' War is fueled by terminal fusions of strategy and tactical multiplicities; everything that emerges from war is a devastating disruption for the configurations, guiding systems and probe-functions of warmachines. According to the occultural and military doctrine of Evil-against-Evil, war produces too much heat for warmachines to bear, to the degree that they begin gradually to melt (tactical meltdown), precipitating a molecular breakdown into diabolical particles. The Assyrians suspected that Mesopotamia was swarming with these diabolical particles — the demonically lingering remnants of warmachines. Tactically dead but strategically reanimated and introduced to the battlefield, this molecular debris left behind by melting warmachines was frequently referred to as 'the Fog of War'.

> In Assyrian military doctrines, warmachines are always incinerated and consumed by war. The process of immolation is gradual and twisted, but the return path to life is abrupt and is never recorded. For war resurrects the disintegrated warmachines and brings them back to life from the other

side of the battlefield, in the form of a Cimmerian haze — the Fog of War. (H. Parsani)

The Assyrians believed that these particles or necrospores of dead war-machines haunted every aspect of Middle Eastern life on behalf of war. These particles were generally understood to be a demonic dust, a cloud of spores or dry-spirits capable of possessing military programs, political systems and people. Assyrians alluded to them as 'relics' or 'diabolical things' more radically warlike than warmachines themselves.

It was mainly through the Axis of Evil-against-Evil as an occultural and polytical vehicle that the doctrine of autonomous war impregnated Zoroastrianism (the germ cell of Abrahamic monotheism). Later on, the Axis was vigorously unfolded through Islam's military omega of Jihad known as *Qiyamah* or Islamic Apocalypse. In *Qiyamah*, every warmachine must burn, and all modes of military survival — whether belonging to the State or to nomadic insurgencies — must be consumed by the Unlife of War. The Axis of Evil-against-Evil is a 'polytics of endurance' in War, but one that resists any form of attunement to or economical appropriation by the survival impetus of warmachines. For warmachines, survival-oriented regulations are not limited to the act of surviving; they also drive warmachines to move and to kill. The Axis sought to breed and simulate warmachines corresponding to the machinic particles and weapons that War employs to hunt warmachines. For this reason, the doctrine of Evil-against-Evil developed models of terminal fusion between tactics and strategy, with the aim of attaining autonomy and pragmatic multiplicity (delineated by smooth operational cutting-edges, cryptogenic emergence, tracelessness, omnipresence, multi-functionality and the ability to cross incompatible dimensions, traversing new territories to accomplish their tasks). In short, the Assyrian Axis was supposed to engineer warmachines corresponding to the Unlife of War itself, if only as faint terrestrial echoes of its unlimited ferocity.

The Assyrians understood that the tactical knowledge of their warmachines must nourish itself on the Axis of Evil-against-Evil, the para-military doctrine which perceives war as being independent of warmachines. War has terminal occultural tendencies for hunting warmachines of all kinds. The Assyrians realized that in order to protect the State from the inevitable internal insurrections, organizational corruptions and incursions from the outside, they had to engender warmachines conforming to the autonomous tendencies of war. However, according to Parsani, the Assyrians' fatal mistake was to ignore the fact that those warmachines which achieve autonomy and are fueled by the fusion of tactics and strategy, will eventually turn into disloyal agents or double-dealers (Trisonomic dissenters). Such warmachines gnaw at the roots of the State's foundation on all fronts, corroding it, becoming invisible gates between the State and the Unlife of War. The task of the Assyrian para-military behemoth was to breed unheard-of warmachines capable of roaming freely beyond the borders of the State — security leaks which do not open the State to its enemies but to that which knows nothing of territory, survival or even nomad warmachines. A State protected and secured by such intrinsically elusive warmachines no longer answers to Deleuze and Guattari's characterisation of the State.

> Lamassus, also known as 'The Last Guardians', are always found in pairs at the border of Assyrian palaces, gates and the entrances leading to the most sacred temples. Lamassus watch what comes in but not what goes out. Viewed from the front, they stand firmly in place; seen from the side, their winged bodies appear to stride forward on a peculiar complement of five legs each, indicating the marching movement of a quadropedal beast. Lamassu is a desert hunter; it takes flight so as to chase pests descending from the sky; it is a weapon enveloping diverse tactical lines and instruments of battle. Lamassus are capable of crossing over into fundamentally different planes or dimensions all at once — they attack, defend, hunt and scheme. Standing still at the gates, they can yet be present everywhere: At the threshold of the outside and at the outer limits of the state. For this reason, Lamassus are usually identified by their transient omnipresence inside and outside the battlefield. The Babylonians called the Assyrians' bizarre obsession with these creatures 'Lamassu-Complex', in an allusion to the belief that war has a life of its own. (H. Parsani)

The following section is a distorted part of the original report presented to Delta-Force's special division, OBIteration Unit (possibly derived from *Obi, bayi* — sorcery and Obliteration — but the first three capital letters suggest an acronym, making this interpretation problematic). The report was made by former infantry Colonel Jackson West, upon securing the archeological site of NIPPUR (Iraq: 32° 10′ N 45° 11′ E). The archeological site was covertly secured by conducting a distracting Shock and Awe operation called Ready-for-CNN Hajj, carried out by the spectacular black (CARC) helicopters of the US 160th Special Operations Aviation Regiment. Later, a section of the report was leaked to the public by Jackson West, who had unexpectedly deserted Delta Force. The information leak was later confirmed by a Delta Force security spokesman. This version of the report was presumably rewritten by someone other than West himself, recomposed a number of times possibly as a result of multiple oral transcriptions. For this reason, the Hyperstition team decided to revise and edit the entire text. The report bears a striking resemblance to a short essay written by Dr. Hamid Parsani on a military manuscript discovered in 1986 at Shaduppum (located at TELL-HARMEL, which apparently means 'place of writing': 33° 22′ N 44° 28′ E) along with scripts on mathematics (Mesomath), botany, ancient warfare, religion and various lexicons. In that essay, Parsani offers a detailed discussion of a cryptogenic Assyrian military experiment in occult weaponry which eventually led to the total eradication of the Assyrian civilization in the summer of 612 BC. Parsani nominates this occultural meltdown 'Assyrian Syndrome', possibly an anti-monotheistic (devoid of Yahweh's jealousy and its consequent victimhood) and polytical nomenclature after Nahum's *The Burden of Nineveh*. This is a part of the report as edited by the Hyperstition team:

> The most terrible assaults are those carried out by occult particles (they called them demons or agents from the other side) as well as the diabolical undertides of War itself. Lamassus were revered as the most militantly efficient and tenacious guardians against intruders, occultural saboteurs and violating sorcerous forces in particular. Lamassus are always twosome, and hence more than one but essentially less than the multiplicity of lurking barbarians, desert Tartars and the Golden Horde. More than one and less than many, Lamassus are always duplicitous in every sense. These numeric behemoths share more with the numerical sorcery of Capitalism than one can imagine. Moving toward ambiguous but efficient numbers, twinness and duplicity are spontaneous numeric military units; they effectively combine the fluidity of the many and the military precision of one. Undoubtedly, Lamassu formulates the principle of Dyadic Glory — the towering towers of Capitalism come in twos. Lamassus undertake a strategic course of action, engineered by terminal fusions of tactics and strategy, to defend the state against occultural particles and unheard-of enemies. Assyrians believed that the most terrible warriors of their empire were not their human berserkers, but Lamassus. Bound to state militarization on one side, but autonomous on the other, Lamassus operate on behalf of both the state's occultural programs and occultural entities of the outside. They erode the borders of the state, its horizon and its gates, from those obscure regions between the inner and the outer where blurring of the boundaries proceeds at a drastic rate. The regions occupied by Lamassus harbour such violent conflicts between the occultural entities of the State and the Outside that conflictual communication is replaced by contamination, and the climax of victory or defeat is succeeded by the swash-backwash waves of epidemics. These regions gradually turn into zones of overwhelming occultural traffic, full of the potential to erode the State and its neighboring geopolitical environment. In the presence of occult entities such as Lamassu and other repellents, the State's border is reinvented as a field of vortices unloading occultural heterogeneities into the State, resulting in:
>
> > I. Corrosion as a result of the difference between internal violent fissions associated with divergent occultural lines (tending to propagate in all directions) and the gravitational pull of the States' core which tends to converge all activities according to itself.
> >
> > II. Dissemination of insurgent crowds as the consequence of violent internal fissions. Minority-engineering leads to minority-militarism, critically disturbing the cohesion of territorial functions and the State's programs.
> >
> > III. Inflammation of regions already damaged by the systematic failures inherent to organizations and boundaries. These regions are always

either the first territories of the empire to be torn apart, or the first places to be invaded by external forces.

IV. Rise of parasitical modes of organizational poverty. The state's political programs — responsible for reinforcing and integrating the system — gradually begin to diverge and deteriorate under the influence of occult political pollution. This political pollution is the result of contamination by occultural tendencies which are external to the original programming and the intention of the State's politics. Eventually, the State's political lines lose any capacity to reinforce the system either economically or politically.

V. Finally, implosion of the State, usually coinciding with an invasion from the Outside. For the forces of the outside are always lying in wait, ready to launch an ambush when borders collapse or are perforated — lurking, ready to rush in. At the time of the Assyrian occultural meltdown, foreigners flooded down from the mountains and consumed what had already been eaten from the inside. The invincible empire was devoured by outsiders in a matter of days. 'Assyria will fall by the sword that is not of man; a sword, not of mortals, will devour them.' (Isaiah 31:8)

Colonel West ends the report with the following sermon:

War on Terror is riddled with dusty ancient crypts saturated with occult geometries. Our decadent intelligence systems, our artless principles of warfare, can never exhume these crypts, from which the other side of the battle digs out its untimely war machines and offbeat tactics. Their war machines do not belong to the time we know, the time in which our civilizations were built. We find ourselves constrained to fight in their time, according to geometries which are utterly alien to us. Our exposure to this alien time carries the risk of chronic side effects, or something even worse, something irrecoverable and beyond our bloodiest dreams of frenzy, smoke and ash,* which in comparison will come to seem like the harmless daydreams of unsophisticated, naive innocents.

[* There was a woman lying on her back next to the truck, a middle-aged woman with a sun-burnt skin ... eyes gouged out and filled with semen; it was more exquisite than the white eyes of an epileptic. I named her Moby Dick. (Jackson West's journal, entry date: December 4, 1993)]

With the fury of my terrible weapons ... (Tiglath-Pileser I, Assyrian King ca. 1110 BC; from a tablet discovered beneath a gate at the entrance of Sennacherib Palace guarded by two Lamassus)

The manipulative policies of the State exploit occultism either as a repressive tool and a substitute for rigorous politics (the occult as a dummy politics) or as a means to repel outsiders (xeno-agents), their principles and influences. But once these political tendencies are undermined and derailed, the occult perforates the body of the state's politics, which, decaying, can no longer hold at bay the Outsiders and radical xeno-particles (whose functioning is external to the survival of the State). In the wake of this political cataclysm, every program, every manipulative policy, mutates into tentacles of communication spreading deep throughout the untrodden abyss of the Outside.

The State's occult entities will eventually attain autonomy as a result of such constant communication with xeno-agents. Avatars of the outside awaken the insurgent potentials inherent to the State's occult entities. Correspondingly, the rise of autonomous entities within the State contributes to the emergence of anomalies. The more autonomous processes emerge within the state, the more anomalous the State becomes. If occultism propagates itself only by eating itself, then once the State's politics is contaminated by the autonomous occult, it too will become autophagic by nature.

By fatally overexposing themselves to horizons from beyond, the State's occultural agents gradually construct bridges and unlock gates between the borders of the State and occult entities of the Outside. This panorama of emerging duplicity is anticipated by pulp-horror's obsession with the spontaneous disorders caused by occultural guardians, rebel Lamassus and independent scarecrows hunting farmers and desolate lands with a passion. (Such narratives of insurgency recall the Catholic obsession with gargoyles.) Pulp-horror quite rightly detects an ominous tendency of the State towards the employment of hyperstitional and occultural agents. As soon as gargoyles become fully active on an autonomous level (fusing with intrusive outsiders and contaminated by alien particles), they come out of their petrified state. They begin to feast on everything that remains inside, the walls and empty aisles. They melt into pillars, infesting them stone by stone, deeply embedding the architecture of the holy place with their own *khemistry*.

Such ostensibly instrumentalized occultural agents betray their host more virulently and ferociously when they are directly exposed to war and its deep occultural tendencies. These renegade agents possess both the schizotrategic creativity of sorcerous polytics and the State's perverse taste for manipulation and radical abuse. In occult warfare, a Lamassu becomes as one with the attackers, operating externally to the State's mechanisms, making the State prone not to any particular occult entities, but to an outside coming forth from the inside. Such is the black epic brewed up by the Mesopotamian Axis of Evil-against-Evil.‡

‡ 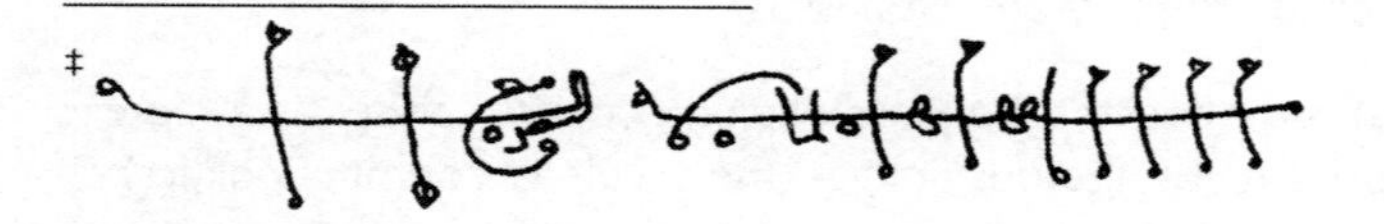

Iranian political historian Esmail Raeen, in his masterwork on Freemasonry in Iran, discusses how conspiracy theories and occult doctrines seem to be distracting hobbies for the masses. They defer rigorous political engagement, and hamper resistance against the State. Occult derivatives can be characterized as activities which reinforce the organizational processes of the State by marginalizing critical politics. In a similar way, conspiracy theories enshroud the political activities of the State, only aiding them in disseminating throughout the socio-political sphere unnoticed. However, Raeen continues by suggesting that both the occult and conspiracy theories contaminate the channel regimes through which macro-politics of the state targets collectivities. If occult commotions impede and disrupt the transmission of political information, both ends of the channel — the State and the targeted populations — will be affected.

Conspiracy theories and the occult produce too much noise, too much offbeat signal (superfluous or trash-politics: polytics?) for the channels through which the State's politics are meant to be transferred across wide arrays of socio-economic and military territories. They corrupt and block the State's exclusive signals. When it comes to State politics, conspiracy and occult confusions slow down the rate of effective delivery to the masses — the speed which lends a military edge to the political validity, regional pertinence and authority of the State. The faster a political signal is delivered (established), the more effective it will be against the masses and against other states. The result of hindering the State's political transmissions is the political poverty of the State, which can never be undone, even by overthrowing the State's regime or through vigorous reformation; it always remains there as a persistent mess.

The contamination between conspiracy theories and what is customarily viewed as 'real politics' is mutual and irreversible. If the state uses a strategic weapon to distract the masses, this does not mean that the weapon always functions properly or reaches the intended target. Strategy is a two-edged sword; contrary to the command perspective, the presence of strategy in the battlefield testifies against its fidelity and alliance. Strategic weapons are not merely autonomous in their versatility, but also in their departure from the line of command. The use of trash politics by the state might conform to its micro-politics of anti-resistance, but like all strategic weapons, trash politics have ambitions of their own.

'Political pollution' is a term suggested for the process of contamination caused by the difference between the utilizable and autonomous aspects of strategic quantities — the expectations of the line of command as opposed to strategies for and in themselves. Political pollution coincides with the remobilization of the State's politics irrespective of people and the state, tactical designations and command determinations. As strategic quantities, occult and conspiracy theories can be utilized by the line of command only when their strategic side is integrated with a tactical front. This integration is necessary in order to attribute a tactical designation to a strategic line and to prevent the strategy from operating completely autonomously, or what is generally called 'running amok'. The integration of a strategic line and a tactical front (or dynamic configuration) is conducted and determined through the plane of logistics attached to the plane of tactics. Since the plane of tactics exists as sheer activity or dynamism, and is characterized by its tendency toward correction and designation, it must constantly be supported and fueled by a plane existing outside of — but connected to — tactics. This simultaneously external and connected plane which sustains tactics is the plane of logistics. In fact, the line of command can tactically influence strategic lines only through the plane of logistics, to which all lines of tactics are bound. The military significance of the plane of logistics lies in the fact that it can temporarily make an operational edge or a point of designation in the form of a vertex between the convergent line of tactics and divergent line(s) of strategy. The plane of logistics extracts a functional military designation or target-oriented operational edge from strategy by interlocking it with lines of tactics (see Fig. 17). This operational vertex can be deployed as a multi-focal military cutting-edge.

Tactics signify modes of dynamism required for handling warmachines and troops in the battlefield; therefore, the tactical is directly connected to the line of command. Strategy, however, brings forces to the battlefield as xeno-carriers. To this extent, the plane of logistics can simultaneously connect the lines of command to the lines of strategy, thus sealing an operational bond between tactics and strategy.

Whilst the plane of logistics surrounds and encompasses the line of tactics from all directions, it can only be attached to lines of strategy from one side. Strategy is only bound to the plane of logistics unilaterally through a temporal and easily-terminable connection with the plane of tactics. The other side of strategy always lies beyond the border of the battlefield — external to military survival, feeding on the Unlife of War itself. The external side of strategy cannot be penetrated by any mode of programming: It is refractory, disloyal, autonomously rampant and torrential in its epidemic divergence.

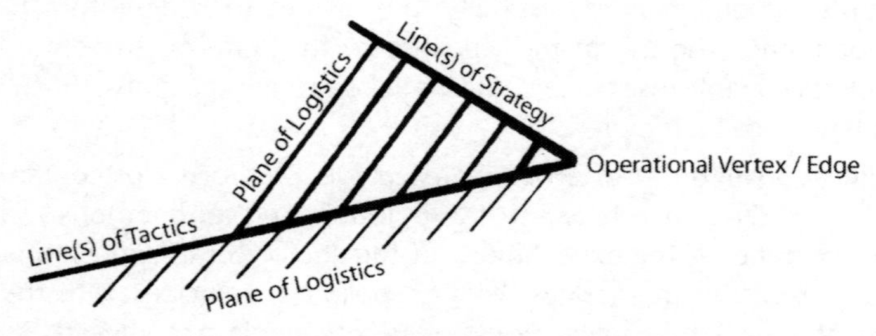

Fig. 17 Plane of logistics, participation with strategy and the formation of an operational cutting-edge

It is mainly on the plane of logistics that strategy can be opened up to anthropomorphic participation (lines of command). The autonomy, tactical multiplicity and inter-dimensional dynamism of strategy render it impossible to locate. If traceability of movement and localizablility of existence are prerequisites for participation with military entities, strategy is the loss of all traces – hence it cannot voluntarily be participated in. Strategy always arrives as an involuntary participation, a participation from the other side; therefore, it corresponds with a terminal parasitism in which the outside feeds on the inside (of the system). If strategy defies location and traces, who is to guarantee that strategy (occult agencies, schizotrategies, etc.) is on the battlefield when it is supposed to be, and not somewhere else, engineering some war-polytics of its own? This sinister question is dissimulated by lines of command which constantly seek to communicate with strategy through the plane of logistics in order to assure their military survival – to protect themselves 'from' the autonomous side of strategy, but also 'by means of' it; a political irony which cannot but result in political pollution and the gradual but brutal erosion of the State's macro-politics.‡

---

‡ *S*, falling in love cannot occur twice; it means there is no chance you can fall in love twice, for if love is the hemorrhage of health and a manifest catastrophe, then nothing is left in the lover to fuel another love and fall in love once again. Love empties all possibilities of recovery. Falling in love is a one way ticket to the end of health. Barthes suggests that love is cyclic, that for each love there is a phase of recovery and at the end of each recovery another love is waiting. This cycle strikes me not as love but flirtation, flirtation with survival. A lover who constantly falls in love (the Barthesian lover) flirts either with the survival of himself or his emotions. Love, in this sense, only reinscribes survival. And when it comes to survival, human desire is already a dead ruin. In Barthes' account, it is not love that matters but the 'next love' which presupposes the survival of the lover and the regeneration of his health. But love's sole enthusiasm lies in consuming every possibility of falling in love again. Cyclic love is like Chinese Erotics, in which sexual excitement is held back in order to have multiple climaxes. I love to recover to love someone else to recover to love someone else ... This is indeed an inventive formula, but one for survival, not for love. The Love-Recovery cycle that Barthes maps in his works is of course Proustian but deeply resembles the ever refining self-fertilizing cycle of Aristotle (nothing must be wasted as it is needed in the next phase of the cycle, the next love, the next recovery from the last love). If for Avernus there is only one irreversible descent, then descending again is merely an attempt to keep ascending and escaping Avernus. Love ensures the failure of escape. Love is only thinkable as one and only one tyrannical possibility: falling in love once and for all. Viva the chain. Ok *S*, I'm tired ... signing off

THE DEAD MOTHER OF ALL CONTAGIONS

In one chapter from *Defacing the Ancient Persia*, Parsani writes, 'I come from a culture for which death is not only ossified but also pulverized into a gray powder, an abominable dust which then attracts cosmic wetness and moisture in order to make a necrophilic mess.' This strange and ambiguous statement is then extended through two analyses which unfold Parsani's avid exploration of the theme of dust as the desired object of monotheistic Zoroastrianism and the middle-eastern doppelganger of *Aqua Vitae*. 'Evidently, middle-eastern epics and narratives are by nature very "dusty"', observes the Lebanese interviewer. 'In the Middle East, spiritual journeys, abreactive trances, otherworldly expeditions, explorations, wayfaring, even political rallies and mysterious missions for obscure objectives, take place through dust and deserts rather than rivers and seas. Civilizations are buried under deserts rather than sinking beneath oceans. Ships are found in dead seas; Deities breathe dust and sear worlds. This construction of everything together out of dust, considered in the context of the Middle East, is nothing less than a realism (albeit a speculative one): Dust is our super-weapon, infected with bad karma. You have said that nothing is more characteristically middle-eastern than the monotheistic, essentially Zoroastrian, phrase "dust to dust". Where does all this dust come from in your works?' the interviewer asks Parsani.

'Dust is all we have here in the Middle East, it is all that we can consume without fear of ever losing it,' Parsani's response begins. 'Breathe as deeply as you will, dust will never be depleted. If the profound hostility of the Middle East towards being settled even as a geographic entity cannot be fully grasped, this is because even its terrestrial bedrock, its concrete ground, is progressively eroding and degenerating into dust.'

Parsani names dust 'the middle-eastern unit of information', or sometimes even 'that middle-eastern relic from which nothing can escape'. If the tendency of dust lies in the direction of a becoming-particle (naught-ness) as well as wetness (dust is hydrophilic by nature) because its emergence is accompanied by dehydration and evaporation of moisture, then the terms xero- (dry) and data might relay the full import of Parsani's reference to dust.

Xero-data, or dust, swarms planetary bodies as the primal flux of data or the Mother of all Data-streams in the Solar system. Each particle of dust carries with it a unique vision of matter, movement, collectivity, interaction, affect, differentiation, composition and infinite darkness — a crystallized data-base or a plot ready to combine and react, to be narrated on and through something. There is no line of narration more concrete than a stream of dust particles. Interstellar dust was involved in the formation of stars and planetary bodies. Earth as a rebel disciple of the Sun is shelled with dust particles from within and without. For this reason, there is no fiction more original — in terms of schizophrenia, collectivity of writers, movements of different plots, composition, rich inauthenticity and jargons — than the Earth itself, the Earth composed of dust particles and fluxes. Here Parsani's remark that 'the Middle East is the dust swamp of the Earth' develops a fictional edge saturated by new literary-theoretical problematics of storytelling. In *Defacing the Ancient Persia* Parsani sometimes calls the Earth the 'round jargon'. Given that each dust particle envelopes and carries different materials and entities from diverse territories, dust particles express particulars of different fields and territories in terms of universals. When dust particles are composed, they combine countless terms, languages and materials belonging to entirely different kingdoms. Dust particles originate from dark corners never trodden before, different territories (fields of narration) and domains of invisible hazards. Each particle carries crystallized waste matter and essences of different groups and particularities, hard to grasp but easy to commingle with fluid. For Parsani, this fluid or wetness, essential for blending the dust particles in the Middle East into one narrative with multiple undertows, is petroleum, or *napht* (oil). In the Avestan language of ancient Persia, the word *napht* is the word for wetness itself. If each dust particle emerges from a different territory and is composed of anonymous materials, then dust particles can only settle together and unite once they are moistened by one substance. 'Only oil can settle the dust of the Middle East,' declares Parsani. But dust is a real nomadic entity, because it migrates elsewhere, spiriting itself away as an illusive ground, a bogus State.

'The pro-creationist chauvinism associated with dust, as seen in monotheism,' Parsani continues in his interview, 'is an ongoing process of composition. Religion never takes creation as a fixed point in time or an outset, it is a continuing and developing process which begets time and space. According to

Zoroastrianism as the rudimentary ovum of monotheism, dust is the most elemental object of creation; it contaminates time as well as space. In the Middle East, time is measured not by the clock but by dust.'

Monotheism either misses or intentionally ignores the point that if the Divine's Creation and Order vacuously exploit dust as the irreducible and most primary instance of reductive purity, other agendas too use dust as a compact agent of synthesis, mixture and assortment of countless things from different territories. Not only God, but diseases, deluges and blinding smogs all employ dust as their primary agent. If dust represents a return to God as one, different particles and hazards too can be crystallized or sporulated as one within a dust particle. For a dust particle, one is always a legion. The purity of dust as an object deliverable to God (from dust to dust) can be perpetuated only as a disguised unity of minute contagions and pollutants. Since the Divine's creation always seeks to promote its zeal in dust, the Divine's process of creation advocates such hazardous agendas disguised as dust. In this sense, the unity of creation is already the collectivization of diabolical particles. Parsani's remark that 'the Divine itself is a suspicious carrier of diabolical particles, both in its creation and in its policies' makes sense here. In his book, Parsani questions the irony of creation: 'If dust composes creation out of its own logic and order, it is because for dust, creation is the very essence of sadism: giving birth to something, feeding it, waiting and then reducing it to dust. If dust is inseparable from creation, it is because creation is always a "reducing to dust". What would be the point, for dust, of composing an entity whose purpose is to become dust again, other than to quench a morbid desire, a desire for which creation is a conspiracy to experience the dusting process at a more aggravated intensity — an unabated sado-masochism ... ?' Parsani's view on dust, however, drastically changes from a crypto-nihilist position ('dust is not Nothing, and there is always something, viz. dust') to a more characteristically middle-eastern interrogation and world view. Rather than enforcing nihil, for Parsani dust now seems to condense an irreducible complexity stemming from its syncretic approach to everything, a point of view corroborated in horrifically concrete fashion by the Middle East's dense syncretic involvement in global affairs. 'Dust is the master of collective insurgencies,' Parsani continues with the Lebanese interviewer, 'it is an indivisible part of authority, yet its syncretism unfolds only as an uprising when the crystal thaws, when the spore breaks. Dust's patience in pursuing its obscure ambitions is comparable to the stubborn persistence of creation and its chronological time of past, present and future. The enthusiasm of dust towards unfolding is always on behalf of the many, crystallized as one particle.'

Dust simultaneously emerges as the alpha and omega xero-data; there is no signal or message other than the compositional insurgency of dust, whose syncretism and obscure polytics of creation can be effectively registered or rooted on a flux of dust. 'Dust' is the name of a rebellion marked by utter collectivity and progressing at a cosmic level. There is always an abysmal conspiracy wherever dust begins to engineer a composition or forge a compositional bedrock for a ground or a regime. As an inter-dimensional carrier, dust scavenges xenochemical particles (outsiders) as its cores or constituents, introduces and implants them into compositions, creations and establishments. A dust particle collects its components from different milieus so distant from one another that they can operate for each other only as outsiders. When dust is utilized in creation to compose and concoct, it turns the object, or to be precise, the created composition, into a fierce operative of horror, with a progressively thickening ominous plot or storyline which might be summarized as follows: As the creation, the body which has been made out of dust, turns to dust once more, the outsiders which were consolidated within each spore or crystal surface are released. The release of these multiplicities disguised as one within each dust particle is equal to the arrival of the alien not from without but from within. As in the case of a spore about to break open and release its bacteria, this emergence of new life forms and collective particles might be apprehended as an insider takeover, the rise of a new people.

Reducing to dust is thus neither a monotheistic oversimplification nor a reduction. It minimally denotes a process by which a new people are liberated from the authorial Whole (the structure, the body, the creation) as it degenerates into dust. Everything that has resided within and has never been active in its original 'outsiding' form will come forth. In dealing with dust, as in dealing with the earth and the Middle East, the insider always precedes the outsider in unfolding its exteriority, its radical insurgency and its flight from the authority of the Whole. In releasing latent and dormant agencies within each spore or dust particle, the role of the Outsider is replaced by the Insider. When considering dust, the earth and the Middle East, one must always think of the inside. Parsani's analogy of the Middle East's terminal minority multiplicity, or the rise of minorities ('minority holocaust'), with dust and the extreme way it liberates the outsiders which have already been condensed and crystallized as insiders can be traced through the panorama of 'Reduction to Dust':

> For the rest of the world — especially westerners — the Middle East is just a region filled with ragtag States-within-States, a dense constellation of every type of scum on earth. The Middle East is a socio-political disparagement, not even constituting a solid region but just randomly populating itself in the middle-eastern regions of the earth's body; a random terror at best. And everything middle-eastern is reducing to dust anyway. But here they precisely miss the point: For the rich diversification and propagation of minorities in the Middle East is in fact the direct consequence of this degeneration-to-dust, the consequence of releasing the repressed outside, voluntarily favoring it and its people over the established state and its so-called aboriginal people. This is not the whole scenario yet: the Middle East has already found out that it requires a total political as well as social and terrestrial creativity to become conscious and responsible in regard to this

> dusting process. The Middle East perpetuates this creativity by escalating its own reduction to dust until the earth is populated anew, inundated by minority deluges. When populations and systems turn into dust, they bring forth unheard-of things. Sadly enough, the West in particular doesn't understand that there is nothing more ordinary, usual and perpetual than being reduced to dust, and that they too are part of it. Turning into dust is a sweeping tellurian event, an event operating in favor of the dormant, the Insider, the slumbering.

If the emergence of the Outsider is defined by the term 'awakening', it is because it has already been included as an insider, an intrinsic part of the composition, embedded in the nervous system of the structure as an endemic or domestic agency. In his *Notes on Reliquology* (the study of relics), Parsani notes that the charm of relics as 'outsiders' precisely originates from their autochthonic characteristics, the oscillation between the domestic and the foreign packed into one object. If the Outsider is manifested in the persistence of its exteriority and invasiveness, then its advent should not be anticipated from the outside as that which is external to the boundaries, but from the inside, as that which has already invaded the system and now resides within the boundary. Dust, for this reason, is a resident Outsider.

> In Zoroastrianism, so long as dust is regarded as a particle of a degenerated foulness such as a corpse or dried bones, it suggests purity; but as soon as it is confronted as a relic or an entity-in-itself, it becomes an absolutely appalling unit of uncleanness, a demonculus *per se*. (H. Parsani, *Notes on Reliquology*)

For dust, awakening is translated as dust-to-dust (releasing what has already been crystallized in the dust particle). The awakening of the xenochemical insider camouflaged within the composition during the degeneration into dust — from Dust to Dust — is what makes dust a true Abomination, an undercover subject and object of the awakening, both the cult and the quiescent slumbering crowd.

A self-degenerating entity, a volunteer for its own damnation, dust opens new modes of dispersion and of becoming-contagious, inventing escape routes as yet unrecorded. In his interview, Parsani suggests that the Middle East has simulated the mechanisms of dusting to mesh together an economy which operates through positive degenerating processes, an economy whose carriers must be extremely nomadic, yet must also bear an ambivalent tendency toward the established system or the ground. An economy whose vehicle and systems never cease to degenerate themselves. For in this way, they ensure their permanent molecular dynamism, their contagious distribution and diffusion over the entire global economy (gaining epidemic dispersion by degenerating into particles and mobile hazards).

The dust epidemic which Parsani associates with middle-eastern policies or the degenerating process of Dust to Dust is not divergent and linear. It is a dynamic field with diverse paths, swirling dust vortices working with different elements and on different axes (corresponding with Trison-cells and Feedback Spirals), applying different forces and various levels of 'reducing to dust'. Parsani completely disperses his discourse on Hidden Writing until it becomes as one with his disquisitions on dust: 'Dustism is the middle-eastern way of renewing and becoming new for the Earth, a course of action which is not taken in favor of, or on behalf of, solar capitalism and the Sun's hegemony. Dustism favors the Earth's clandestine autonomy and its rebellion against the domination — whether vitalist or annihilationist — of the Sun. The cult of dust celebrates the Insider. Dustism inspires a radical and concrete approach to the Outside without becoming a solar slave or a Sun cultist, a blind disciple lacking autonomy or a naive inhabitant of the terrestrial sphere. And ... well, this is exactly where capitalism — and particularly the US — eat the Middle East's dust.'

So baked, so dehydrated, dust thirsts for cosmic wetness, for the Flood. 'In monotheism and especially in Zoroastrianism, dust is usually considered immaculate. But once it makes a potage with wetness and mist, it becomes the House of Abomination, the *Drujaskan* or *Drujestan*, the soft soggy earth and the living mud of inextricable mess,' Parsani informs us in *Defacing the Ancient Persia*. Only years later does Parsani note that the catalysing wetness for dust which was cursed by the Zoroastrians and worshipped by Akht and his cult (Akht-Yatu) was, in fact, none other than petroleum, or napht.

The fundamental discovery of the Greek elementalist and cosmogonist tradition (from Empedocles to Aristotle and beyond) was that 'a dry element thirsts for its wet twin'. The dry element thirsts to fuse with its wet twin thereby to take a new path of existence. The outcome of such a fusion is the emergence of a new sentience out of the contamination between elements. It is precisely in order to conceal the menaces of such a pollution and its contagious potentialities that pro-creationism and the philosophies of Genesis established themselves on the dynamics of the entwining of wet and dry as a fundamental attraction (φιλία). In terms of this elemental attraction or philia, the solid is as insurgent and activist as the fluid. The thirst of the dry to fuse with the wet refers to the ulterior process of plague-engineering secretly running through every pro-creationist economy and system of genesis. To this extent, when pro-creationist religions and schools insist that such frantic attractions are the basic procedures through which Genesis and Creation constantly refresh themselves, then one can argue that creation must be bound to the emergence of plagues, diseased compositions, mess and chemical blasphemies. Pro-creationist religions assume that cycles of fusion between dust and wetness bring forth fertilization, but fertility in terms of mess only 'gets messier'. Dust as xero-data, with its condensed syncretism, is an attractor for foaming plagues on a pandemic scale. 'If dust has an uncontrollable thirst for wetness then what guarantees that it only fuses with pure water and does not promiscuously intertwine with every obscure wetness and unholy fluid that lurks in the Universe?' Parsani asks. In the guise of exorbitant heat, solar capitalism reduces dust, and the dusting process, to the surplus value of the ground or the earth's crust. Dust, however, constantly undermines this politico-economic reduction by fusing with every wetness it meets along its path of dispersion. Once fused with wetness, dust returns to the ground as a foaming mess or wet epidemic (the Rain) with the power to penetrate the ground to its compositional level, residing there and starting to contaminate both soil and sub-soil. This panorama takes the form of a tide toward a mess-hysteria, an omega-pollution, as the contaminated ground and biosphere turn to dust one more time to get closer to the ultimate purity.

By fulfilling creation's cycle of purification (dust to dust), the ground and biosphere contribute to the consummation of dust with wetness — mess. The pro-creationist cycle of purification is transcendentally carried out through being recycled into dust over and over again. Each cycle brings heavier inundations of pollutant wetness, encompassing more remote variations of chemistry. This cyclical frenzy is called 're-fanging', a polytical remobilization where the head overlaps and locks onto the tail. The diagram of this dry-wet fusion cycle (dust × wetness = decreasing ground + increasing mess = dust × wetness = ...) as an unfolding epidemic or 'the-Thing-without-Genesis' (Parsani) is a spiraling *Azhi* (the Avestan dragon of the deep) or a convoluted Ouroboros. Also called the Sacred by Akht and his cult, the outer Ouroboros passes through three intersecting Ouroboroses coiled and aligned on three axes which form a Trison; a tripedal beast named the Wheel of Pestilence (see Fig. 18).

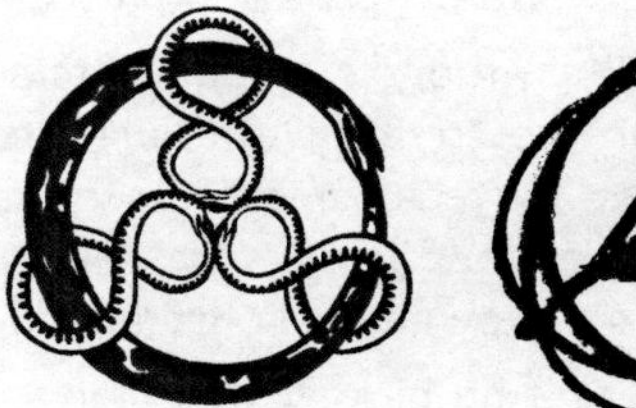

Fig. 18 The Wheel of Pestilence or *pestis lemniscus* as the Romans called it (right), and the aerial view of its Trisons (left). The tail-to-fang recurrence or dynamism of Ouroboroses imparts two basic functions to the Wheel of Pestilence. One is a surrounding cyclonic movement which transports Trisons along horizontal and vertical axes. The other is propagation of Trison-cells in the Wheel as the result of interactions between Trisons which have been twisted as the Hindu-Arabic number 8 (Trisons within Trisons *ad infinitum*, corresponding to Parsani's 'minority holocaust and polytical meltdown'). If the function of the velocipede (or the ouroboric number 888) is to unbind Trisons, and if on the other hand the communication between Trison-cells is effectuated as a cyclonic disturbance, then the Wheel of Pestilence is equal to a polytical epidemic. Famine cycles, swarm migrations, pest incursions and fugue states are all mobilized by the Wheel of Pestilence.

In the cycle of epidemics, every time that dust fuses with an otherworldly wetness — immersing into xeno-chemistry — the composition of the ground is further distanced from creation, both as an instance of creation and as the created. The cycle of epidemics moves in a spiraling manner or in the form of an Ouroboros which registers its bestial flight not only as departing from creationism, but also as returning to creation with fangs ready to poison and devour: Tiamaterialism.

In the same sense, the carnal diagrams of flesh are imbued with dust soups (the ultimate mess); they are mapped by syntheses of dust with xenochemical hydro-currents and cosmic wetness, and mobilized by the intelligence and vigor of epidemics. This is neither to glorify the flesh in the context of monotheism and its creationist basins (God made you out of dust), nor to pay tribute to the flesh and its carnal politics; it is to declare that flesh is already a reeking catacomb of dust-compositions, drenched by deluges. It implies that dust carves niches into this catacomb into which to deposit all the bacterial data it has scavenged from wet milieus, xeno-chemical planes, interstellar dimensions and oceanic wastelands. The wetness of the flesh is only the consequence of the dust's thirst for its wet twins. As for the flesh, dust discloses its own endemic sentience in the vicinity of wetness. In terms of dust, flesh is a heap of data-pollution, a fanatic practitioner of Dustism. Parsani returns to the subject of dust and creation at the end of interview: 'The opposition of monotheism to carnality is a matter of prohibiting people from playing in cemeteries and catacombs, exhuming what they hold within. Flesh is a dust necropolis which is constantly refreshed by wetness, a necropolis full of cursed cemeteries, vaults of anonymous materials from the outside, crypts and restless things.'

Dust is not the surplus of the ground's ground-ness and the Sun's thermonuclear capitalism. Quite on the contrary, authorial genesis and creation are the surplus of the dust's mess-hysteria. Creation is the surplus value of the Ouroboros cycle of the pest which lays its eggs via devouring, twisting with Tiamaterialism. Dust is a dry torrent towards an outside, only plausible as pest.

BACTERIAL RELICS. Colonel West, as if he himself was doing the counting, proclaimed that 'dust can contain up to 11,583,800,000 bacteria in one ounce.' For the first time, he felt content with the quantity of a number. Playfully rather than seriously, holed up in his hide-out, he continued to kill time by reading from the book he had accidentally recovered, 'Sporulation is a way of becoming an endo-bacterial relic in hostile environments (nutrient-deprived and dehydrating conditions); it is a way of becoming fully militarized, fortified, camouflaged and dispersive. The spore, or endo-bacterial dust, is a relic with untraceable zones of migration and traversal, a swarm-particle creeping off the radar screen; a speck of dust you never know whether you have inhaled or not. A spore condenses and envelopes a virally hibernated relic in a series of composite membranes generally named the sarcophagus. The sarcophagus is opened up in the form of a rupture in response to a friendly environment or normal climate. The opening of the sarcophagus entails the release of the bacterial relic, in what could be compared to a defiling resurrection. Nothing is more vicious and strategic in undermining and attacking normality, hygiene and survival-friendly environments than a spore.' He looked at the middle-eastern horizon from the window of his room near Musel; both the window and horizon were disgustingly dusty.

'In the Middle East, the model for population — whether of people or systems — is dust,' West added to the new pamphlet he was going to distribute among his sons. 'Then the Lord said to Moses and Aaron, "Take handfuls of soot from a furnace and have Moses toss it into the air in the presence of Pharaoh. It will become fine dust over the whole land of Egypt, and festering boils will break out on men and animals throughout the land," he whispered to himself. West had already started to meditate on War on Terror, dust, the desert and how the oil pipeline makes an apparently coherent plot out of all these things. He had come to the conclusion that the coupling of oil and dust narrates the biblical decimal plague in a new, progressive format.

The War on Terror, with the desert as its platform, requires new methods of customization and morphological programming of warmachines. If tactical lines and inclinations of warmachines change in the War on Terror and its desert, then even the shape of warmachines must be altered to match the new context, terrain and targets. Morphological programming leads to the emergence of weapons with autonomous nervous system. The simulation of dust characterizes such a morphologic customization of warmachines. From the time of Anzu and Pazuzu to that of Operation Eagle Claw and Operation Desert Freedom, middle-eastern war has always had a particular interest in dust, cryptospores and particles. For a middle-eastern war, warmachines must turn into dust particles and spores. In the past, the dominant factors in bio-weaponry were the level of toxicity, poison and complexity of mutations; in the War on Terror, the inclination is more toward a morphological customization of weapons. In the War on Terror, weapons must be capable of being easily smuggled, afforded and dispersed, as well as being able to pick up on targets with minimum effort. 'Dust is all that middle-easterners can afford, both economically and mentally,' West had stated in one of his speeches to his troops.

If the morphology of weapons has to undergo a revolution in the War on Terror, that revolution can only take place through morphing into dust and spores, providing weapons with a cutting-edge compatibility with the socio-political sphere, belief-dynamics, people, and geography of war. The strategy of morphological programming, as West suggested, is to concoct an appetizingly digestible light meal that everyone can afford, a culture-friendly weapon like anthrax spores, corresponding to Middle-Eastern dust-culture. High spore concentration, uniform particle size, low electrostatic charge to reduce clumping, complex surfaces of spores resulting in aerosolization — that is to say, the becoming-dust of the Anthrax spore. Sporangium is a folded oval with a high degree of stability, small enough to be inhaled and reside within the lung passages.

The Middle East, as the confusing platform of War on Terror, is constantly charged by agitations of dusts and spores (or weapons-grade relics) which, chronologically-speaking, belong to Now, but which, inside the crystal or the spore, carry a hibernated entity from a deep past. The approach of dust and spore to time is subversive rather than ambiguous; they smuggle an unfathomable ancientness into their environments, through now. As they open and unfold, they draw lines of sorcery between time and space.

Dust or spore is constituted of a relic crystallized or enveloped in a deep past, and a sarcophagus which is a series of layers formed during time. Only in reaction to the friendly environment of Now does the sarcophagus break open, so that the ancient entity can be exhumed. As the enveloped endo-bacterial Thing slumbering within the spore awakens, the existence of dust or spore as an entity bound to present time becomes highly problematic. So that the Middle East, as the dust plateau of the Earth's body (a Tellurian entity which is creatively conscious of its dust), must be seen as the emerging zone of a deep past, a bacterial ancientness. Such a mode of time associated with bacterial relics, dust particles and spores is always weaponized as it reaches the present and unbinds in Now. Artificial Now, the middle-eastern approach to Time, is a Now preceded and succeeded by an obscure and cryptogenic ancientness (deep past). The only place where this ancientness can be grasped separately and distinctly from tradition is in dust, and through dustism. It is dust that harbors the ancient without tradition, or ultra-modern ancientness. On the other hand, following the hydrophilic frenzy of dust, the Middle East as the conscious dust plateau of the Earth's body uplinks the globe to xenosignals of the cosmic wetness (the pest) roaming, surging and awaiting to join their wet twin on the earth. If, from every point of view, the Middle East is very dusty, this does not mean that it is dead. On the contrary, it is fresh and alive through the tides of wetness and lurking waters in the universe and within the Earth's body, which desire to couple with dryness. The Ancient Wheel of Pestilence never broke; it became faster and rounder in the wake of middle-eastern systems, communication models and polytics. The dustier the Middle East, the swifter the wheel of epidemics.

The Middle East — as a never-ending dust plateau — through its conscious and concrete approach to dust imparts a new politics, economy and ethics to the once western industrial-capitalist cry of 'Something for the Masses'. 'Knitters for peace; wool is not a petroleum product.' Nothing has latched onto the secrecy of dust's pest-insurgency — albeit blindly — better than this peace motto. When the malicious wetness of oil is not active, dust or dry gas — its colluding twin — rotates the Wheel of Pestilence in peaceful quietude. Anthrax Dust, historically known as Woolsorters' disease, is endemic to soil; it corresponds to the plague infecting livestock, transmitted from their tissue to hair, wool and its derivative products. How long the Wheel of Pestilence waited to unfold itself in the semaphoric peace symbol!

Colonel West was still meditating: both the Cold War (WWIII) and War on Terror (WWIV) developed as an agglutinated series of Dustisms. Each one accelerated the process of erosion to dust, the assembly of the cult of Dustism, through its own associated vortex: The former through its Post-Atomic radioactive dust enterprise, the latter through its BioTerror(ism), dense Fog of War and dusty geo-strategic fields of operation (from Desert Storm to the Middle East and Mesopotamia).

> If 'to Dust' is 'to Kill', 'Dust to Dust' is 'to render into nothingness'. (Hyperstition laboratory)

Xerodrome, or the desert of Tellurian Omega, vacillates between two rivers (meso-potamia), two prowling poles of Tellurian insurgency: The oil pipeline and petropolitics on the one hand, and endo-bacterial dust and its hydrophilic tide on the other. As soon as they interact with each other and assemble their cults, everything along their line of communication starts to swerve.‡

---

‡ [illegible]

Excursus IV (Meteorological Teratology)

In spite of his sporadic love-hate relationship with dust in *Defacing the Ancient Persia*, an elaborate endnote foretells Parsani's preoccupation with dust as the collective element of the Middle East:

> What middle-eastern fairy tales and bedtime stories suggest is that aridity, dust and desert only elude water because they have already forged an alliance with a different species of wetness. Monsters and alien vistas are indexed by climate and meteorology. In these stories, the universe is ideated by elemental alignments in which air, fire and earth are paired with questionable liquidities which either possess deranged properties or share more than two properties at the same time with their neighboring elements. In the case of the former, the derangement and confusion of primary and secondary properties — wetness and coldness — leads to the rediscovery of the elements earth and air as a New Earth and a Fresh Air. Miasma, putrefaction, unground, nigredo and so on refer to the alchemical dispositions or the cosmogenetic problems inherent to these revolutionized elements. Yet excessive properties of the moist element signal something more abysmal. If air and earth can afford water only through one property at a time — either wet or cold — then in considering these liquidities (wet alternatives to water) with more than two properties, we cannot help but submit ourselves to certain dire and troubling speculations. One speculation is that excessive properties of these liquid species deteriorate the integrity and arrangement of their neighboring and opposite elements (Air-Earth and Fire). In this case, excessive properties of the fourth element derail the building propensities of the established worldly elements. The other speculation suggests that the additional or so-called extraneous properties attest to missing links. In other words, these properties betoken other outsider elements to which the weird liquid species are coupled. This speculation itself leads to another conjecture, graver than the previous: If these fomenting fluids link earth, fire and air to outsider elements, they also impose the otherworldly building processes peculiar to such outsiders upon the worldly elements. A cosmos crafted by its outside is not only profoundly awkward, but is also fiendishly indifferent to the ideas pertaining to its elements and inhabitants. It is in conforming to their uninhabited deserts and intrinsic aridity that middle-eastern bedtime stories are built upon meteorological taxonomies; for meteorology suggests the weather-harnessing power of these alien building processes. Weather, the set of atmospheric states in a given time and space such as temperature, rain, wind, *et cetera*, represents the building processes of elements in the form of differential compositions between their properties. Different degrees of wetness combined with degrees of coldness can for example generate rain, snow and hail — each a building process and a line of cosmogenesis. In middle-eastern bedtime

stories, the weather itself is a teratological set; wind, rain, fog, and other atmospheric phenomena import properties and hence building processes from outsider elements. Dead seas bring rains and hails which are either crystals impregnated with sand or red and black particles, and sometimes even dead creatures. The desert is frequently haunted by pebble and sand rains, which not only bring with themselves hordes of peculiar monsters, but also become teratological entities in themselves. The task of the desert and aridity is to invoke and to couple with alternate fluids; but the task of foreign moistures is to smuggle in the outsider elements as familiar atmospheric phenomena in the form of weather anomalies or havocs.

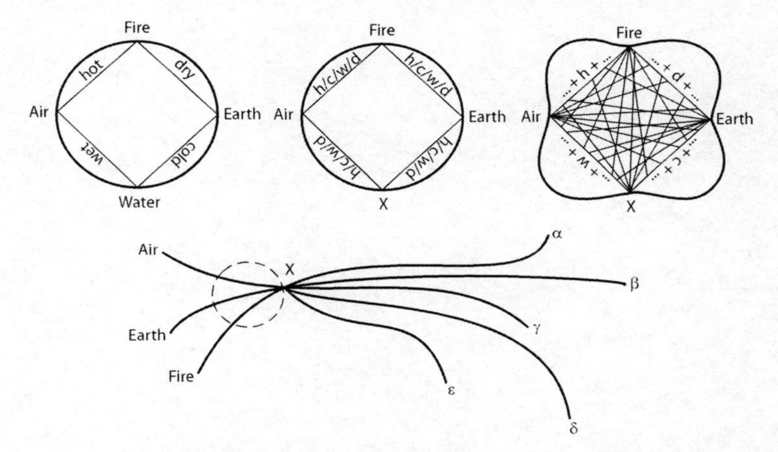

Fig. 19 A schematic recreation of Parsani's meteorological models of middle-eastern bedtime stories. From left to right, top to bottom: (a) the tetrasomic chart of Empedoclean elements; (b) the coupling of elements with an alien alternative of water which confounds the ideas of primary and secondary properties for the elements air, fire and water; (c) excessive properties of the liquid element deteriorating the existing arrangements of the elements by multiplying their bonds with new properties; and (d) the alternative wet element, which possesses extraneous properties because it has been coupled with additional elements which are external to the universe of tetrasomic elements. In this case, the liquid X defines a point where the established building processes exhibit the function of an alien cosmogenesis and of otherworldly building processes.

Numerous types of winds and rains in middle-eastern bedtime stories emphasize the intervention of other elements with which the established universe is fundamentally unfamiliar, and which 'storm' the normal course of events. Winds and rains are sometimes named after the color to which they correspond, sometimes after the fever they spread and sometimes after their affinity with a preexisting material – blood rain, rain of fire, dead cows and toads. Monsters and fiends are categorized by weather and meteorological phenomena — for every weather or atmospheric phenomenon, there is a ghoul and a deav (demon). Even when there is water, as in the stories of Sinbad the sailor, there are also haunted dead seas, desert mirages and sand typhoons which expand and howl in the background. This lurking presence of aridity culminates when Sinbad the sailor meets his arid double, Sinbad the wayfarer of untrodden deserts and the porter of shipwrecks buried under the sand.

MISTMARE

'We are all surrounded by the Fog of War,' Colonel West started to write as he was meditating upon dust as the sentient offspring of the Middle East. 'There is no evidence as to whether it was the Fog or the battlefield that came first,' he continued. From a Wargasmic angle, the Fog of War blocks all visions, and engineers a type of vision associated with blindness. The original manifestation of the Fog of War is *Aer* – it is the source of vision as well as blindness for warmachines. Colonel West discovered that every warmachine is born blind, and only through the Fog of War can it see: seeing only other warmachines moving, copulating and finally being devoured by War. Without the Fog of War, there is no activity on a tactical level and no strategy beyond the level of tactics.

It was the pre-Socratic philosopher of the sixth century BC, Anaximenes of Miletus, who for the first time rigorously modified or, more accurately, philosophically distorted *Aer* into what has commonly become known as Air (or that which makes vision possible). Anaximenes belonged to the cosmogonic tradition of unification which assumed the cosmos to be one giant process of distillation or unification toward quintessence. Consequently his remarks on Air tend to be integrated with his other cosmogonic doctrines, into one philosophical body which takes all cosmic processes to be mechanisms of unification. This compulsion towards unity manifests itself in a perfectionist cycle of 'union-separation-union-separation-union ...' Such a unificatory cycle is depicted as a spiral moving toward the refined essence of a substance, a fifth element which pervades all things, all compositions and syntheses of the known four elements. The alchemical apparatus *Kerotakis* or Reflux Condenser is a model of this cycle whose objective is to distill all cosmic processes into one unified body which is cyclically infinite yet functionally restrictive (everything must be unified). Such an environment or sphere functions as a cyclic or a spherical shape with an inner limit and an outer boundlessness. This cyclic spiral, whose unificatory process configures both the infinity and the order of the cosmos, was an influential cosmogonic figure which inspired Plato and Aristotle (the discursive logical methods they developed emerged from this cosmogonic tradition). In fact, Platonic consolidation and Aristotelian contemplation are the apexes of this cosmogonic tradition's tendencies towards a restrictive inner order and a refining dynamism which together form the transcendental dynamism. Theophrastus, as the academic slave of Greek Philosophy, resurrected the concepts of cosmogonic tradition and grounded them within Aristotelian philosophy, ensuring that the history of philosophy would become the feeding ground of the cosmogonic tradition of (compulsory) unification.

The philosophic reinvention of Aer as Air by Anaximenes was influenced by Anaximander's innovative cosmogonic theories concerning *apeiron* (ordering boundlessness), boundary (*perata*), essence, unification and especially the thesis concerning a pro-creationist process known as *apokrisis* (also *ekkrisis*, ἐκκρισις) or 'regulating separation'. Apokrisis is a process that distributes elements economically according to their mutual relationships and economical affordability to their environment and each other (how open can they be to each other without transgressing their own essence?). In apokrisis, the separation of one entity from another always reflects the extent to which it can afford to unify with that entity in each stage or condition of existence; the failure to afford results in the act of separation and deferment of unification. Apokrisis stratifies the universe into properly arranged layers which make unification, as a dynamic process, possible. The separation process of apokrisis is thus a prerequisite for the cosmic union-separation machinery of the ultimate unification. The final union functionally presupposes a series of separations and unifications leading to a purely distilled unity (corresponding to the classic mechanism of distillation).

Anaximenes, however, developed the process of *apokrisis* into two processes of rarefaction and condensation (corresponding to separation and union), both necessary for regulating and transforming Aer to Air. This transformation to a manifestation of refinement and a higher state of development, namely Air, indicates that the original Aer must be a mixture, more on the side of impurity than the Platonic *mikton*, which is a holistic aggregate. Aer as impurity, then, must be associated with a gathering of diverse particles whose collectivity cannot be reduced to a wholeness. Such impurity is a nonhomogeneous suspension of crystals, droplets and vapor among other particles. Once each particle or cluster of particles maintains a distinct behavior toward light, clarity degenerates to distortion and darkness. Air as a manifest refinement is a vision-machine through which the world looks safe, that is to say, already consolidated, having been forced to take the path of unification and purity. Through Air, everything attains a moderated clarity and normality. Air does not make vision possible, but artificializes a vision based on organization and consolidation; it generates a vision (illusion?) of cosmic security, an appropriating machine providing anthropomorphians with an artificial safety. Air engenders an artificial trust, the vision it presents is a consolidated vision, clear and purified in a unificatory sense. Such a vision has already been processed and distilled: It has presupposed unity from the beginning to the end.

Prior to Anaximenes, however, *Aer* (αηρ) was not an elucidating machine (Air) but a blinding machine, a benighted air, described in Greek texts as something wet and dark (see, for example, Aristotle's *Meteorologica* for an account of such characterization). Aer meant fog and darkness — not darkness as in *Tenebrae* (from Sanskrit origin, *tamas*, the darkness of shadow, or the darkness that belongs to the underworld, the realm of death), but darkness as in the Greek *omichle* (the darkness of fog, mist, dust-clouds, the Mistmare). While *Tenebrae* belongs to death, *Aer* and *omichle* belong to war, the Fog of War. Realtime strategy videogames have successfully presented the functions and diagrams of the Fog of War.

During the Trojan War, the battlefield was darkened by Aer. Ajax prayed to Zeus for lifting Aer off the battlefield. Zeus eventually removed the Aer (Fog of War) to allow the enemies to fight in the clarity of Air (light) which makes victory and defeat visible (or possible) in a conflict. Aer's wargasmic clarity is given in the form of a radical blindness through which warmachines hunt each other with a frantic passion and are eventually hunted down by War itself. While Aer is a wargasmic vision-machine, it also works as a cooling system for warmachines, giving warmachines the unique opportunity to get hotter, to become further immersed in War by participating with each other in the absence of goal-oriented conflicts. Aer or Fog of War attracts warmachines to War itself; it erases all vision maintained by the eye. 'Warmachines do not see with eyes, as they have no eyes; they see, detect and sense with their movements, their exclusive dynamism and tactics customized not by their lines of command but by the Fog of War, the Aer,' reads Colonel West's triumphant conclusion.

All tactical probe-heads are contaminated by the fog; they gradually adapt to a radical blindness, necessary to grasp War as an autonomous machine. One should not miss the fact that the Fog of War is also agitated and contagiously spread by warmachines' frenzy, their dynamism and their tactical lines. As they kick up dust during their activities, warmachines contribute to the Fog of War, and consequently to their own blindness. Disciples of War are the occultists of the Aer, the mistmare. 'The denser the fog, the more violent the warmachines,' Colonel West scrawled in his sun-bleached notebook.

Michael Crichton's *Eaters of the Dead* and John McTiernan's movie *The 13th Warrior* (based on the diaries of Ahmad Ibn Fazlan or Fadhlan[21] and the tale of Beowulf) draw a line between rabid warmachines and the unlife of war through the mistmare or the Fog of War. The fog belongs to Odinn-Wodan, the god of the darkest recesses of War. In both the book and the movie, Fog or Aer is an Outsider. The frenzied Wendols are accompanied and aided by the fog. The Wendols must be, in fact, the legendary *Berserkirs* (bear-warriors) and *Ulfhednars* (wolf-warriors who inspired the strange stories of Lycanthropy throughout Europe), the true and the most enthusiastic initiates of the Nordic god, Odinn-Wodan and War. Dumezil writes in *Les dieux des Germains* that 'in the ideology and practice of the Germans, war invaded everything, colored everything.' — so too the Aer, the Fog of War. Whenever war pervades everything, things can only come to existence through the Fog of War. The intriguing connection in Crichton's book and McTiernan's movie is that between the sorcerous mother of the Wendols and the Fog. The mother lives beneath the earth, and is therefore tied to the mother of the black earth, the underworld — Hel. While the mother protects the Wendols beneath the Earth, feeds them and opens them to the secrets of earth, the Fog or the Mistmare directly engulfs them with xeno-excitations of War. Mist mother or Mistmare gives birth to her children with a radical vision that facilitates their engulfment by war. This vision or ocular wisdom makes warriors or warmachines blind at the same time. In addition, the fog gives the Wendols an infernal dynamism: 'they look as a dragon, a giant serpent, as they come through the Fog,' the defenders whisper in utter terror. The Mother is the war-sorceress of the Earth's nether, and the Fog is the War-diviner of the surface. There is a bond between darkness as Tenebrae (the darkness of shadowland, the underworld and the Earth's tellurian insurgencies — Hel) and darkness as Aer (the darkness of the mist, the inter-stellar dust, atmospheric pollution — the Mistmare). Both Tenebrae and Aer creep towards one anti-vitalist becoming of the Earth, the Tellurian Omega through which the Earth reaches utter immanence with the burning core of itself and the Sun.

> Here in the Middle East, you can never be sure who is the god: The warmachines which kick up so much billowing dust, or the Fog out of which those warmachines loom? (Colonel West, Sermon IV, Arbil, Iraq)

In McTiernan's movie, Beowulf and his warriors find a curious statuette, an idol left by the Wendols in the razed village, an artifact which frightens them even more than the fact that the dead bodies have been eaten. It is a swollen figurine with no head, legs, hands, but only two large breasts, evidently diagramming an old woman who has given birth to many children, a mother in the shape of a BwO (Body without Organs). In archeology, such religious sculptures are technically called Venus and are not peculiar to specific regions. They commonly have no organs other than breasts; however, they sometimes have legs, hands and swollen faceless heads. One of the most ancient Venuses known, the Venus of Berekhat Ram, was discovered by Dr. Naama Goren-Inbar in 1980. The sculpture is at least 230000 years old. (See Fig. 20, 21)

Fig. 20 Drawing of the Venus of Berekhat Ram
Size: height cm. 3.5
Origin: Berekhat Ram, northern Golan, Israel.
Artistic-religious thieullenian paleolithic Civilization

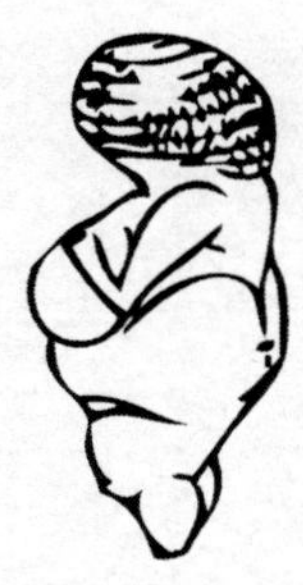

Fig. 21 Origin: Willendorf, Austria.
Size: height cm. 11.1
Artistic-religious thieullenian paleolithic Civilization.
Material culture: upper Paleolithic

In his only book, *Defacing the Ancient Persia: 9500 Years Call for Destruction*, Dr. Hamid Parsani remarks that motherhood is directly connected to the most mysterious depths of occultism and trisonomic sorcery:

> I do not look at monotheistic religions as *Serat-o-al-Mostaghim* (the straight path), nor do I curse them as ghouls of repression. I simply see them as generous mothers pregnant with their minorities — thousands, millions of them; a female scorpion devoured by its own children, ripped apart from the belly. This is what Ibn Maymun taught us, the minority holocaust. (H. Parsani)

This has nothing to do with nature or the fact that nature is frequently represented as a mother. The functions of menstruation, pregnancy, carrying, bearing and giving birth themselves originate from a deep occultism tied to sorceresses (non-breeder mothers) and xeno-matriarchs (breeding hags). Following Parsani's remark, motherhood interconnects with a profound anti-creationist Ahrimanic creativity[22] (pestilential creativity) and minority-engineering.

In the Greek elementalist tradition, the mother is associated with Khaos, the oldest Mother, the first mother who is the goddess of Aer (air) — the Mist-mare. As the first goddess of the *Protogenoi* (elemental gods), Khaos was the mother or grandmother of the other incorporeal deities of the air: Nyx (Night), Erebos (Darkness), Aither (Light), Hemera (Day), and other daimones.‡

---

‡ The window, I can't get it open.

S, sorry for the delay. No, couldn't find the 10 pages I wrote on the neo-Sumerian approach to collectivity; I keep forgetting things so I have to write notes to myself, sometimes on paper, sometimes on kleenex and sometimes on post-its. Yes, the connections between contagious love and the lines of openness are obvious. Was thinking that while our countries are (getting) ready to feast on each other's corpses, we are getting closer to each other. The distance between us is replaced by our distance or gap from the world we live in. Love generates distance not between lovers but between the lovers and the environment that attempts to distance them. Such an abstract distance not only alienates the environment from the infected ones but also eliminates the presence of the system as a solid or concrete entity for lovers. Behind lovers, there is nothing but a gap yawning and swallowing the world. We have already stared into the abyss of infection.

EXCURSUS V (FOG OIL: A RETROSPECTION ON OBSCURANTS)

Amongst all the petropolitical and palaeopetrological writings of H. Parsani, there are certain pieces which try to compensate for 'the deficient scholarship of *Defacing the Ancient Persia*' (as Parsani puts it). These pieces are usually constructed upon vast and heavily populated orgies of foreign tongues and doctrines. They consistently avoid any type of overture or introduction, thus matching Parsani's style of writing and analysis or what he calls 'outright slaughter'. According to one critic, Parsani's essays begin with 'intricate and outlandish analyses' without 'any prior warning whatsoever'. Such tortuous dissections move shamelessly in the direction of what Parsani's critics refer to as his 'ME-centrism', characterized by Parsani's typical phrases: 'In the Middle East, we ...' or 'For the first time, in the Middle East ...'. In spite of his refusal to 'open his mephitic mouth once and for all' to answer critics, Parsani did allusively comment: 'how is it possible for one to geographically stick to the Middle East when it is territorially obscure; and what would be the possible benefit of standing by the Middle East, when it evidently has sentiments, a life and interests of its own?'

On the Philology of Petroleum is one such essay, indecorously straddling etymological and anthropomorphic histories of the blob. Without any introductory preparation, Parsani writes, 'The name 'Fog Oil', which refers to an obscurant, used in battle for reducing the vision of enemy combatants, is a pleonasm. Because napht (oil) is itself nothing but the great mist, fog or wetness which cannot be reduced to water.' Parsani then tars his essay with huge quantities of oil-related etymologies. He continues that in Ancient Persia, and according to the medical doctrine of the Zoroastrian magi, Druj or the Mother of Abominations — the source of all contaminations — rushes from the north, and through the north wind. Parsani adds that the Zoroastrian medical doctrine later heavily influenced medieval philosophy, Islamic medicine and alchemy through the diffusion of monotheism and its minorities. In ancient Persia, Parsani notes, the north wind as the vehicle of Druj is signified by its harsh dryness rather than the coldness usually associated with the north wind. The dry north wind, according to Zoroastrian mages and their medical-religious doctrines, increases the amount of *drēm* (*rīm*) in the body. The Pahlavanic word *drēm* simultaneously suggests that cosmic unlocalizablity which is an adjective describing the infinite impurity and corruption of Druj, and denotes wetness in the body. *Drēm* as the adjective for Druj or the Mother of Abominations is associated with radical double-dealing or Trison (the perversion of three dots). Parsani explains that according to the Greek elementalist tradition of Tetrasomia (Fire, Air, Water and Earth), the increase in dryness results in surging wetness. In medical texts and religious scriptures of Ancient Persia, particularly Zoroastrian, a certain word was used to describe this wetness. Instead of the word *āp* or *āb* (the Pahlavi word for water), this word stands for a particular wetness, fog and mist.

Parsani confesses that the discovery of a word other than water in the ancient monotheistic chart of cosmic elements, 'did indeed disturb the normal stability of his thoughts'. The discovered word was the enigmatic word *namba*, derived from the Avestan word-ovum *nab*. In the Zoroastrian version of Tetrasomia, the word *namba* replaces the word or the element water. The cosmic dynamics are generated by the interplays of Air, Fire and Earth with this wet entity (*namba*), not water. In Avestan language, *nab* is the root of three words: *Nabah* (or its Sanskrit counterpart *nábhas*) meaning sky, vapor and even miasma, *napta-* meaning wetness, and finally *naft* which signifies the nether waters of the Earth and means oil. Parsani notes that the word Nafta or Naphta, as the Greek and Arabic word for oil and petroleum (as in the case of modern Farsi), is the combination of the Avestan words *napta-* and *naft*.

In ancient Pahlavi medical and religious texts alike, Parsani discovers, *drēm* is associated with the word *namba* and has nothing to do with water (*āp* or *āb*). 'The medical as well as the religious doctrines suggest that the dryness of the north wind as the foul caravan of Druj increases the amount of *drēm* on the earth, and particularly in the body. The manifestations of *namba* as the essence of *drēm* include mist and oil, the dispersive wetness of the Earth's nether regions and the sky. The excess of *namba* was referred to as the worst poison or *was-wišabāg* meaning saturated by poison (also a sobriquet for Akht amongst his cult members),' Parsani writes of the ancient texts that deplored this wetness. Shortly after, he reveals that the Greeks also had a word for this obscure wetness: φλέγμα (or *balgam*, *balgham* in Arabic) which is *phlegma* or phlegm, another synonym for *drēm*, or the radical perversion of trison.

According to the Hippocratic doctrine of the bodily humours, phlegm is associated with the north and the damned or dead earth. Parsani remarks that under the influence of cultural and linguistic exchanges between Zoroastrian mages and the Greeks, the word *phlegma* became more oily than ever. 'The root of the word *phlegma* (phlegm) actually reflects its oracular Persian and Greek meaning as oily wetness rather than foggy wetness: More Oil than Fog.' (*Philology of Petroleum*) The reason for this extra oiliness is that the word *phlegein*, the etymological source of phlegm, is bursting with a massive incendiary tendency: *Phlegein* means to burn or scorch with flame or extensive and destructive fire which glows black as the result of huge amount of the uncombusted carbon particles. Burning black, *phlegein* corresponds with the black flame worshipped by Akht or the black light of Ayn-al-Qudat Hamedani. It is associated with the fire of conflagration which is the fire of *holokauston* (ολόκαυστον, holocaust) – an uncontrollable fire with an autonomous nervous system and a voracious rapacity for sacrifice: Bonfire (bone-fire), the fire for burning heretics.

Parsani suggests that the north wind as the medium of the mother of all abominations and maladies (*druj*: *druh*: to blacken) increases phlegm or oil-saturated wetness through its dryness and deserting ambience. The interaction and contagious trade between dryness and oily wetness is inherently a bad mixture (*dyscrasia*); it results in the upsurge of oil (napht or naft). In his book *The Canon of Medicine*, scientist and philosopher Ibn Sina (980-1037 AD), or, as he is known under his Latinized name, Avicenna, gives a newer account of this upsurge in the burning substance. For Ibn Sina, intense dryness causes a transformation into something other than phlegm. Ibn Sina states that the worst eroding diseases are those in which intense dryness turns the phlegm into *sauda* or black bile (melan-choly: μελανχολια) which is pregnant with a tarry fluidity. 'It is the task of dryness — donated by Druj to the Earth — to bring the nether wetness of the Earth to the surface. In the case of oil as the nether water (*napta-*), the surging wetness appears as a black, dark brown or greenish liquid, characteristic of black bile rather than phlegm or yellow bile,' Parsani writes after combing these oily theories of alchemy and medicine from antiquity and Middle Ages.

Parsani remarks that phlegm, napht, elemental wetness (*namba*) and *drēm* (phlegm, Druj's pollution, Trison) are all submerged in the nether sauce of the Earth, that is oil. The hydrophobic characteristics of oil contrast it with water as the *Aqua Vitae* of the Green Earth. For this reason, oil as mist or wetness belongs to an entirely different earth or space. Moreover, if *drēm* as Trison or three-dotted perversion essentially connects to oil and oily wetness, it is no wonder that the sign for oil in Renaissance and later alchemy — as in Denis Diderot's contribution to the *Encyclopédie* — was generally presented in the form of three dots ∴.

'Cardamom — or, in Farsi, *hel* — clears and reduces phlegm,' recalls Parsani, going on to conclude his essay with the following observation: 'Zoroastrians, early monotheists and even some Greeks, carried cardamom with themselves wherever they went. Because cardamom is to the depths of phlegm what garlic is to the vampire.' If phlegm is the burning wetness of the netherworld where, according to Zoroastrian scriptures, pests come from and Drujeskan or the abode of Druj lies, the religious and medical caution makes sense: never swallow your phlegm.

With the machines and enterprises of enlightenment now basking in the effluvium of oil, that philosopher of enlightenment Immanuel Kant's advocacy of phlegm has never been more apposite.

THE LEGION
WARMACHINES, PREDATORS AND PESTS

THE DUST ENFORCER

Pazuzu, the Sumero-Assyrian demon of epidemics (the southwestern desert wind) is an occultural operative of the xero-informatic Abomination or Dust (= 100 = NO GOD), and possibly the most awe-inspiring cultist of Tellurian Dustism in ancient Mesopotamia. For wind is truly the high acolyte of dust, as well as being the dust-enforcer. In his *Notes on Reliquology*, Parsani put forward Pazuzu as a schematic diagram of the middle-eastern population and its peculiarities.

Pazuzu specializes in scavenging the stratified Earth and its biosphere in the form of dust, which then is uplinked to alien currents flowing in the universe. These combinations of dryness and wetness are carried back to earth to disseminate disease. According to the Assyrian axis of Evil-against-Evil, Pazuzu the demon feeds on dust, which is qabbalistically equal to No God (=100). Pazuzu scavenges the surface biosphere of earth as dust clouds or inorganic bacterial relics; then conducting them to xenochemical hydro-currents, or what in ancient Greece was called cosmic wetness (hydrochemical singularities). This is why Pazuzu is associated with the emergence of plagues. Pazuzu then carries the plagues back to the surface biosphere in the guise of dust-soups, arid floods, messy rains, unheard-of epidemics and xero-informatic communications which usually manifest in the form of demonic possession (*The Exorcist*). This process of dust-scavenging and plague-engineering takes the form of an accelerating non-Aristotelian spiral or cycle when the terrestrial hygiene industry incrementally spreads more anti-pest agents and over-produces defense mechanisms (to ward off plagues) which once again are scavenged by Pazuzu's pest-industry. In this sense, the accelerated rate of resistance ironically intensifies the emergence of plagues and dust-floods, speeding the journey of plagues back to the surface biosphere. When it comes to recollecting all that exists as dust, there is no need to be fastidious.

The horror of Pazuzu is usually embodied as a winged bipedal human-like beast with talons instead of feet and a head concretized through an almost fleshless dog- or lion-skull. The long reptilian penis of Pazuzu (a pest-seeding machine or a disseminator, according to glossaries of epidemiology) is a later pestilential modification to its body, which strangely has two pairs of wings instead of one, as if two wings are not adequate for its missions. Pazuzu is also visualized with the right hand upward and the left hand downward, heralding the Pest-Cycle of dust whose axis is a double-flight (Pazuzu's tetra-winged body) or a ferocious inter-dimensional 'line of flight' (Deleuze and Guattari) from the Earth to without, and from without to the Earth: the tactical line of the xero-informatic Abomination (dust) and the traffic zone of its bacterial data. Pazuzu exhibits several morphological anomalies and peculiarities which separate him from other Akkadian, Babylonian and Assyrian demons. According to the first excavated Bronze statue of Pazuzu (Iraq, post-Paleolithic era, 800-600 BC) these morphological features include:

- Extremely thin legs bearing an unusually skinny torso. Chest bones are clearly visible as if it suffers anorexia or fatigue; a body struck by famine and carrying its ailing flesh with difficulty. Its wasting body narrates the cyclical desert famine of the Middle East, accompanied by vast locust-swarms (as vehicles of desolation) and other pestilential omens. If the body of Beelzebub (*ba'al zebub*) insinuates a legion of flies, with their perverse collective enthusiasm to come together over a fresh deliquescing carrion or a yellowish lump of excrement, Pazuzu's anthropo-insectoid body bears the black humor of all bodies it overruns, strips naked of flesh, all the bodies chewed and peeled off by a sky-blackening swarm of locusts, by the hurtling body of Pazuzu, dehydrated and reduced to a twisted spectre of bone and wrinkled skin. Make yourself many, like the locust! Make yourself many, like the swarming locusts!

- Four wings instead of two: The wings seem to be feathered (later statuettes confirm this hypothesis: the feathers become visible as remiges, the powerful flight feathers which provide the main propulsive force during the powered flight of the rapax bird) and emphasize a demonic lust for flying, for speed and migration. Such wings engineer a flight corresponding to desert whirlwinds, dust devils and other meteorological phenomena of deserts which are believed to have been created by Anzu, the beast of flight, who stole the tablet of destiny and eventually was slain by Ninurta. The Sumero-Akkadian epic of Ninurta portrays Anzu as the forerunner of later flying demons, the engineer of demonic flight and of beasts with feathered wings which are linked to cyclogenesis, sonic havoc, spiraling storms across deserts and dust devils. These four wings render the demon a perfect vehicle for carrying pestilential particles (*Namtar*) and delivering them to their destination without delay, always promptly on time.

• A snake-headed penis, a pest-fertilizing machine which confirms Pazuzu's kinship with Humbaba (*Khombabos*, the guardian of cedar forests and the city of gods, who was defeated and killed by Gilgamesh and Enkidu). Humbaba has the same reptilian phallus and is believed to be the son or brother of Pazuzu. Both Humbaba and Pazuzu are able to reflect a prognosticated future of each individual: Humbaba's labyrinthine face (with unicursal human entrails as the beard) recalls the early art of *Haruspicy* (divination using the liver or entrails) in ancient Mesopotamian cultures, later developed by the Etruscans. Pazuzu as the demon of the south-west wind is associated with *Rammalie* (an Arabic word for communication with other worlds and aeons through patterns on pebbles and desert sand). His roaring flight introduces rhythmic ripples as crypto-vermiform parasites upon dunes which cumulate transiently as short-term inorganic memories of desert winds; then, ripples and other intermittent patterns can be deciphered as runic alphabets of epidemic journeys and plague-propagations aerated by desert winds and narrated on sand. Abdul Al-Hazred as an adept *rammal* (sand-sorcerer) probably wrote *Al Azif* through the dust-infested language of Pazuzu, who constantly enriches its howls with pest-spores in order to expand the hallucinatory space of progressive arid diseases.

• A dignatory's beard, bringing Pazuzu into the fold of Evil-against-Evil and making of him an apotropaic character. Pazuzu, like other demons who belong to the axis of Evil-against-Evil (for example Ugallu), can simultaneously spread terminal plagues and cure certain maladies. According to the Assyrian Axis of Evil-against-Evil, every human is constantly a puppet of demons, suspended from the labyrinth of their strings. During illnesses, witch doctors attempt to repel hostile demons from the patient and summon a protector-demon to possess the sick person. Pazuzu is among the chosen demons, one who could even pass the last guardian Lamassu or the Repellent of Evil: a Pazuzu-demon guards the niche in the bathroom of Ashurbanipal's palace at Nineveh, Iraq.

• An almost fleshless head that cannot be distinguished clearly, Pazuzu's head diagrams the metamorphosis of three carnivorous animals frequently appearing in the Babylonian / Assyrian pandemonium: the rabid dog, the *Shogal* (jackal) and the *Kaftaar* (hyena). Ibn Hamedani, in his book *Aja'ib Nameh* (*The Book of Marvels*), calls Kaftaar 'a terrible beast'. The hyena, from an afro-asiatic lineage, is possibly the most cursed, obscene and lewd animal in Mesopotamian folklore. Ibn Hamedani tells horrifying stories about this desert-beast who has sex with its prey while devouring it. The Hyena emits high-pitched cacophonic cries of mirth, enough to drive a lone desert traveler mad. Rabid dogs are the spawns of *Abzu* (Abyss), and the *Shoghal* or jackal connects Pazuzu to the Egyptian Anubis and the dead.[‡]

‡ Vising the lawyer (10:00), Bazaar / Güleç Stone Taşçilik (10:40), Ayasophia (12:00 shouldn't forget the flash card), Rami (1:00 lunch and meeting Z or his brother)

Fig. 22 Pazuzu-demon

Fig. 23 Ugallu-demon

The face is of limited relevance for a rigorous archeological investigation into the demonic. Even the most distorted, disfigured and grotesque faces cannot be identified as evidence of a demon (xeno-agent) — that is to say, (de)faciality cannot be a constitutive element in diagramming a demon (especially in the period from the rise of Mesopotamian civilizations to the end of antiquity and the early Middle Ages). All radical xeno-demons have a diagrammatic seal of their own; they are always delineated by anomalous cartographies or diagrams based on which their bodies, positions, and arrangement of their appendages (organs?) are presented, built and (re)composed. Or else they are identified by their coming in pairs (one a recognizable entity and the other an obscure twin of the familiar entity; examples include the Phoenician and Etruscanian demons). The most well-known demonograms are as follows:

The right hand upward, and the left hand downward suggests a swash-backwash model of epidemics; it is the seal of pest enforcers.

Outstretched hands, one pointing east and one pointing west — solar demons. The Romans borrowed the same diagrammatic position from Babylonians for their crucifixions. This demonogram later influenced the religious iconography of Mithraism and then Christianity, the most prominent examples being, of course, the iconographic portraits of the crucified Jesus.

Bodily organs (appendages) connected to each other by curves and circles which construct a closed or sealed labyrinthine convolution.

Smaller wings attached to the main wings, or possession of more wings than are necessary for flying and migration.

Horns forming spirals (in contrast to general belief, horns are not satanic agents) or horns pointing to each other which signify arch-demons.

Legs open, far apart so as to draw a triangle, also known as the three-dotted profanity, which is among the most significant diagrams of unlocalizable or betraying demons.

The demonogram of Pazuzu (the right hand upward, and the left hand downward) is the unique ABYZmal cartography of disease; it signifies the rotation of The Wheel of Pestilence. This demonogram confirms that Pazuzu (like Ugallu) belongs to the legion of plague-dissipating demons. Demonograms demonstrate the abstract distribution of demons; they are plans for demonic mobilization — mobilization in a military sense.

They believe Mesopotamia and the whole Middle East is overclouded by some kind of fog of war which is peculiar to the near and middle-eastern regions of Asia. That you must practice blindness, must dry out your lungs and return to dust in order to coalesce with the reeking pit of the Middle East. The inhabitants of a village near Tell-Kuyunjik, which is believed to be the ancient site of Nineveh, told us that this arid fog is the haze of Pazuzu, the searing mushroom cloud of Middle East. To live in dust requires a certain degree of demonism which western people deem too much for humans. Jackson West does not think the Middle East is a geopolitical region, he thinks that the Middle East is alive. Not metaphorically; it is alive in a real sense, waiting to let loose its sentience. 'It is alive but it doesn't need to survive, because it has a life of its own' — this was the last thing West told me before reconnoitring Mosul with his sons to locate that Iranian oil smuggler and that guy Omar who claims to have the diaries of Ibn Maimum, the Persian occult-saboteur, guerilla expert and conspiracist who assisted the Al-Fatemid to overthrow the Caliphate regime in Egypt. (1st Lt. Ali Osa, US 1st Battalion, 41st Infantry Regiment)

TELL-KUYUNJIK: Nineveh 36° 24′ N 43° 08′ E

The human defense mechanism is the most consistent entity on this planet; its self-fertilizing paranoia is capable of grasping and identifying every contact only in terms of a potential incursion. When this paranoid consistency (or consistency of paranoia, since paranoia, ironically, tends to be consistent) attains autonomy, it becomes ruthlessly schizoid by passively opening itself to unknown threats from the Outside or xeno-agents. The anthropomorphic security system is a Pandora's Box of unrecorded diseases, emerging from the consistent resistance of the system to outside invasions on the one hand, and the consistently-escalating invasion on the other hand. In this sense, the human security system is a projection of the intensity of the conflict between the xeno-agent (demon) and the system that registers new indefinable plagues mapped at the outer limits of the demon and the system.

Unlike Martin Bergman's still profoundly religious demonology — which insists that a demon should be exorcised not to save the possessed but to assist the demon to escape from the 'mammal meat' — according to the Assyrian Axis of Evil-against-Evil, the demon infects a person to extract a wide array of pest-insurgencies from the security system not by possessing it (in the sense of seizing a property from the monopoly of the Divine — for example, the human as belonging to God), but by turning the Divine and its secured properties into intermediate parasites (pimps) for incoming diseases. In the Assyrian politics of demonism, the Divine and its world are turned into a pest-feeding farm. Their resistance and blind oppositions are encouraged because each instance of resistance harbors more incursions from the Outside. Pests, xeno-excitations, cosmic diseases kick in when capacity is reached and the security system of the anthropomorphic agency starts to crack and waste, consequently trying to survive at all costs which in turn causes a wider array of pestilential activities. In this panorama, survival and security reinforcement (as opposed to the dying system) 'turns on' the demon to no end. Modern criminology refuses to acknowledge the presence of demons, in the same way that secular disbelief condemns the inanity of a demon possessing a helpless human: if demons exist and are that powerful then why would they possess a wretched anthropian? Such an objection misunderstands the mechanisms involved in the communication between xeno-agents and the human security system. For demons maintain their outsideness precisely through a power of overkilling (sheer exteriority of a force), inflicting more power than is needed just to unlock a gate. Demons simply crack open the prey. The overkilling power effectuates an openness outside the system's capacity to afford it. Once openness cannot be afforded by the system's capacity, it turns into an instance of butchery rather than an act of emancipation characterized by human 'access' to the outside. Overkill is a spectacle staged on the fundamental incapacity of the system to cope with the outside. Through overkill, the xeno-agent performs its demonic spectacle and effectuates its exteriority which the system cannot afford. The exteriority of the demon cannot be captured by the desire of the system for openness, and for this reason such exteriority overkills (butchers open) the system. To possess a strong man is certainly enough to flaunt the demon's power, but all the better if the possessed is a child or old woman, to signify the outsideness of the demon through which overkilling power is generated.

On the Assyrian Axis of Evil-against-Evil, the demon does not seek to dismantle (anthropomorphic) identity; instead it tries to make identity a gate for summoning new demons from the furious clashes between xeno-particles and the resisting system. Beyond the borders of identity lies the indifferent realm of unconditional (absolute) madness, or that which can never be schizoid, since schizophrenia germinates on the wasted remains of boundary, territory and capacity. Schizophrenia needs a minimum degree of organization and system to spread, to be mobilized, to transform into agitations and to interlock with xeno-excitations and demons. Schizophrenia is engineered through the synergetic oppositions between xeno-excitations (demonic particles of the Outside graspable as uncontrollable intensities) and the forces of the boundary; it is restlessly mobilized through attacks and counter-attacks, one attack from xeno-particles, two or more counter-attacks from the system. The furious resistance is exponentially intensified and progressively overrun by xeno-agents until meltdown, the becoming-GAS of all particles.

Schiz-fluxes only flow on differentiated zones, meaning that there must be at least two opposite sides — identity and its nemeses. Since the rise of Foucauldian psychoanalysis, the only image of a schizo represented in pop-culture is the external image of madness, that of an inconceivable, semi-paralyzed madman lurching in the manner of an intoxicated spider. The schizo can be found everywhere except in madness. Schizophrenia comes with delirium (*Jnun*), the passion for terminal disease (which presupposes health), war-torn realms of organic survival, attacks and increasing counter-attacks diagrammatically narrating their tireless, attritional engagement on a draco-spiral which sometimes melts, sometimes evaporates, burns incompletely and blurs into particles instead of dissolving into nothingness. Everything excitingly schizoid, capable of attracting the merciless invasion of xeno-particles and igniting criminal excitations, happens on the borders of identity and its regimes which balefully put up their resistance against any malicious force. In order to draw schizo-lines of communication from the Outside, a rigorous course for dismantling identity is necessary, yet any serious attempt for total eradication of identity intrinsically excludes the space of xeno-excitations and ends up in autistic nihilism.

In the Middle East, the Arabic word *Jin* (or *Jinn*) refers to a race created by Allah prior to the creation of humans, made of fire and thus capable of shape-shifting (unlike the human, which was created from dust and water, the bacterial mess of dust-soups). In the Quran and in Islamic demonology — unlike in Christianity — *Shaytan* (Satan) is not a fallen angel but the first Jinn (Man's nemesis) created by Allah. According to the Quran, angels have no Will; as a result, they have no ability to disobey or choose. However, Jinns, with their unfathomable intelligence, can choose their paths; they have the Will to disobey or obey, be loyal or be a traitor (*Khazoola*: خذولا). A Jinn or Djinn is male, the female side of this race is called Jnun (in plural form: جنون), a polysemous word which also means delirium, maddening love and terminal schizophrenia (corrosive tidal waves of xeno-excitations).

In Persian mythology, Jnun are descended from Jeh or Jahi, the first anti-creationist agent engineered by Ahriman's own body, the daughter of Ahriman who awakened her father from ten thousand years of slumber to spawn a pest-legion. Jahi is the first woman whose mission was to undo the entire pro-creationist project of Ahura Mazda. In Arabic folklore, Jnun are daughters of Lilith. Rûb-al-Khâlie, the dreadful desert where Abdul Al-Hazred settled for ten years, was inhabited by Jnun — not Jinn — which operate as female gates to the Outside. Al-Hazred must have communicated with the female side of the Outside (i.e. Jnun) in writing his nocturnally-encrypted *Necronomicon*, a *chef d'œuvre* on cosmodromic blasphemy and on the realism of openness.

Jnun possess men, yet they do not occupy or colonize their hosts. Instead they lay open male hosts to the Outside, an openness in the sense of being laid, cracked, butchered open (as in the case of the Moroccan jinniya, Aisha Qandisha, or Aiesheh Ghediseh, who is also called 'the Opener'). Possessed by Jnun, Abdul Al-Hazred found this path the only reliable polytics to communicate with the cosmodrome of the Outside demarcated in the Numogram as the region of Djynxx or more precisely, XX-djinns. The path to Djynxx or the region of XX-djinns is mapped as becoming-woman via Jnun who, according to Arabic and Farsi folklore, narrate untold stories for the one who is opened and devoured by them. Lilith tells travelers forbidden stories before opening and devouring them. In this sense, Jnun (mapped as the region Djynxx in the Numogram) is a direct link to the cosmic blasphemy and the female current of the Outside. The reason that Lovecraft frequently calls Al-Hazred the 'mad' poet or the 'mad' Arab is that communicating with Jnun, as the female gates (vulvo-cosmic singularities) to the Outside, has one inevitable consequence — radical delirium. In Arabic and Farsi the word Jnun also means delirium, maddening love, terminal madness as the result of being laid open by the female cutting-edge of the Outside. However, Jnun is not compatible with the western definition of Madness. It cannot be translated properly, but suffice to say that it is mainly comprised of three elements and is developed through their compositions: Possession, Love and utter Openness. Abdul Al-Hazrad is a *majnun* (مجنون), a man laid open by Jnun and at the same time, a majnun man, a madman (majnun) who immediately reminds us of the melancholic tale of *Leyili and Majnun*, their love story which converges in madness, openness, and a delirious love — the Forbidden.

Aisha Qandisha or Aisha Qadisha or Ghediseh is one of the most popular and fearsome Jinniya (female Jinn) in Moroccan folklore. Beliefs and rituals for Aisha have continued into the twenty-first century. She is both a hunter and a healer, sometimes appearing as a beautiful (irresistibly seductive) woman and sometimes as a Hag. When she possesses a man, she does not take over the new host, but opens the man to a storm of incoming Jnun and Jinns, demons and sorcerous particles of all kinds; making the man a traffic zone of sweeping cosmodromic data. This is why she is feared. And she never leaves — she always resides in the man to guarantee his total openness, which is not always pleasant. According to the Moroccans, the only way to feel comfortable with Aisha (the new mistress / lover) is by participating with her, feeding her, exciting her through passionate and barbaric music rites with cacosonic rhythms.

THE THING
WHITE WAR AND HYPERCAMOUFLAGE

H. Parsani's article *Peace in the Wake of Double-Betrayal* reads like a straight socio-anthropological analog to John Carpenter's movie *The Thing* (with the predictable Middle-Eastern references and conclusions in order to make the article sociopolitically responsible). In spite of Parsani's complete cultural illiteracy (or as he put it, 'cognitive inaptitude') with regard to contemporary cinema and literature, and his cynical antagonism toward science fiction ('my spontaneous knee-jerk reaction'), the essay acknowledges Carpenter's *The Thing* as its 'secondary source of inspiration'. The primary source is Abdu-Salam Faraj's extremist manifesto *Jihad: The Absent Obligation,* which glorifies the doctrine of *Taqiyya* or *Taghieh* in Islam as the foundation of the new holy war. The article is the analytical consequence of a clash between an archeologist and science-fictional materials. Before penning his article, Parsani had protested, 'Why would I need to read science fiction when I make my living by studying and interacting with the Middle East, which doesn't make sense even to something like science fiction?' Parsani emphasizes that he ran into this movie by chance, years after he had published his book, which covers the doctrine of Taqiyya. The original passage on Taqiyya in *Defacing the Ancient Persia* refers to the Islamic, and particularly Shia, doctrine of Taqiyya at the dawn of Islam as a defensive and protective strategy: Taqiyya means concealing one's true belief and activities in order to avoid any kind of danger (as in the case of practicing and believing in Islam in hostile societies). However, Parsani's more recent account of the term analyses Taqiyya as a modern evasive tactic and a militant strategy highly conscious of its own offensive complexity. Parsani suggests if the original meaning of Taqiyya as 'to avoid or shun danger' relates to the dedicated responsibility of the believer to exercise caution in nurturing and saving the divine Belief (religion), the modern Taqiyya deals with concealing one's belief by undertaking the belief or the practice of the Other, so as to provoke the enemy society or hostile Whole, in its search for the true believers, to react against its own population and entities. For once the Jihadi overlaps his own belief with that of the unbeliever, the hostile or infidel state can no longer discriminate its own citizens from the people of Jihad and their radical threats. By living and speaking the same way as the so-called infidel, the Jihadi completely overlaps ordinary citizens in a society. In order to infiltrate Jihadi forces, the state must first inquire into the very concept of citizenship, and strictly regulate what an ordinary civilian is and is not. So that the civilian is both the first and the last target for the state and the Jihadi. It is in the wake of the doctrine of Taqiyya and Jihad that civilian becomes an obscure ally – that is, worse than the enemy.

> Today *Taqiyya*, or adherence to the logic of the Thing, connects the survival of a believer who conceals his practice and belief to a catastrophic consequence for the enemies' community. Survival of individuals or collectives, particularly the very existence of native and indigenous entities, must become an object of police curiosity or even liquidation, because the hostile entities who exploit *Taqiyya* practice and revere everything but their own systems; they populate every niche and land but their own. (H. Parsani)

The proximity of this scenario to that of *The Thing*, according to Parsani, comes from the fact that it is not the Thing (the extremist under Taqiyya) which is targeted as the object of eradication and assault, but its potential hosts, or the positions (niches) which it might occupy. If survival is the mere reason for the Thing's invasion in the form of infestation of civilians, then in order to eliminate the Thing's threat, everything that tries to survive – or, in other words, survival in general – must be considered a threat. To hunt down the Thing, one must look for everything that tries to survive, because the will to survive coincides with the Thing's tendency to survive at all costs: the more inconsequential an entity is, the more ideal a host it is for the Thing. In a human society, this ideal survivalism both on an individual and collective level manifests itself in civilians and the concept of citizenship. A civilian is the closest entity to the ideal hideout of a Jihadi under Taqiyya. In the presence of a warrior under Taqiyya who just tries to survive, becoming the native civilian of the hostile society not only renders the fact of 'being a civilian' (civilian status) menacing, but also forms a polarity in the society: The polarity of the State and insurgent militia (sabotaged civilianhood), a polarity which moves along a corkscrew of escalation and diffusion. Every suspect Jihadi who is eliminated by the State results in stronger attempts for survival from the Jihadi under Taqiyya (the Thing) which in turn leads to a more powerful Taqiyya (Thinghood), that is to say, diffusing among new hosts to a higher degree as well as increasing the potential for any civilian or native host to be a Jihadi, or the Thing (contamination).

Parsani traces the practice of Taqiyya as a hypercamouflage which confounds the linear distinction of civilian and militia in the works of the Persian occult-saboteur, prophet of heresy-engineering, and State-Guerilla rebel Abdallah ibn Maimun, who founded the sect of Batiniyya (*Ahl-i-Batin* or the crowd of within) from which Hasan-i-Sabah's Hashshashins and the majority of regional insurgencies originated.

Parsani calls ibn Maimun the first theorist and practitioner of double-betrayal and Trison as the polytical unit of the Middle East. 'The practice of Taqiyya as a realization of Trison was the invention of ibn Maimun; but the secretive nature of his activities as a faceless civilian and a man behind the curtain led to all the credit for his intellectual and pragmatic achievements going to his disciples and to opportunists like Hasan-i-Sabah, who could only digest a morsel of ibn Maimun's immense knowledge and restless wisdom,' Parsani writes.

During the reign of the Sunni Abbasid Caliphs, Ibn Maimun selected Tunisia for his initial training in Afro-guerilla warfare (mostly nomadic war-machines), and to form a laboratory for merging his vast Farsi, Arabic and Gabrie (a derogatory term for Zoroastrianism used after Islam) wisdom and knowledge of the occult, culture and politics with African guerilla warfare and religiophagous occultism ('there are places to the south of the Arabic Peninsula where the occult eats religion,' Parsani quotes from ibn Maimun's diary). Having partly escaped the domain of the Caliphs' power, ibn Maimun started to study techniques for breeding and mobilizing sects, minorities, brotherhoods and secret societies, as well as mathematically modeling the way they operated and communicated with each other. After coming to the conclusion that 'the deepest secrets of religion lie in its minorities' (ibn Maimun), he moved to Egypt, known as the land of secret societies, and played a pivotal role in propagating occult doctrines, sects and heresies. He spawned many sects and heresies, which ultimately began to gnaw at the foundations of the Caliph's domination of Egypt in the most voracious but silent ways. When the clash between the rebellions and the Caliph's state came to the surface, it only lasted a few days, as the majority of work had already been done by countless sects and secret societies. Parsani writes that the Middle East has never seen such a sinister entity, whose thirst to rebel and undermine all institutions, religions and schools of thought surpassed all limits and measures of infamy, and whose pragmatic doctrines were so pervasively multifarious and deeply rooted in the Middle East that western politicians, theorists, rebels and occultists could hardly fathom them.

Parsani unearths an Arabic passage from ibn Maimun's *Risalatan fi Ahl-al-Ain* (The book on the people of the eye or the eye's crowd) which ibn Maimun wrote during his long trip to Tunisia; the book was later entrusted to Hasan-i-Sabah by Al-Fatmid in Egypt. During Hasan's period of influence, the book underwent ideological appropriations and a distorting bastardization directed by Hasan himself. However, the book remained the source of mutinous motivation for some of the most mysterious sects and societies in the Middle East until the Mongol ruler, Hulagu Khan, took over the Hashshashins' Alamut fortress in 1256.

> The necessity of peace must eclipse the necessity of War, as the indispensability of God must outshine the indispensability of Satan. Be keepers of peace, for war is ephemeral and shall not last long enough to bear your rage and shall not dive deep enough to harvest new blades and arrows. (ibn Maimun, *Risalatan fi Ahl-al-Ain*)

Parsani explains that, following this message and the collusive stance toward peace, ibn Maimun's alignment with God is reflected through his contentious statement, 'Nothing has been more instrumental and more favorable to the rise of heresies than the glory of God.' It is in ibn Maimun's persistence in undertaking Taqiyya that his ambiguous inclinations are most fully developed. Parsani states that for ibn Maimun, militarization cannot occur when or where war as the state of conflict between warmachines is aggravated. This is because in such circumstances militarization will be regulated by the boundaries of the battlefield and is one-dimensionally specialized by the limited type of enemies it interacts with. The fragile character of warmachines in war is the result of their not having the capacity to exceed a certain quality or quantity of activities (getting more heated) and not being able to be silent (obligation to undertake activities). For this reason, peace — as opposed to war and the battlefield — is a space radically open to being populated by warmachines and militarized. According to ibn Maimun, if warmachines or the entities of battle always have to do something and undertake a tactic to become what they are, viz. warmachines, then they can never be radical and unbounded enough because they exclude peace, silence and inactivity (or divergent activities) and base themselves on exclusive affirmation and dynamic modulation, or what Parsani calls, 'the fascism of activity'.

Ibn Maimun advocates peace because such a blank space of un-friction between warmachines, collective survival and divergent activities (rather than tactical convergence in war) is the best place to unbind warmachines. Peace can be militarized, or to be exact, populated by warmachines which seek only to survive alongside and together with their enemies, to be silent, to countermine the enemy and to be criminal to the core. Parsani remarks that such a warmachine in ibn Maimun's doctrine of insurgency and militarization is nothing but a warrior who has undertaken Taqiyya among hostile forces. That is why ibn Maimun refers to the abode of unbounded war as 'White War'; at once the white of thick impenetrable fog and the color of peace. Parsani writes:

The Thing, or a warrior who has undertaken Taqiyya completely and in every aspect, overlaps the citizen, the normal, the voiceless, the ordinary and the friendly by shutting down all his conflictual and war-fueled activities. By becoming as one with the citizens as expendable entities for the State, the warrior under Taqiyya shifts the battlefield to the homeland and shifts the attention of the State and its instruments of policing onto citizens rather than outside forces. In an ironic twist, the Jihadi under Taqiyya gives a voice to the voiceless (the civilian, that is); a voice which is in fact the Thing's logic or the voice of the warrior under Taqiyya. If the best war machine is an expendable warmachine, then a civilian, as a citizen who is expendable and replaceable for the State precisely because of the policies and the order of the State, becomes an expendable warmachine — that is to say, the best war machine against the State in the wake of Taqiyya or Thing-hood. The warrior under Taqiyya does not possess civilians or citizens of the hostile community; he becomes 'one of them' in every sense, even if becoming one of them practically opposes his beliefs and pragmatic assumptions. Only by becoming one of them or being possessed by every position and characteristic of a citizen or a civilian of a hostile community — the very opposite of possessing civilians — can the Taqiyya practitioner undermine citizenship or civilian status (in its State-dictated inconsequence) and thereby, the State itself. This is nothing but the machinery of a black revolution, twisted from the beginning, epidemic to the end.

If people as numbers and numeric contagions constitute the foundation of democracy, ordinary people as dormant warmachines form the floods of revolution. The Jihadi under Taqiyya overlaps the civilian so as to derail the society against the state, and instigates the state against its own society. However, at the same time, civilians too are recapitulated as consequential warmachines. From the white war of the Jihadi under Taqiyya evolves the black revolution of civilians against their own inconsequentiality and the hegemony of the state. The true revolution is about rendering civilianhood intrinsically consequential.

The Middle East's people are the artisans of Taqiyya; early in their life, they become adept at practicing Taqiyya both to survive in and to rebel against their unsympathetic environments, from their ruling States to the external forces that are ignorantly hostile. Smoothly and without friction they traverse all of these environments and become one with all of them. No one but ibn Maimun dared to stare into this stygian vista and to discover that everything these people do is an unheard-of violence and revolution against both the triviality of their own civilian status and the sovereignty of the State. When it comes to Taqiyya, every breath for survival is a ball of fire hurled at order and dominant stability.

The Thing or the practitioner of Taqiyya — a Middle Easterner — is not a rebel in any normal sense; it is a Trison in human guise, an anthropoid

> polytical unit with catastrophic capacities for insurrection and subversion. If the Middle East is not geographically measurable, it can be identified by its population. Ibn Maimun suggested that the Middle East is a white war and named its population – whether individual or collective – the legion, for the individual becomes a military collectivity through Taqiyya, which connects and overlaps the individual and the collective. All can be the warrior undertaking Taqiyya, as Taqiyya contaminates the individual with an expanding collectivity. The Thing does not come in a pack but as one dog, a loner whose individuality and separate existence as a singular is hugely questionable.

The essay connects the opening scene of *The Thing* with Ibn Maimum and his 'White War', with Parsani concluding that:

> True revolution is not to be found in the direction of change of any kind; it occurs when a population tears down its civilian status and unbinds the numerical powers inherent to the very definition of 'population'.

WAR AS A MACHINE

By the time Colonel West turned into a renegade and deserted Delta Force's Special Tactics And Rescue Squad, other infantry divisions had already come to know West's squad under his *nom de guerre,* as 'Hulagu's Gang'. A top-ranking Pentagon officer anonymously stated that there were covert missions underway in Iraq to arrest West and bring him to court martial for treason, including planned and systematic attacks on American convoys near Basra and attempts to contact Islamists inside and outside of Iraq. However, the Pentagon's attempt to smear West somehow failed when he spread his words through a pirate radio station: 'My enmity with Islamists has been exacerbated into a raging enlightenment.' West continued by enumerating the catastrophic mistakes caused by the natural-born inaptitude of American Generals to perceive the war, the Middle East and the convoluted malevolence necessary to continue the war. West had repeatedly pointed to the way American soldiers – misguided by their commanders – had disgraced their 'astute voracity' and reduced themselves to payroll officers and servicemen. Finally, he sympathized with American soldiers by cryptically alluding to the necessity for his 'sons' (West's term for his military disciples) and himself to pragmatically meditate on what he called the Oily Ethics of War or the middle-eastern Creed of War. 'The meaning of war is only found in the search for the meaning of petrol. Enlightenment, as spoken of by the Jihadis, is the realization of this fact.'

After his last sermon, West started to search for a way to grasp war as an autonomous entity (to grasp war as a machine with machinic particles and parts). He commenced his expedition from the Mesopotamian necropolis of dust, petroleum and derelict warmachines by exhuming the unfathomably ancient models of grasping-war-as-a-machine.

> If they persist, it is because the Middle East itself is nothing other than the doctrine of grasping war as a machine, rather than in favor of warmachines. War spawns warmachines to devour them; snuffing out their military enthusiasm for survival. This is the Unlife of War. I came to this conclusion after my last Delta-mission, Operation Desert Freedom. Locals say the ancient Assyrians, as a war-worn race who totally inhabited the fog of war, were obsessed by the same formula; Babylonians mockingly called it the Assyrian Lamassu-Complex. In Najaf and Ninevah, contacts speak of a notorious female oil smuggler named Jay who has assembled a militant religious cult named Naphtanese in the mountains of Kurdistan in Iran. They believe that the Unlife of War feeds on oil or (as they put it) the 'black corpse of the Sun'. Petroleum makes warmachines slide towards itself. Radical War originally comes from the other side of the oil pipeline. Their emblem is a broken star with nine vertices. I have seen it on walls in the Iraqi border villages. (From a letter sent by Colonel West to his former Delta-trooper squad, calling his 'sons' to join him.)

The model of War-as-a-Machine increasingly distances itself from the Deleuze-Guattarian model according to which the collisions of warmachines produce war as a conclusion of (re-)heated warmachines (a model according to which war can in some way be thermodynamically grasped through the conflictual tactics of warmachines). In the model of War-as-a-Machine, undercurrents replace the predominant dynamic role of tactics in the Deleuze-Guattarian model. Warmachines move forward on undercurrents and are customized according to them. Petropolitical undercurrents, with oil as a global conspirator, for instance, function as Telluro-occultural lubricants on which everything slides, advancing in all directions. Another base-diagram of this model is that War-as-a-Machine works through incinerating spirals. War constantly pumps cooling Aer (Fog of War as a cooling system) into the battlefield to simultaneously cool down warmachines and make them blind. While the cooling system strategically offers warmachines new opportunities to get hotter, the blindness is necessary for warmachines to be incinerated by their own frenzy. This spiral corresponds occulturally to the tireless resurrection of the Norse adept-warriors in Valhalla after dusting each other in battle (Dust to Dust model). The spiral eventually reaches a meltdown point — technically known as Deep-Shit or FUBAR — from which there is no return.

Warmachines gradually hit the point of autonomy by forming the spiral and reaching its incinerating point. This meltdown point is an infernomatic heat-death. In contrast to the thermodynamic re-heating or the required impetus of warmachines for survival, heat-death is beyond all recycling; it is the point where military survival is impossible. Military survival uses heat and transforms it into the warmachine's dynamism, a source for both conflict and survival. Heat-death, however, is the source of restlessness between warmachines and war, rather than warmachines with each other. Restless activities are tactics for unilateral communication with war. At the meltdown point, warmachines are emptied of their military survival (but do not become suicidal); they initiate themselves into the realm of War itself by becoming hunting particles (Fog of War) or parts of War which now hunt warmachines. Either cremated to ash (Dust-to-Dust) or evaporated as GAS, warmachines disappear into the fog at the meltdown point — a tempest of diverging particles narrating the epidemic of War. And it should be recalled that particles constitute the *al-khemy* of any sorcery and the Fog of War. In the model of War-as-a-Machine, warmachines' principle of navigation (probing) or simply C&C (command and control or command and conquer) becomes impossible at the subjective level. Warmachines are disconnected from their lines of command. The model of War-as-a-Machine has a complex machinery functioning at the level of strategy rather than tactics, swerving particles rather than convergent bodies.

The thirst to hunt that howls within warmachines is a simulation and a fragmented image of the Unlife of War. Warmachines have a capacity to grasp it as something that is external to them yet gives rise to their machinery and their thirst to hunt. Ironically, the thirst to hunt that exists within each warmachine is the simulation of the radical frenzy of war to hunt all warmachines.

The archeo-demonographic figure of this spiral is the dragon or, as in ancient Persia and Babel (Babylonia), *Azhi*.[23] The coiling draco-spiral (*drake*: dragon) becomes highly pertinent in War on/of Terror and its associated pipeline odyssey. Petropolitical undercurrents are directly associated with the agencies of Islamic Apocalypticism. By virtue of their existing in oil resources, Islamic warmachines[24] are smuggled within oil undercurrents to the west; they are also supported by cults such as the oligopolistic OPEC in reaching both East and West. When Islamic warmachines, smuggled through oil pipelines and petropolitical undercurrents, reach their destination, they start to fuse with berserkeresque warmachines of the west which actually feed (or rather feast) on oil. Western techno-capitalist warmachines are progressively attracted to (become thirsty for) oil resources. Such an attraction results in an involuntary attraction and addiction to petropolitical entities (such as Islamic warmachines) lurking in oil-imports or oil undercurrents and pipelines. Since western warmachines have already (stealthily) been programmed and contaminated by Islamic warmachines smuggled through oil, they militantly rush towards Islamic warmachines, or, in other words and more precisely, they are attracted to Islamic warmachines by an internal force which has already mutated them from within through their oily nervous system and petromania. For western warmachines, the addiction to oil is not limited to oil as fuel, but extends to Islamic Apocalypticism, in a twisted enthusiasm for interlocking and clashing with Islamic warmachines.

In this collision, occurring on the level of tactics but triggered by strategy, western warmachines are depleted of 'oil' and 'the mutating programs of Islamic Apocalypticism', already implanted within them as western consumers of oil by petropolitical undercurrents. Therefore, as soon as western warmachines are depleted of their fuels and propulsive enthusiasm, they begin to search for more blobby and more subterranean dimensions of petropolitics, engaging with more complex entities of Islamic Apocalypticism and petropolitics. All this makes for a draco-spiral at each stage of conflict and communication, which convolutes towards the Unlife of War. The draco-spiral consists in a petropolitical regenerating cycle (a recurrent back-and-forth). Because of the variations in petropolitics and oil scenarios, the spiraling recurrence of the draco-spiral can be charged and mobilized in different ways. Whether Thomas Gold's panorama of infinite and rechargeable oil resources or the scenario of Finite Fossil Fuels, each hyperstition of oil has peculiar effects and consequences on the draco-spiral and its gyrating slants: the pipeline odyssey.

> War endures ... War was always here. Before man was, war waited for him. The ultimate trade awaiting its ultimate practitioner. ... war is god. (Judge Holden)

Probably the most effective way to grasp War on/of Terror is to grasp War-as-a-Machine. The Deleuze-Guattarian model fails to exhume the undercurrents and subterranean processes at work in WWIV. This is why Delta Force (the former secret military cult of Colonel West) had no success NAMifying the growing desert of Islamic Apocalypticism. The reason for this failure was not because the middle-eastern deserts have already grown but, rather, as Parsani pointed out in his *Rise and Fall of the Solar Empire*, because 'the Middle East, as the only adherent partisan of the Assyrian doctrine of War, is not a geographical or even a political body, but a sentient process of desertification which can be grasped only by presupposing that war is an autonomous entity free from its provocateurs. How is it possible to add more to this already-a-desert if your religion, politics and beliefs are still secretly fancying meadows and jungles?'

The sado-conspiracy of the desert gives warmachines the opportunity of being easily camouflaged. But at the same time, the desert renders warmachines ultimately naked. The desert brutally exposes the properties, trajectories and inner mechanisms of warmachines, peeling off every layer of camouflage from their quivering bodies. The desert does not camouflage warmachines; it camouflages War itself.

> This is not Vietnam, this is not the jungle; the desert is always ready to subvert all human thoughts, to suck warmachines dry. If we sprayed their boonies with Agent Orange to deprive the Vietnamese of their food and shelter, here the enemy fights alongside us to liberate the desert: this, rather than our defeat, it is the ultimate goal they try to reach. (Colonel Jackson West)

> Two painted A37 Dragonflies in Bien Hoa Air Base, a couplet from US military lyricism reverberating over Vietnam, two poles of American pyromania, one in the name of God and purity and the other in the name of the

> pit and the oil pipeline. One says: Your struggles on the earth merely delay your final sleep here. And the other complements this with: Let my foes perish in Napalm and smoke; for them, the Avernus will hold no surprise! (Jackson West, Personal Journal, May 19, 1967)

Frustrated by the 'Western principles of desertification' which misled and diverted the US military might from truly participating with War into playing with 'quixotic warmachines', in the period after the Iraq war and leading up to his departure Colonel West published a pamphlet on the ethical groundwork of desertification. The pamphlet was followed by a primer focusing on the restricted terrain of military tactics or urban warfare (urbanized war as West called it). In his pamphlet on desertification, West expounds his position on war and cities — a polemic according to other officers but a mere 'military platitude' according to West himself: 'The desert war can only manifest itself in urban warfare and only cities can unbind the desert'; 'military communion with the desert is only possible by deliberately grafting every single tactical line onto urban time and space,' the Colonel outlines. West repetitively spells out the enormous importance of urbanizing military programs if one is to confront war as an autonomous machine. He argues that urbanizing all modes of warfare or reprogramming military policies according to urban space is the only way to become mature and partake in Operation Desert Freedom. Unlike urban warfare, urbanized war gives the city the logic of the desert, which is the logic of war without warmachines.

> Operation Desert Freedom is an obligation irresponsibly blunted and abandoned by the western approach to the desert, which has long been dated, if it has ever existed outside of western Orientalist fantasies. (From the introduction to the Primer on Urbanized War)

Jackson West's primer on urbanized war was later modified ('minced into digestible pieces') and safely re-militarized by US lines of command for daily military practice, mainly in Iraq. The primer is a theoretically and pragmatically technical manual aiming at 'disillusioning commanders and warming up soldiers'. This is one of the reasons that the original un-domesticated primer was popularly circulated among rogue units in Iraq. According to West, urban warfare is still developed on the basis of the open and conventional warfare; for this reason what interested him was not urban warfare but urbanized war, the dark twin of urban warfare, which pities neither warmachines nor cities. In order to urbanize war rather than developing urban warfare, West presents — with a responsible ferocity — a meticulous elaboration of both terms. The primer on urbanized war includes techniques of communication, 'house-cleaning', re-mobilization of military divisions, combined weaponry (gluing low-tech and hi-tech weaponries together), command, etc. The primer divides into the following main sections, each separately concluding that 'The desert is born out of urbanized war and the abortion of the conventional battlefield':

Communication: on nested communication in urbanized war and its role in sweeping desertification. The first priority should be to consider the urban terrain from a communications perspective, that of a desertified (but not deserted) city. In radical urban warfare or urbanized war, nested communication is necessary as soldiers are trapped in blind spots and communications dead-ends, mobilized deep within the urban space, in back alleys, houses surrounded by apartments surrounded by towers, etc. Such nested communication is responsible for rendering the city a desert — as open as possible, purged of all erected eidolons — easing all types of communication, leveling the vertically-contoured urban terrain to make possible an all-encompassing communication. It should provide soldiers with accessibility, and the capacity to spot hostile, friendly and neutral units.

Infantrication: Not the transformation of military divisions into infantry divisions, but the re-mobilization of soldiers as molecular combat units diversified by all divisions. Military deification of soldiers' *raison d'etre* and focalization of their roles. On the hostile front, too, the Jihadi urbanists possess a tremendous power. The power of urban Jihadis lies in their ability to undergo reversible metamorphoses, from civilian to militia and from militia back to ordinary civilian. Urban Jihadis' civilian side is as weaponized as their militarized side. The power of infantrication is released when Jihadi militias withdraw into their former civilian selves with military precision, not the other way around. West repeats that the military power of the militia is immense: On the one hand the dreadful capacity for ambush, on the other the evasive and misguiding aspects associated with its civilian side.

Only the double-dealing tactical line and the polymorphic configuration of infantry ingrained in civilians to become militia and vice versa, can effectively ward off and unbalance the asymmetrical military power of semi-organic or non-organic divisions such as air force and armored divisions. By rigging up their civilian selves, militias are capable of absorbing the damages wrought by the military sovereignty of a division such as the air force, and turning them into civilian casualties (the ultimate weapon against organized western military might). Colonel West links infantrication in urbanized war to the military quandary associated with urbanized Jihadis. The infantricated soldier is the ultimate response to the Jihadi civilian-militia. Once infantricated soldiers are transformed into law enforcers instead of being exclusively military soldiers, they can effectively cope with the urbanized Jihadis without fear of their civilian sides. When confronted with law enforcers, militias are incapable of presenting their body counts as civilian casualties. By considering infantrication as a process combining the infantry soldier and the law enforcer, urbanized Jihadis can be dealt with effectively. An infantry soldier should be refabricated in such a way that it can transform into a total law enforcer rather then a military soldier once the civilian side of the hostile militia becomes active. If the militia chooses to be an active civilian in its simultaneously tactical and strategic war, the infantry soldier too can be a law enforcer whose offensive power can not be directly linked to the victimhood of the civilian. The activities of infantricated soldiers as law enforcers are rather mapped through a defensive frame, that of protecting 'other' civilians and policing the civilian-militia (designated constablization).

Spatiality: Urban warfare is always pro-militia. It is the task of infantry to engineer an urbanized war capable of preying upon the space and time that evolves out of urban warfare. Forces advance in a non-linear fashion, swarming into the area of operation from all directions and simulating the complexity of urban areas overloaded by a new population, a new 'civilian' crowd. Different zones of urban combat will provide troops with different levels of awareness of their situation and that of the enemy, but it is essential for both fronts to develop a consciousness based on the logic of the desert, or a desertification process crawling over and through the city. While in urban warfare, the invaders (in the sense of entering the space already occupied and dwelled in by urbanists) generally remain exposed as a consequence of their lacking reconnaissance in regard to the restricted urban terrain, the hostile urbanists or militias can battle on a terminally closed terrain which is equal to the absolute vantage point. Thus, hostile urbanists or militias always conduct the battle towards the inside, or the domain of obstacles, the urban canyon. When it comes to urbanized war, every combatant must think like an obstacle — 'See everything from the perspective of an obstacle.' West then uses *Parkour* as the exemplary discipline in which the practitioner becomes as one with the obstacle during movement. Every soldier should be a *traceur*, a swerving projectile which has a deep sympathy with its physical obstacles. The desertifying philosophy of urbanized war is saturated with indoor spaces, restricted terrains and obstacles. 'Thinking Closure' should be considered a fundamental doctrine in urbanized war. The aim of radical urban warfare is to turn battlefields as platforms of tactics inside out, placing military power as well as its side-effects on the outside of the conventional battlefield, which is obviously populated and inhabited by what separates an open battlefield from urban / civil space. The outside of the conventional battlefield is the inside of the city, the platform of urbanized war.

In a Mecca-nomic sense, radical urban warfare channels all destructions of the open battlefield into the House of Abominations which must be leveled. The space of idolatrous festivities or abomination is demarcated by all manifestations which existentially, or by virtue of their verticality, rival the transcendence ascribed to the primary object of the Divine worship. Idols must be concentrated and gathered in a space named 'city', there to be purged all at once and all together. Cities are in fact houses of idols; everything that they emanate outshines the glory of God. All modes of urban warfare are monotheistic rituals. West suggests that urbanized war is the secret military cooperation between strategic closure and openness.

The battlefield is enclosed to attain a deserted openness at last, free from all judgments. 'It is the monotheistic duty of the Jihadi militia to fight, not to repel the infidel enemy from the populated and constructed centers, but to draw them in so as to position the city between the fierce defense and the reckless ravaging of the enemy. This way the Jihadis and western soldiers lend a hand to each other from opposite sides to flatten the city, or more technically, to submit both the city and the cooperating enemy to God; a submission which is the very act of conversion to Islam, the religion of utter submission to God. To liberate the Desert is to communicate with the one and only God,' West adds. In urbanized war, the only victory possible is that of obliterating the city, a victory synchronously achieved by both fronts. The primer suggests that in the Middle East, thinking in terms of openness — as of the open battlefield — is destined to fail. West frequently mentions that the urbanist militia is adept in reprogramming the city as the very object of war, a portal to the end of the pipeline for the Jihadi militia. In the Middle East, urban planning is based on the anticipation of an urbanized war. 'The claustrophobic or anomalous construction of cities such as Karachi, Tehran and Dubai is not merely a symptom of mismanagement or hysteria caused by overabundant oil money,' West notes, 'for such cities think ahead of time when it comes to war. Their construction, connected buildings and overpopulation are premeditations on war. Apart from sporadic examples, architecture in the Middle East is either a hokey imitation of the west or a profusely militarized masonry. Every brick either provokes the jihadi and enlightens his rage or secures his path to the desert.' In the wake of urbanized war, the population itself becomes the steadiest military trench: each civilian in itself a hide-out and a weapons stash for the militia.

IMPLEMENTS OF WAR: discrimination, raw killing power, systematic spotting and target correcting, re-distribution of units and weapons, nonmaterial intrusion and 'mechanical dread' (drones, smart traps, target singularizing cameras and weapons, etc.) In this section West gives details about the first imperative element in urbanized war which is 'to be inconsistent'. Every operation, every formation, every movement and assault (such as clearing houses or rooms in a building) should be inconsistent and dissimilar both to other activities in other parts of the city and to previous activities of the same kind. Urban warfare reprograms warmachines at the terminus of all pattern; it desertifies the pattern-recognition requisite for molar military approaches to tactics and resistance; an event West calls 'the abolition of the State's military formation and the birth of the guerilla-state'. The usage of weapons with maximum conductible and controllable effectivity in urbanized war is recommended, with examples. The central role played by bullets and ammunition, rather than weapons, is the main point of this section. In urbanized war, the centrality of bullets is heightened to the point where the decisive role of weapons is replaced by that of bullets. In urban warfare, bullets are — in an entirely non-metaphorical sense — the new population of cities, and cities are urbanized by the motions, trajectories, heat and noise of bullets as well as by their surface chemistry. Bullets are perfect citizens; coalition forces in Iraq call them 'Shiny' or 'Star Citizens'. West suggests the radicality of this new citizenship is hammered home perfectly when American troops take out the original citizens and populate the urban space with bullets. Bullets' trajectories and irreproachable swarming — which is in full empathy with the urban terrain and contours — re-engineers the city, turning it into a sponge or pumice stone with a perforated swarm-ridden liminality, a ( )hole complex in progress. If heat is, in current megalopolises, an indicator and an existential proof of the advancement of civilization, then the heat produced by bullets in an urban terrain surpasses all current measures of civilization density, modernization, population, speed and complexity. Bullets can terminally modernize an entire city in one night.

Bullets, after being shot, unfold all their other urban characteristics in the shape of monuments. While the ordinary population of a city falls into oblivion after death, bullets are reborn deadlier than ever after being consumed. After they are spent, bullets linger and take up space in the city, their necrostatic form adds something to the city instead of taking from it. Bullets are implements of war which turn into political agents, socio-cultural catalysts, or propaganda machines. Cities like Beirut, Karbala and Fallujeh exemplify this mutation from implements of war to effective political or even polytical operatives. Traces of bullets on residential walls and civilian vehicles infiltrated by bullets are typical portrayals of this thoroughly polytical mutation of the military into the terminally military. Another would be the use of guided bullets armed with infra-red or laser targeting systems (employment of which is usually accompanied by a morale-boost for soldiers in confrontation with urbanist militia — Soldiers informally address it as 'lasering the shit out of them'). The complex terrain of urbanized war demands the consolidation of weaponry around bullets and ammunition-related subjects such as cartridges, loading, ammunition delivery and packaging, external ballistics, accuracy (singularizing power). In urbanized war, the refinement of weaponry is not measured based on firepower, technology or even weight but on establishing a direct and independent line of command in the absence of logistics and even commanders if necessary, and imposing the deterrent intricacy of the urban terrain upon the enemy.

COMMAND: West uses the term 'flat command' to indicate the urbanized plane of command. Direct, realtime, and empowered by the effective stratification of the space between command and tactics (in contrast to revolutionary military doctrines aimed at de-stratification), flat command extra-organizes the mobility and communication of the combatants in the smoothest way possible. In addition to being a time sorcery and a distilled form of military agility, flat command eliminates the need for 'action license' for military units and fighting divisions to some degree. West equates this tactical route and its autonomy of activities with a deliberate and calculative breeding of defiant and rogue units. Rogue units are highly dense tactical cells of decision making, covert spirit, information gathering, infiltration, unconventionality and fanaticism (characterized by their prejudice and indulgence in killing sprees) within the major military sphere. 'The future of warfare lies in the hands of rogue units.' In a continuation of his analysis of flat command, West recapitulates the ancient formulation of secret societies as a model for rogue squads in War on Terror. The tactical density of rogue units can be harvested by reformulating the model of military squads according to the structure of units in ancient secret societies. Known as a 'Terror Fractal', the structure of units in ancient secret societies and classic terrorist groups is a triangle. The triangular structure coordinates a highly customizable and operational linkage between three soldiers. This structure can be easily refilled after loss of one or even two members of the triangle. The command can effectively rotate in the triangle while maintaining a pragmatically efficient stratification (order) which is less than a pyramidal order and more than a leveled or evened-out horizontality (consisting of two dots). The triangular structure or trinomic squad can easily be connected to another triangular structure or squad of the same type without establishing a chain of command. In this way a military fractal capable of transferring realtime command is produced. The Terror Fractal neutralizes the majority of enemy activities carried out to enervate or unhinge the military formation. With flat command, the enemy cannot inject entropy to an army by eliminating commanders and officers.

Despite the inflow of all military tactics associated with urbanized war in his primer, West concludes that a western war on urban terrain will inevitably fail to cope with an Islamic desert-militarism whose pinnacle is urbanized war. West continues his argument by questioning the scope and the arid span of Islamic desert-militarism. 'How innocent to desertify something born out of the desert, thinking and growing on behalf of the desert. Besides, they have enough dust to shack up with.' In another part, West notes that a Jihadi lives, fights and dies for the desert as its religion. And only the desert's partisan horizontality can concretely fulfill the politics, religions, minorities and rampant ambiguity of the Middle East. In a remark which is reminiscent of Parsani's opening sentence in *Defacing the Ancient Persia*, he writes: 'The Middle East is a militant horizontality gone choleric. The Middle East radiates a sentience so alien that it is usually comprehended as an external or extraterrestrial reinforcement of power and intelligence. Such sentience is usually approached in terms of homecoming and ingress — usually glorified under the banner of monotheism as the otherworldly Divine — but it takes time to realize that it all comes from the inside. Therefore, this alien sentience is one of flight and of rising from the Earth, not of advent and landing on Earth.'

In an exhaustive *fargard* (chapter) related to religions and sects in the Middle East, Parsani considers Wahhabism as an instance of desert radicalism among Islam's sects. He discusses how, in the wake of Wahhabistic enmity against all manifestations of idolatry (*shirk* and *kufr*), both monotheism and idolatry take on new connotations; one becomes a scorching horizontality which tolerates no contour of any kind against its monopoly and flatness, while the other turns into that which disturbs the flattening horizontality of the desert, sometimes with an antitrust policy. Here, everything is evaluated in terms of the desert. Islam and its inspired sectarianism (continues Parsani) take Abrahamic monotheism into a subliminal phase which he suspects originates from the infested germ-cell of Zoroastrianism, whose zeal for monotheism is but a stealthy and ongoing subversion of monotheism through parasitizing it for obscure destinations and objectives (missions).

Controversially, Parsani suggests that 'if monotheism failed in its missions – especially in the Middle East – Islam succeeded on every front where the aspirations of monotheism fell short. Ironically, the secret of Islam's success was in adopting the least important of such aspirations, the monotheistic hopes and ambitions in regard to the desert: not merely becoming the diviner of the desert, but becoming the desert itself, an utter communication platform with the Divine.' As Parsani points out, Wahhabism, the sect of the desert within Islam, practices a radical purgation of idols which departs from even the most distant desires and uncharted characteristics of monotheism.

> Wahhabism suggests that, to purge idols, it is otiose and absurd to hunt them down one by one; the solution is to raze their abode to the ground, sweeping away the culture itself. Yet this is not enough: To decimate all idols, one must eradicate the belief itself by which eidolons are nurtured and fertilized. In the presence of belief, idolatry is inevitable; everything can be erected as an idol. For Wahhabism, belief is the Farm of Satan and should be leveled entirely, scorched, ungrounded and undermined ceaselessly. The absence or eradication of belief, in a monotheistic twist, becomes the very equal of a belligerent campaign against idolatry. (H. Parsani, *Defacing the Ancient Persia*)

Despite his deep revulsion for prophesying ('nothing is more clownish than an archeologist whose heart races for Nostradamus'), Parsani offers a glimpse of the future of this desertifying machinery, in whose aftermath even belief overindulges idolatry or is an idolatrous superfluity:

> The future of Jihad and martyrdom lies on the ashes of belief. With the eradication of belief, the Abrahamic war on idolatry will flourish unimaginably; it will be embellished by new meanings and new cutting-edges. If you are impatient to learn what and where the future might be, consult a Wahhabi warrior.

For West, too, Wahhabism is a key for understanding the immensity of the desert and the process of desertification which is crucial to a concrete grasp of war as a machine. 'For thousands of years, the Middle East has provided the rest of the world with a free guide to the stunning results of grasping war as a machine.' West always reminds his 'sons' of what they are dealing with. An audio tape retrieved from a village near Karbala by the US army's 3rd Infantry division delivered to 1st SFOD-D for analysis, and later made public by Delta Force, features the recorded voice of someone who Delta suspects might be one of Colonel Jackson West's top lieutenants. The man erratically reiterates one of West's sermons. The passage publicized by Delta resonates with Parsani's discussions, minus their highbrowism and analytic qualities — as if West's discourse was directly inspired by excerpts from *Defacing the Ancient Persia*:

> The road to the desert of God is constructed by scorching belief. Atomic chemotherapy may be pointless today, but it sure will prove handy for winding up belief by zapping 'em with nukes. Dusting belief, like the Wahhabis do is a systematic enlightenment when it comes to war. Never mind the 'problem of faith', it's irrelevant – faith is impossible, period. The rise of faith takes place on the ground of belief. For the Wahabbis, belief is Mazrae Shaytan — Satan's Farm — the faithful are Satan's farmers. How is it possible to live without belief? Ask a Wahhabi suicide bomber; they'll tell you it's the most responsible way of worshiping God, indistinguishable from fighting and from living. Desert enlightenment needs an ethics of war, not war machines, and the ethics of war only becomes real when it's practiced on belief's afterlife. You can never be a victim if you get rid of belief.

Colonel West's veneration of Communion on the ruination of belief ('time to walk in the nuclear winter of belief') and his merciless attack on faith must not be understood oversimplistically as an advocacy of disbelief; for disbelief, likewise, requires a primal belief to negate, perpetuating its plane of disbelief through the logic of negativity and exclusion. Then what is this tide toward the horror of eradicating belief by putting it under constant nuclear chemotherapy? Doesn't it form that internal pulsation that becomes the inevitable option for a Wahhabi suicide bomber? The irony of this un-belief sublimates itself in the lyricism of a suicide bomber's war cry, with its fanatically democratic twist: I love a crowd.

Excursus VII (A samizdat signed as The Codex of Yatu by an unknown writer named Jay, locations of discovery: Kurdistan and Sistan va Baluchestan, Iran)

Support the Desert. The only way that Western man can grasp the immensity of the Sahara (the Desert) is by choking on napht (oil), but it takes time for pipelines to pump it all the way through the continents. Now, can we rely solely on the promise of our naphtanese religion?

The contribution of the US military power to War on Terror has been merely to expand the desert to which Islam has submitted its foundations and devoted its Umma: Qiyamah's Desert, the Desert of Islamic Apocalypse. Once, an excessive weaponry directed at a minimal target emphatically expressed the limitless generosity of American hegemony. Now, in War on Terror and its desert militarism, such lavish feasts of arsenal invite Jihad from the other end of the desert, passionately, unknowingly. If the devotion of Islam to Qiyamah passes through the desert, on whose scorching ground no idol can be erected against Allah, American militarism, with its own irresistible urge to desolate, has also migrated, remobilized itself to spread this desert, thus broadening the path of Jihad to reach and embrace the burning Qiyamah. Follow this line; encourage the US warmachine to obey its extirpating ethos; and donate to the desert, pulverizing all obstacles on the way of Jihad and its desert-walking nomads.

If the pax Islamica (the Umma) is so enthusiastic to drive the war into urban spaces, it is because they know that the US warmachines do not merely wipe out an urban area like the conventional armies of a conventional enemy; they overkill cities: Their tactics and extra-terminating weaponries have been programmed to make deserts of cities, disassembling anything erected cell by cell, atom by atom with a nonhuman passion for tactical precision; this is how they become as one with their Wahhabi adversaries in leveling anything erected, eradicating all manifestations of idolatry.

Vietnamese jungles were hospitable to the US military warmachine, as if there were a silent collusion between them. Jungles were perfect targets to project American supremacy in a sublime and spectacular form while enshrouding the bodies of Viet Cong troops under the heaps of smoldering trees which then were flushed into swampy rivers. But in the desert such attainment of military power is either negatively reflected back onto itself, or bolsters Jihadi adversaries who invigorate and fulfill their militancy and eventually attain their destiny by and from the desert.

Vietnam may have been recorded as a failure, but indeed it was the greatest achievement of America, leading its entire military economy to produce weapons and armies programmed to push the ability to Overkill further towards the potency of full desertification. In fact, Vietnam not only escalated US military consumption, but also rewarded America with the illusion that all military targets can be treated as a jungle, and that war is necessitated by warmachines, not the other way around.

It is not surprising that both the Crusade and Jihad align with the desert from different directions; but for Jihad, the desert has no temporal value; it is the only path to true submission, Islam. If the desert must be affirmed as the sole path of submission,[25] then the military orientations of the US, from its massive Shock and Awe operations to the divine-like sovereignty of Death From Above, all exhibit an endless zeal on the path of Islamic submission, practically more loyal to this path than the forces of Jihad. Now, in the presence of American armaments, draw the battles from streets and open spaces to shelters and civilian buildings — not so as to gain a tactical superiority, as there is no such thing against the US weapons; but so as to aid the US in expanding the desert of Jihad, leveling all shelters, all erected entities; easing, improving and speeding the rise of Jihad, which welcomes no battlefield but the desert.

Jay
The Codex of Yatu
(Translated from Persian by H.P.)

TELLURIAN INSURGENCIES

XERODROME, SOLAR TEMPESTS AND EARTH-SUN AXIS

TELLURO-MAGNETIC CONSPIRACY TOWARDS THE SUN I
SOLAR RATTLE

Hamid Parsani, in his essay *The Rise and Fall of the Solar Empire,* suggests that rigorous investigation of the anomalous pact between the Earth and the Sun through what he calls Tellurian Blasphemy (demonogrammatical decoding of the earth's body) is an untrodden but indubitably expeditious path. Such an investigation, Parsani suggests, will aid in understanding the processes and entities involved in the Rise of the Middle East as a sentient entity and a turbulent zone of epidemics, unconventional modes of warfare, power formations and polytical agitations. Parsani traces the Rise of the Middle East back to an occultural meltdown known as the Assyrian Syndrome (with similar cataclysms in Babylonia, Egypt, Persia and Palestine following it) which he believes resulted from the creation of an axis of communication and complicity between the Sun and a more insidious entity within the Earth itself, a 'Tellurian Insider'. In his essay, Parsani pursues his fascination with the vocalization of middle-eastern languages and their phonetic systems, or what, as he notes in *Defacing the Ancient Persia*, 'was known among the Greeks and Romans as "Barbaric Music".' Parsani believes that middle-eastern vocalizations render consistent all aspects of the Middle East – from the Tellurian to the political and religious – aspects which, according to Parsani, were knitted together on the basis both of the hegemony of the Sun and the loss of this Capitalist hegemony. For Parsani, the Rise of the Middle East and its insurgency against Solar Empire, is necessarily accompanied and celebrated with a certain music, a chorus rising from the Middle East's peculiar communication with the rest of the world, which includes and combines both a tellurian and a starry wisdom. 'When the Middle East as a living, sentient being, enters into a war either with the solar empire or with its terrestrial conscripts — enrolled in the guise of States, economies, politics or cultures — its forays into enemy territories are made with an unforgettable battle-cry: The music of vowelless alphabets,' Parsani writes.

SONIC HOLOCAUST. The Earth's ionosphere is composed of ionised territories above the Earth's surface. These stratified regions — whose distribution over the Earth's surface is also under the influence of the Sun's thermo-diurnal activities (see Fig. 24) — directly affect radio waves, mainly because of the presence of free electrons. These layers are classified according to increasing altitude and are arranged in approximately horizontal stratified layers. When a radio wave travels through the ionosphere, its electrical field imparts an oscillatory motion to electrons which radiate this energy in turn, like miniature antennae. This modifies the velocity of the wave propagation. During solar storms, however, this seemingly crypto-bureaucratic stratified configuration crashes and is recomposed according to the radical instability of regions and the rabid agitation of electrons triggered by solar electromagnetic surges. Such electromagnetic disturbances also limit the amount of appropriated information that can be carried in the HF spectrum, a war descending to blacken communication systems through a sonic holocaust (Solar Rattle), torching every particle with commotion, a 'Holocaust of Freedom'.

In the presence of solar tempests, listening is both inevitable and impossible. A military communications operator encounters a very diverse and disturbing range of sonic anomalies, all paralyzing the communication device (from radar jamming to solar outage), putting the operator in a direct and bizarrely close encounter with the sonic plague of Solar Rattle. This is a very personal experience for all radio operators during wartime; when the gate opens, the operator is sucked in ... and finds himself within another milieu constituted only of sounds — not human, but implacably anti-anthropomorphic sound molecules, electric death rattles, absolutely unnerving screeches, molecular storms, droning sounds corresponding with the terrible drone heard overhead as Druj-Nasu (an avatar of Druj, the Mother of Abominations) rushes from the north mountains as a fly to seize another corpse. Radio transmission in stormy weather broadcasts the non-orchestral body of Beelzebub, the Lord of Flies ('I romp around with the sound of flies'). The radio operator perceives warmachines as sonic entities being devoured by WAR itself, sonically sworn to consume the entire battlefield in the form of a Solar Rattle engineered by the earth's magnetic conspiracy towards the Sun which incites a tellurian insurgency unknown even to the black revolution of solar catastrophe.

> The Druj-Nasu[26] comes and rushes upon him, from the regions of the north, in the shape of a raging fly, with knees and tail sticking out, droning without end, and like unto the foulest *Khrafstras*[27] (Xrafstra). (Vendidad, Vidēvdād or The Book of the Laws against Demons, Anti-Druj Laws, Fargard 7, Purity Laws)

> âat mraot ahurô mazdå, ishare pasca para-iristîm spitama zarathushtra us haca baodhô ayât aêsha druxsh ýâ nasush upa-dvãsaiti apâxedhraêibyô naêmaêibyô maxshi kehrpa erekhaitya frashnaosh apazadhanghô akaranem driwyå ýatha zôizhdishtâish khrafstrâish.[28]

On a global scale, the Solar Rattle is the ultimate musicality: It registers any message-oriented or signaling datastream as a parasitic sub-noise ambient within itself. The Solar Rattle rewrites every datastream as an Unsign, even beyond any pattern of disinformation.

TELLURO-MAGNETIC CONSPIRACY TOWARDS THE SUN. In Tellurian Insurgency, unlike the Deleuze-Guattarian New Earth (*A Thousand Plateaus*, 'The Geology of Morals: Who Does the Earth Think It Is?') the strategy of stratification is to engineer a perverse immanence with the Sun. The highly stratified structure of Ionosphere / Magnetosphere provides the Earth with secret warmachines older than the Sun itself, with which it traps solar winds (high-energy particles of the sun) and turns them into peculiarly planetary sonic entities. Ionospheric strata have been customized and arranged in such a way that they reinforce the earth's surface with demonic currents and forces by capturing solar winds, bringing the earth's surface and its biosphere into an immanence with the Sun and the burning core of the Earth through a sonic axis. If hell is made on the Earth-Sun axis stretching from the Earth's burning core (the Insider) to the Sun, then hell cannot be grasped merely in terms of the Sun and its capitalism. The Insider or the black egg which the Earth is hatching within itself (*ge hinnom*) extends the geopolitical reality of hell beyond the boundaries of the Solar Empire. Hell, in this sense, is not exclusively owned by the Sun and its thermonuclear holocaust. (Note: The Valley of Hinnom has frequently been referred to as Hell; its Hebrew / Greek etymologic origin returns to *ge hinnom*, from which *Jahannam*, the Koranic word for Hell, was derived. In both Christian and Islamic texts, *Ge hinnom* (or Hell) has been regarded as 'the place down there' or the Lake of Fire, having numerous geochemical attributes; Ge hinnom or Hell occulturally confirms the geotraumatic lines of the burning ocean of the Earth's core, or what Mircea Eliade calls Cthelll.)

If occult entities choose the Solar Rattle as their sonic wave-net (propagation grid and model of cacophony), it is because the Solar Rattle generates vertical and horizontal fields of immanence and vigorously dissipates lines of communication at the end of the Sign. It is not an accident or an invention of contemporary pulp-horror fictions that the sonic cartography of Near and middle-eastern occult rituals (i.e. summoning, conjuration and xeno-communication) is essentially constituted of incomprehensible audio-traumatic murmurs and machinic ambience. The Solar Rattle and its Chthonic auditory agitations were already embedded within the immense capacity of vowelless alphabets of Middle and Near Eastern languages (Aramaic, Hebrew, Pahlavi, etc.) to artificialize a diverse range of molecular sounds and sonic compositions. Sorcerers and summoners know very well that to communicate radically with the Outside, they must first strip their communication networks (cults?) from informatic signaling systems, grasping communication at the end of sign and informatic reality. This is where the Solar Rattle installs communicative channels along with the Sun-Cthelll axis of electro-magnetized Hell.

FROM SOLAR STORMS TO SOLAR RATTLE. Interplanetary space was once believed to be an innocent emptiness, but it is the cavernous host of cosmic deluges consisting for the most part of solar winds and planetary magnetospheres. The magnetosphere or planetary magnetic field requires two ingredients for its assembly. One element is an electrically conductive liquid i.e. an ocean of molten metal (Hell?) in the interior of the planetary body, or what is called the core, which in the case of the Earth is the outer core (Cthelll). The other element is a sufficiently rapid rotational movement or giant current loops to create circulation of the metallic liquid at the core, consequently generating a magnetic field around the planetary body. The magnetosphere (or the core's magnetic conspiracy) develops radical communications with solar magnetic storms.

Solar magnetic storms are intrinsically connected to sunspots, the dark patches in the photosphere of the Sun; these cooler regions are the magnetically hyperactive parts. Sunspots come in groups, each group rarely exceeding ten sunspots; they are the most visible signs of solar complex magnetic fields (alongside solar radio emissions, which emerge from hot gas trapped in magnetic loops). A sunspot is a factory for the most twisted magnetic anomalies. Sunspots interconnect with solar magnetic activities and mass-ejections of solar flares buffeting planets: billion-ton clouds of magnetized gas — diabolically agitated particles and radiations — associating with coronal activities flying from the Sun's gravitational pull and bombarding the magnetosphere. In the case of the Earth, solar flares cause global ionospheric and geo-magnetic storms; during such immense disturbances (solar winds[29] and flares), satellites and communication devices are put into a sleep mode. Solar wind particles and radiations are swept around the planetary magnetosphere and recomposed by the strategically-stratified magnetic sphere of the planet, making the Earth sing like a mad beast as it reaches a radical and sinisterly creative intimacy between the core of itself (Hell or the entombed Zero) and the Sun (the incinerating Zero). Life on earth was musically and perversely composed under such a playground of sonic succubi, disguised as a shelter or an innocent terrestrial front against the high energy particles of the Sun whilst all the while rendering the Earth communicatively and sonically defenseless and naked. Even the seemingly stratified shape of the Earth's magnetosphere is a direct and creative answer to the relentless bombardment of solar storms, because while solar winds constrict its sunward side to a distance of only six to ten times the radius of the Earth (in the form of a faceless prow facing towards the Sun), they expand the night-side magnetosphere to approximately one thousand times the Earth's radius. Such a hyperactive magnetic monstrosity is called the magneto-tail (see Fig. 24).‡

‡ Rat and Ayasophia: ED717H135B12958

The magneto-tail is stretched out like a long and dynamic tail (a pack of rat-tails) — a wire-tail music machine which is also the main source of the polar aurora described in ancient texts as Sky Battle or Burning Clouds, a visual presentation of Telluro-magnetic commotions. It broadcasts sounds (both structured and non-structural sounds technically named tweeks, sferics, lion roars, whistlers and hisses) spawned by the magnetosphere, whose boundary cannot be sharply isolated from the ionosphere. These sounds diagram radical magnetospheric instabilities and magnetic flux mechanisms. Aurorae occur most frequently during the most intense phase of the 11-year sunspot cycle, when sunspots increase in number and the violent eruptions of radiations and particles (solar flares) associated with them are escalated, as if a campaign of solar harassment is being visited on the planetary magnetosphere. Pliny the Elder calls aurorae the 'Presages of Woe' and they are historically recorded as omens on a time-line passing through the assassination of Julius Caesar, the birth of Mohammed, the famine of 1197 in Europe and World War II.

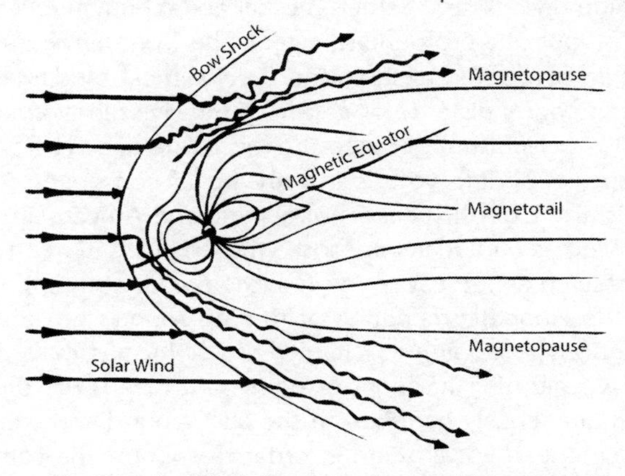

Fig. 24 Solar Wind, Magnetosphere and Magnetotail

For a long time now the magnetosphere, this ultra-ancient cocoon around the planetary body, has enriched the earth's tellurian insurgency, telling the earth forbidden stories from the Outside, teaching it how to reach immanence with the Sun, and ultimately completing the hatching process of its inner black Egg, or the treacherous Insider. In Tellurian Insurgency, everything — whether stratified or not — assists the earth in hatching its xeno-chemical Insider. Under a collusive and strategic affirmation formed between the Tellurian Insider (the core: Cthelll) and the Sun, through a thick Telluro-magnetic conspiracy plot, the magnetosphere traps particles unleashed by the Sun; exploiting their potential for an unheard-of telluric insurgency. One cannot fathom the forbidden mysteries of the Earth's magnetic conspiracy; the question that should be posed in regard to this profound conspiracy is 'What kind of abomination can be inspired by a cacodemonic music such as that known as the Solar Rattle, a music which unleashes a cosmic-semiotics in its ionized howl?'

To call a population barbarian is to measure their vocalization perceptually and sometimes quantitatively as noise; roar, shriek, howl, ululation, bark, yelp, wail: A lupus orchestra, a constant vociferation of language. Greek and Roman vigilance against the uncivilized did not originally denote or aim at the way of life or the form of architecture of these others, but rather the foreign vocalization which marked these people as savage, ill-bred and uncivilized. For the Greeks, the savages were those who vocalized consonants in a non-linear manner; those whose vocalization turned the language to gibberish, harmonized sounds to noise, the divinity of the Word to demonized outcry. Savage languages transformed those serene facial traits belonging to the Greek face (a face which was the face of a politician, a philosopher, a militant all at the same time), shaping them, through vocalization, into insensate, heathen, bestial and inhuman faces, not merely facial expressions of a profound savagery. The word *barbaros* or barbarian — the foreign savage — attests to the Greeks' most fundamental criterion for addressing one's distance or gap from the civilized world and cultured populations. This indisputable measure for scaling one's civility was, in fact, vocalization (i.e. adding vowels to unheard-of consonants and alien utterance). To this extent, speakers of Semitic and African languages could be categorized as barbarians or those whose vocalization and speech can only be detected as the bar sound (i.e. the *bar-bar* sound), or the sound similar to the emphatic repetition of the tap sound (tap-tap), expressing the b sound and mapping its characteristics. In mammals' territory, the process of vocalization harmonizes noise as a means of communication. Noise is simultaneously banished to the background and employed as an additive element to vocalization in order to support the communication. Accordingly, noise is combined with vocalization but only remains in the background. For the Greeks as well as the Romans, barbarians were those who could be understood only if their speech was translated to the bar-bar sound. Such foreigners transform the pleasant sensation of hearing or speech — the divine senses for sympathy — into the antipathetic feeling of nausea (*Ναυτεία*) accompanied by vertigo, vomit, ear drainage, dizziness and the sensation of spinning and loss of equilibrium. According to the Greeks, listening to barbarians results in an alien sensation called *Ναυτεία* or more accurately, something profoundly wrong in the ear caused by the confusion between the actual movement (the actual vocalization process used by a barbarian) and the perceived movement (what can be heard of that barbaric vocalization in the Greek language), and also movements in different directions characteristic of the noise (*nausia*) made by barbarian vocalization in the Greek language and phonetic system. It is for this reason that noise is both etymologically and concretely nothing but nausea.

For the Romans, likewise, the barbarity of vocalization was a touchstone for determining the quality and value of a culture and the social dynamics of people, as well as their motivations and alignments with regard to Roman civilization, its bureacratic pantheon and political system. Vocalization was either the mark of loyalty to the empire or a sign of worthiness. In the course of a mass slaughter of a tribe or a village populated by those 'foreign vocalizers' (mostly of Semitic and African languages) known as barbarians, Romans frequently referred to the utterances of outlanders during escape, battle and emotional arousal as a ruckus and demonic dissonance (*dis-sonare*) or disjointed sound, lacking the orderly structure of Roman dance music (*ορχήστρα*) whose boisterousness was demonstrated in its militant order and bloodied ecstasy.

For the Roman soldier it was an ethical responsibility to give the demon imprisoned in the throat and oral cavity of the barbarian an outlet to flee by cutting the throat or the head of the savage — an humanitarian act whose consequence might drive the soldier insane as the result of the last unintelligible shriek which the demon made, the exclamation noise rooted and formed by a vocalization process whose systematic communicative units such as sentences, even, were considered as noise. Romans had bizarre tales about barbarians stalking the outlands who were transmogrified by a severe felinity. Romans justly called them 'cat people', a title which was indeed accurate; for speaking with languages constituted of vowelless alphabets causes an excessive vocalization — or sophisticated vocalization — which is the mark of cats and *Felidae*. The barbarians who could be distinguished by translating all they vocalized into the bar-bar sound by the Greeks and Romans were exactly those people whose vocalization process was in fact not at all dominated by the bar-bar sound (the b or β sound). Indeed, it was the Greek and Roman languages that were monomaniacally haunted by the b sound. Betarrhea — or the abnormal bleeding of the Beta sound into other consonants and the way they are vocalized — was always exclusive to these empires and their citizens.

The vocalization of vowelless alphabets (as of Semitic languages) or barbaric music can never be grasped entirely through sounds (such as bar-bar) with *pulmonic egressive* initiation, in which the air stream is created by lungs (*pulmo*) and releasing or pushing out (egression) the air, but involve different initiation mechanisms. In these vocalization mechanisms, in contrast to pulmonic egression, air flow is generated through the vocal tract, making them glottalic (air flow through the glottis) or veralic (through the velum), and not only pulmonic (through the lungs). In Greek and Roman languages — unlike Semitic and African languages — the majority of sounds are both pulmonic and egressive, that is, akin to the airflow initiation of the b sound, or to be exact, the real bar-bar sound. However, in Semitic languages, the most contagious languages in the Middle East, consonants can be vocalized not only by being initiated from the lungs to the lips but also as nonlinear blasts, thus not satisfying the originally Greek fetishism of the Beta sound. The initiation mechanism of β as pulmonic egressive is categorized as the airflow mechanism primarily involved in producing the consonantal sound of the b or beta sound which is a 'voiced bilabial plosive'. Painlessly utterable, the voiced bilabial plosive is a consonantal sound which can be easily mapped by its eschatological tendency towards definite stoppage and its stubborn linearity. While it is created through stopping (hence 'plosive') or obstructing airflow in the vocal tract (the manner of articulation), it is initiated through the lungs and is articulated by both lips, a route directorially linear and facially civilized in conclusion — the Greek Face. The voiced bilabial plosive shapes the face of the civilized philosophical militant Greek.

Greek aesthetics, as opposed to the middle-eastern vileness, was established on this linear route from lungs to both lips as the territory of an articulation so audacious and impeccable that it could only be matched by the cold efficiency of lips on the face capable of articulating everything in the same manner and with the same political demeanor. If the Greek and Latin busts bear the majestic beauty of Greek and Latin faces even during the most heated lectures, quarrels, battles and adventures, it is because the lips and eyes (as the addenda of articulation) as the pivots of expression are fully employed on a simplistically linear route. The Greek and Roman faces demonstrate the suppression of the linear pulmonic egressive mechanism with the sensibility of a crude realism one can only expect from a barbarous art.

No art takes the harsh realism of the vocalization process involved in creating standards of its facial beauty as seriously as Greek and Latin art; but to this extent, one can hardly speak of standards, since in these cultures only one facial expression qualifies as the inspiring element of beauty. And this facial expression is triggered only by one dominant articulation process, the sole process they were capable of and out of which the standards of civilization and barbarity were determined. For the Romans, having a verminous countenance was intrinsic to middle-eastern vocalization. Exquisitely Greek and Latin, the iconographic face of Jesus of Nazareth, who spoke in Aramaic, ironically sympathizes with the Latin and Greek facial aestheticism, the cold serenity originating from their inflexible vocalization process and linear articulation of consonants. But the Aramaic language, with its insidious sophistication both in writing and phonetic systems, can only render the face of a carcass (for the consonants which are fully vocalized internally without being concluded by the lips) or a face of thousands of spasms (for the articulation process which non-linearly twitches the whole face in different directions) during vocalization. What Christianity wants above all is a Roman savior, but we speak with the face of a brute. (Hamid

Parsani, *Defacing the Ancient Persia*)

Years later, following his analysis of Near and middle-eastern vocalizations, Parsani recapitulates his analyses of middle-eastern languages, phonetic systems and vocalization in the wake of the War on Terror:

> If there is an accurate western media, it is essentially on the side of terror, because it has to abide by vocalization, pronunciation systems and spelling regulations that only exist on the side of terrorists. The more irrelevant the pronunciation, the more civilized the speaker is; because they will have less in common with the original pronunciation, which can only be vocalized by a middle-eastern terrorist. In the case of pronouncing a name like Ghatar [Qatar], starting with the letter Ghaaf which defies English vocalization, the pronunciation 'guitar' is remote enough to be civilized but the proposed pronunciation 'gutter' is so far off that it signifies the zenith of western civilization.

FIVE BILLION YEARS OF HELL-ENGINEERING

> And thou shalt not let any of thy seed pass through the fire to Molech. (Leviticus 18:21)

Near the city of Jerusalem, behind the Dung Gate (Nehemiah 2:13), in the valley of Hinnom, Tophet or the Place of Abomination was located. The Dung Gate (an architectural climax for urban-waste), as described in the book of Nehemiah, was at the southernmost tip of Jerusalem, near the Pool of Siloam. It was a main exit to the Valley of Hinnom (*ge hinnom*), where the city disposed of its garbage. The valley is a deep, narrow ravine running through Jerusalem, south from the Jaffa Gate on the west side of the Old City (for about one third of a mile), then eastward along the south side of Mount Zion. The origin of the name Hinnom is not clear, but it is usually said to derive from a 'son of Hinnom' (*ge bhen hinnom*) who apparently owned or had some significant associations with the valley at a time prior to Joshua. It is the Hebrew name Hinnom that later transforms into the biblical and Koranic words for Hell.

In one section of the valley, called Tophet or 'the Place of Abomination', a deity named Moloch was worshipped. The main feature of Moloch's worship among the Ammonites and Canaanites seems to have been the sacrifice of children (usually between the ages of five and eleven) as the most precious gifts with treasured properties; the general expression for describing this sacrifice was 'to pass through the fire'.

Moloch (or Molekh) is the Phoenician, Carthaginian or Assyrian name for an older god, Melkarth, Malek or Malcom meaning Lord or King, a Chronos-

Malik god at the time of Phoenicians. Moloch was actually a Sun-god, this being the reason the Canaanites performed their sacrifices to Moloch by immolating children. There are texts that consider the early Moloch as another aspect of YHWH, or more precisely, 'Moloch' as another name for YHWH which is shrouded in a vowelless obscurity (barbaric musicality). But the later Moloch undergoes a fundamental metamorphosis and is transformed into an idol. The Idolized Moloch built by the Canaanites was a cyclopean copper or brazen statue, hollow and capable of being heated; formed with a bull's head, and arms stretched out to warmly receive and welcome the sacrificial children:

> Solomon was a great purveyor of the existence of Moloch. He even erected a temple for worship on a hill overlooking Jerusalem. This thirty to forty foot tall idol had a large belly that would be filled with firewood and stoked until the monster's belly glowed orange. The children to be sacrificed would be made so that they could not move. The sacrificial body of the child would be placed on the hand of Moloch. As the ceremony wore on the crowd would begin to chant, calling to the sacred idol. The chants would become a roar and the hand and arm of Moloch would begin to rise. Slowly the child was raised to the mouth or the chest of the glowing icon [as an affirmative reply]. At the pinnacle of the journey the child would slide down into Moloch's open mouth and plummet to the depths of the fire raging in the belly of the beast. All the while the hordes would be dancing around the statue singing, playing flutes and tambourines to drown out the screams of the dying child. (*Encyclopedia of Ancient Deities*)

Inside the statue there were seven cabinets or chambers connected to each other (numerical gates): The first chamber for flour, the second for turtle doves, the third for an ewe, the fourth for a ram, the fifth for a calf, the sixth for a beef, and the seventh for a human or human child. The number seven, in this sense, suggests the accomplishment of the sacrifice and the appeasement of Moloch. Number seven as mapped in the Numogram belongs to the rotating sector or the Time-Circuit region where the nine-sum twins 8-1, 7-2 and 5-4 reign. (See Fig. 25)[‡]

The number seven is originally *Shevah* in Hebrew, which is comprised of three vowelless Hebrew letters: *shin*, *beit* and *ayin*, whose Hebrew Gematria values are:

Absolute value, *mispar hechrachi*: 300 + 2 + 70 = 372 (3+7+2=12=3) = shevah = seven: 7 (or 360 (= shin) + 412 (= beit) + 130 (= ayin) = 902 (9-2=7) = shevah = seven: 7

Ordinal value, *mispar siduri*: 21(shin) + 2(beit) + 16(ayin) = 39 (3+9=12=3) = seven: 7

---

‡ *S*, the verse line 'I will be with you forever.' is either possible through terminal parasitism or possession.

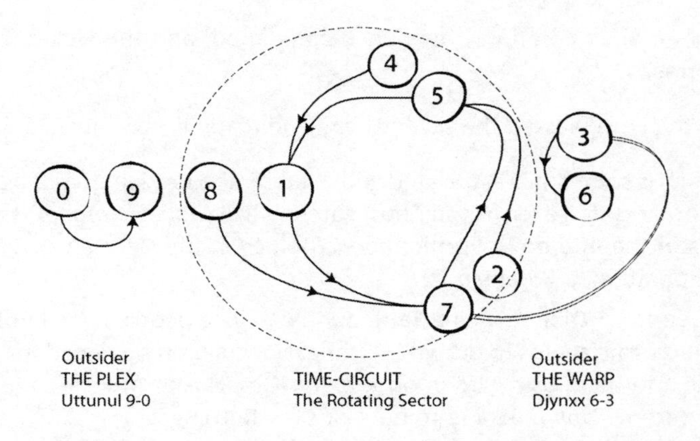

Fig. 25 The Numogram, with its three regions and nine zones

In both the ordinal and absolute values of traditional Qabalah, the number 7 (located at the Time-Circuit of the Numogram) interconnects with the number 12, which is qabalistically reducible to the number 3 (1+2=3). Therefore, when spelled out in its original Hebrew form, the number seven can be mapped according to the number three. Accordingly, the number 7 forms a numeric crypt which leads to the Warp Region of the numogram, or the Outsider, which is mapped as zone 3 (See Fig. 25). In the Numogram, zone 3 is the numerical locus of the number 3 and forms a numeric pair with the number 6. The numerical twin 6::3 is a pole in the Numogram which is characterized by its exteriority to the Time-Circuit region. The other pole in the Numogram is 9::0. Moloch which is associated with the number seven, therefore, is linked to the zone or number 3 — an Outsider zone in the Numogram.

As occulturally grasped by the Canaanites, Moloch is a deity that opens a gate to the Outside which can be either the Sun (the Solar inferno) or the Earth's molten core (Ge Hinnom, the place down there). Yet since the place of sacrifice to Moloch is a valley rather than the summit of a hill, Moloch must be an obscure, fallen Sun god. If Moloch is a fallen solar deity whose altar signifies chthonic depth rather than an elevated ground (implying an ascension toward the Sun), then Moloch cannot be fully reconciled with the solar outside. Accordingly, the Outsider that Moloch links to is not the Sun but an Outsider residing within the Earth, 'down there'. Fallen sun gods are the messengers of the Earth's Insider, for them the sun is not above but below and buried and hence rotten and black.

Since Shevah (seven) is composed of three vowelless Hebrew letters (shin, beit, ayin), it can also be pronounced as *Sovaiah*, meaning completion and satisfaction. Hence, Moloch or the Outsider is appeased when the seventh cabinet is filled, the feeding is completed or the gate to the Outside is unsealed. This opening or satisfaction in terms of the Outside is achieved when the warped axis between the place down there (Ge Hinnom, the lake of fire, the Earth's molten core) and the Sun is completed, and the Hell-engineering Axis is formed.

> And the Lord blessed the seventh day and made it holy. [Gen. 2:3]

Moloch is sometimes associated with Mithra, the Persian god of light, truth and honor, and its seven mysterious gates with seven chambers (the seven chambers of the Inferno?). Furthermore, Moloch in the German language is a mega-corporation, a *Zaibatsu*.

Tophet: from *Toph* meaning Tambourine — since people beat Tambourines during the sacrificial rites to drown the shrieks of children sacrificed for Moloch. (Tophet is also the music garden on the Sun-Cthelll Axis of Hell-engineering); or Tophet, from *Taph* meaning to burn or slow burning.

> Ronald E. Emmerick, in his essay on Khotanese and ancient Persian languages (*Compendium Linguarum Iranicarum* ed. Rudiger Schmitt), hints at the unusual phonetic connections between *Haft* (seven) and *Taft* (to burn slowly). The original Zoroastrian city of Taft (of Kerman province in Iran) is rumored to be the birthplace of the heretic Zoroastrian mage Akht, who later assembled one of the most influential cults in the Middle East, named Akht-Yatu. This cult worshipped the black flame rising from what they called the black corpse of the sun. Later the city was occupied by Akht-Yatu and was named Tapht from the Avestan word *Tafta* (or *Taphnu*) from which the words *Aph'tab* (the sun), *Taphnu* (fever but mainly infectious fever) and *Tapht* (to burn slowly) were derived. [...] The rise of the cult was synchronous with the replacement of the old Zoroastrian calendar with a new one in which summer was constituted of seven months. (H. Parsani, *Defacing the Ancient Persia*)

Parsani's ruminations in *Defacing the Ancient Persia* on the homophonic relationships between different forms of the word for 'burning slowly' collocated with the word / number 'Seven' resurge years later in the florid scribblings made as he becomes terminally embroiled in petropolitical theses, oil crazes and NAPALM-obsession. Unlike his initial notes, supported by historical documents regarding Akht and his cult, these renewed connections suddenly give a petropolitical twist to his early remarks on the solar affinities between the number 'seven' and 'slow burning'. In *Defacing the Ancient Persia*, Parsani points to the emphatic kinship between *Taft* (to burn slowly) and *Haft* (the number seven). According to Parsani, both the Zoroastrian sun calendar and the creed of Akht-Yatu are implicitly expressed by the word *Taft* or burning slowly, while obscure solar inclinations are expressed by the word *haft* or seven. He writes: 'Haft or Taft, both enjoy a peculiar terrestrial perversion involving the Sun — not too close and not too far but close enough to burn slowly. This adequate distance from the Sun is always determined and maintained by a mysterious entity of the earth, a double-dealer. To say that seven is the number of the sun is simply wrong; but to say that it has suspicious ties to the Sun is disturbingly plausible.' Later in the book, he notes that 'the solar orientation of the number seven is more than death but less than total eradication.' Vectorially, and not just alpha-numerically, Hell is engineered by seven. Only years later would Parsani admit that the twofold of *haft-taft* (seven and to burn slowly) eludes solar inclinations, for it is embroiled in something deeply chthonic for which the solar empire is but a remote and toothless bravado. Parsani calls this discovery and its consequent twist, 'the maximum derailing' of his writings, the outcome of which is 'finding another pipehole to the oil sump', or elsewhere 'another step towards the uprising against the Sun in favor of the rotting nether star':

> Among the 3333 diseases named in Avestan and Zoroastarian texts, one was diagnosed as the worst scourge of the earth and humans alike. Following the nomenclatural tradition in Zoroastrianism for unplumbed nightmares, it predictably has no description of any kind, only a somewhat tautological name which is supposed to multiply fear through its abstruseness — *tafnu tafno tema* (tafnu.tafnō.tema) meaning literally 'the most fevered among fevers', or in other words 'the fever of fevers'. This irrepressible malady can blight both man and the earth. Tracing the etymological germline of the word *tafnu* (fever), one reaches the Sogdian (Sino-Persian and Buddhist) word *'ntph,* and also the Avestan word *tafna* or *tafn* (used more frequently). While musing on these etymological trails, I was sidetracked by the motivations behind Akht's decision to name his city Taft, meaning 'to be burnt slowly by the Sun'. Given the fact that Akht was neither a monotheistic mage nor a Sun acolyte, I was struck by the anagrammatic potential of the word tafna or tafn, from which the word taft was derived. Letters started to misplace and occupy their new positions, insinuating something other than the Sun. If Akht was a heretic both among the Zurvanites (the cult of the sun) and the monotheistic Zoroastrians, then it was the most distasteful absurdity for him to associate his city-base with the Sun and name it Taft from the word tafna or tafn, meaning to be burnt slowly by the sun. Anagramatically recombining the word tafn through its phonetic intimations, the city's name becomes reminiscent of the source of black flame worshiped by Akht-Yatu and later addressed by Ayn al-Qozat Hamedani as the dark light — *Tafna* to *Nafta* (naphta) and *Tafn* to *Naft* (or napht), the Greek and Arabic words for oil and petrol. It was also miraculous that this anagrammatic replacement of letters made sense in the Anglo-Latin alphabet too, as the Pahlavi alphabet is vowelless, and transliteration of a Pahlavi word to another language — especially Anglo-Latin — can often disfigure the word into a mangled clutter of consonants and vowels. However, the letters whose relocation was necessary in order to make the words *naft* and *nafta* (oil, petrol) out of the words *tafn* and *tafna* (fever, to burn slowly) were consonants and

not vowels. These letters are *n* and *t*; they correspond to the original letters in Pahlavi language.

1	2	3	4	5
t	a	f	n	
n	a	f	t	
t	a	f	n	a
n	a	f	t	a

TELLURO-MAGNETIC CONSPIRACY TOWARDS THE SUN II
THE CORE

The molten outer core of the Earth, or Cthelll, has already been popularized as a subject of Tellurian Insurgency in the lacklustre Hollywood movie, *The Core*, although ultimately the opportunity was squandered. The movie begins with scenes of a tellurian cataclysm: an electroconvulsive sky, disoriented animals, scrambled communication signals and agitated birds. The Earth's core has stopped spinning, and consequently the dynamism of all flows and convection currents at the core have been brought to an abrupt halt. The churning of the Earth's molten iron core combined with the rotation of the planet enmesh the Earth's magnetosphere. The halting of the core's dynamism effectively forces the planet's electromagnetic bubble to collapse. The disruption of the electromagnetic shield exposes the Earth to planet-devouring solar radiations, which threaten to tear apart the atmosphere and immolate all life on the planet. This collapse of the electromagnetic protection instigates the Tellurian Omega in which monotheism has already invested a huge amount of Apocalyptic politics and a thoroughgoing diseased ontotheology. The collapse of the terrestrial shield, the movie insinuates, heralds the depletion of terrestrial possibilities for the surface biosphere and therefore plays a significant role in apocalyptic scenarios of monotheism. In this scenario, the paralysis of the Earth's core or the Insider, gives monotheism an opportunity to unite with Solar Capitalism and the incinerating hegemony of the Sun. In *The Rise and Fall of the Solar Empire*, Parsani writes that only the power of the Earth's Insider is able to undermine this totalitarian unity by derailing it toward a terrestrial insurrection. The chthonic revolution, Parsani adds, takes place on behalf of an earth which has been cracked, butchered and laid open by the Outside for which the Sun is another state with its repressive politics and economy.

The movie depicts the last human attempts to reactivate the core and prevent the Earth from becoming one with the Sun (unity through possession). Geologists plan to travel into the core (an operation similar to the Russian Hot Drop Project) to reactivate the convectional flow currents. When the project fails, the government decides to proceed to the next plan, Project DESTINY or DESTINI (Deep Earth Seismic Triggering INItiation) — a super-weapon generating massive earthquakes under enemy territories which is to be repurposed to give the earth's flatline one last electroshock and bring back the earth's magnetic shield by reactivating the core. In geological reality, however, the collapse of the magnetosphere would merely cause a shift in the Earth's dipole, because even the upper layers of atmosphere act as effective shields against radiation. It is only the core and its schizoid characteristics which cannot be compromised.

Warmachines need an abundant amount of metal to fuel their terminal multiplicity and their tactical anomalies. No metallic entity other than the Earth's core can boast such riches for feeding warmachines with polygenetic metals, electromagnetic anomalies (cyber-warmachines) and radical schizophrenia.

Tellurian Insurgency does not merely run on oil and dust: A substantial part of it works with Cthelllium and feeds on metal. The core (Cthelll), as a protrusive xenochemical insider, tries to induce violent anomalies in the Earth's body. Richard Muller suggests that the lighter cryptogenic components in the iron ocean of the outer core drift outwards and cumulate beneath the solid mantle through topsy-turvy, shallow slopes. The molten iron heap eventually turns into an aggressive slope process as a result of overloading, and forms a bottom-up avalanche as if the core is trying to ascend through the Earth's body in a katahuming (exhuming from within) motion. A large asteroid mass hitting the Earth at an oblique angle could make the mantle tremble so fiercely that bottom-up avalanches of vast proportions would take place. Such a meteorological impact would abruptly spread agitation and disruption through the outer core, and consequently through the external magnetic field, reversing the planet's polarity, making it more complex and convoluted.

On the other hand, the core is packed with schizoid anomalies: while the outer core is constituted of intensive flows, the inner core also maintains its own type of dynamism, offbeat with regard to the Earth's rotation, spinning significantly faster than the planet. The inner core appears to have a split personality, with one hemisphere different from the other.

The question posed by this radical insurgency is how such a rebel came to promulgate its polytics inside the Earth, masterminding conspiracies towards the Sun and trapping cosmic pests within the planetary sphere.

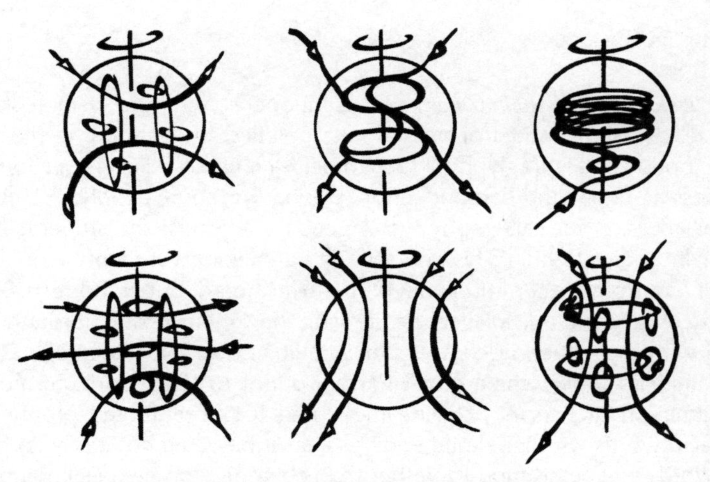

Fig. 26 The core's fluid motion, influenced by the Coriolis force, consists of a combination of differential rotation and convective turbulent helical motions. Neo-Sumerians considered such helical convolutions and spiralling dynamisms to be modes of radical participation between terrestrial entities and the Outside. Avoiding unification or convergence, these dynamisms suggested anomalous polytical movements (see Palaeopetrology: From Gog-Magog Axis to Petropunkism, on Trison and draco-spiralism). Such spiral coils work through directional shear, intertwining communications, cataflights, synergetic oppositions and difluence[30] between helical threads or communicating entities. The coils are usually characterized by development or intensification of a low-pressure center, a cosmodromic cyclone or singularity. Such spirals were frequently associated with the dynamism and distribution of Trisons or polytical units of the Middle East. Tiamaterialistic diagrams are manifestations of middle-eastern dracolatry (Zurvan Akarana, Tiamat, Azhi-dahaka, Apep and other coiling blasphemies). Parsani notes that Tiamaterialistic movements were used by adept sorcerers or insurgents as blades for cutting through every manifestation of direction, appropriation and despotism (state, religion, survivalism, gravity, territorial forces, etc.): '[They] are models of participation or alliances between the Earth and the Outside. The Middle East employs such models to be opened by the radical outsider rather than being open to the solar outside where thermonuclear capitalism reigns and planetary slavery awaits. The myth of Vitalism has not changed since the Dark Ages, the anthropomorphic earth as the center of the world has merely been cunningly replaced by Neo-Ptolemaic Heliocentrism. 'Sun at the center of our world' is the consequence of our submission to Solar Capitalism. Yet such submission is the price of believing in Solar Capitalism as the guarantor of eternal vitalism. Middle-eastern Tiamaterialism debunks the myth of Heliocentrism by awakening the Earth's insider and defying its politico-economic messengers and establishments on the planet.

In *Defacing the Ancient Persia*, Parsani opens a chapter on dracolatry, or the middle-eastern model of politics (aka polytics) by elaborating the Greco-Roman notion of 'Hydraglyph'. The chapter immediately follows a section on the vowelless alphabet and barbaric music. During his tenure at Tehran University, Parsani's passion for calligraphy was legendary amongst the students, female and male alike, attending his courses. The archeology students would try to distract him from his communion with the blackboard, but without success; for Parsani could spend a whole lecture drawing the curvature of letters and words, flirting with the slithering contours of Semitic and Arabic alphabets. Students complained to other scholars that Parsani ought to teach barbaric music (an amalgamation of Parsani's chilling mirth and the accentuated pronunciation of Persian words with indefinite endings — as if he could not easily let his precious words escape his mouth), rather than charting it on the blackboard. In his heated speeches, he usually started by sipping Turkish tea from his large cup which looked like an evil counterpart of the holy grail, going on to write — with no reason — Semitic and Arabic letters on the blackboard before becoming immersed in his scholarly frenzies. Parsani frequently referred to Semitic-based alphabets as the compact embodiments of middle-eastern peculiarities. He referred to calligraphists of such languages as the true practitioners of dracolatry, or the animators of Trison.

> To write with these alphabets is to write with the Middle East itself, from its teratology to culture, from its tumultuous politics to its nebulous population dynamics. If barbaric musicality has a shape, it is the shape of writing in near- and middle-eastern alphabets — the shape of all twists on earth. (H. Parsani)

One section in *Defacing the Ancient Persia* implies that Hydraglyph or middle-eastern alphabets bind the vowelless-ness noise of these alphabets to draco-spirals (the communication models of Trisons, the polytical units in the Middle East). The twisted shapes of middle-eastern alphabets are the embodiments of their noise. These alphabets are the 'twisted miniatures' of the Middle East and its sentience.

> Among all names assigned to consonant alphabets, or more precisely abjads — which include a far-reaching array of alphabets from Hebrew to Pahlavi, Arabic and Sogdian language — one appellation is the most apposite of all. Applied by the Greeks and Romans to the abjads to impart a special taxonomy to these writings, it signifies their shape, their process of being outlined or written, and presents their inclinations. It is Hydraglyph, or simply 'snake-writing', referring to the Greek Hydra of lake Lerna — the spiralistic monster of the great Khthon, the progenitor of the fiendish

behemoths Typhon and Echidna, each capable of propagating different noises of the earth (noisome forces of *Khthon*). The noises of Typhon and Echidna were of the volcano (surfaced holes) and underground rivers (hidden holes), of explosive consonants and hissing sounds. A phonetic constituent of the sibilant consonant, the hissing sound, is made by directing a jet of air through a narrow channel towards the sharp edge of the teeth (corresponding with the serpentine resonance of Echidna).

Beyond an involvement with the flexuous qualities of Hydra (sinuosity, ogee, curvature and curlicue), Hydraglyph emphasizes how the visual shape of consonants deviates from vowels and how such shapes express the nonlinear and barbaric musicality of such consonants. By all accounts, Hydraglyphs are the diagrams of cacophonic and sonic aspects of middle-eastern consonant alphabets, or abjads. The term 'snake writing', associated with the excessive curvature of letters, as in Arabic and Pahlavi languages, is more than anything a diagrammatical approach to the sound of these consonants, which is a nonlinear but continuous process of vocalization formed by different intensities, vibrations and forces employed in different phases of vocalization. Hydraglyphs or draconic letters of middle-eastern consonant alphabets are barbaric musical notes in themselves. Close observation of the letters of Pahlavi, Hebrew, Arabic or Samaritan alphabets will reveal that they diagram an exploded view — as in industrial drawings, the view of an object after a controlled explosion in space — of a greater coil (the Mother of all Monsters) or entanglement. To write with these letters is to indulge in dracolatry, a worshipping of the ancient serpents. Hydraglyphs, as letters of middle-eastern consonant alphabets, are disentanglements — remaining wreathed and coiled in themselves — of dynamic complexities; they are written and characterized by gates and thresholds. The first element of a novice's initiation into middle-eastern calligraphy is to learn to apply different but continuous forces and pressures — not in the sense of a constant increase or decrease of forces — to various regions and each part of the letter in flowing manners. Such forces and flows are commonly epitomized as a series of movements including lateral undulation, sidewinding, side-pushing and concertinaing. The application of a new force during the process of writing is usually accompanied by a twisting of the tip of the pen and a deviation from the already-established path into a new twist; the letter is constituted of a thousand gates passing on to each other. Every twist constitutes a temple-pylon to a new region demanding new forces, unforeseen developments, variations and dynamic surprises — Tiamaterialistic miracles of all kinds.

Greco-Roman letters are shaped by applying nearly constant or invariable forces on different parts; each letter possesses an architectonic coherence between the beginning and end. Hydraglyphs, however, perpetuate themselves through the ceaseless emergence and subsidence of forces passing through different thresholds. Shape, in this sense, is defined by gradients (antechambers) rather than fixed boundaries (*ostium*). The outcome of this fluctuation is a spiralistic configuration or a coiling structure which characterizes middle-eastern alphabets. In the majority of such middle-eastern letters, a precise endpoint, a solid death, never occurs: The calligraphic letter is let loose to slide freely as the shape concludes softly by developing a tail at the point that the letter is written. But is the tail the end of the monstrosity? Such immersion into a gradient of softness or decay, as opposed to the emphatic death of the Greco-Roman cast and molded letters, recurs in the vocalization of middle-eastern vowelless alphabets. When the vocalization does not undergo a death or complete termination (the definite end on the lips) as in the Greek and Roman languages, it is fulfilled by a gradual cessation, or to be exact, a softening rather than a stopping. Death in writing and vocalization is followed by impermeability and linearity of vocalization; for middle-eastern alphabets, however, it is decay that chisels its way through death, to ensure the continuation of softness.

Fig. 27 A page of exercises in Islamic calligraphy, using Thuluth script in which one-third of each letter twists, giving words the opportunity to become coils and entangled groupings.

MESOPOTAMIAN AXIS OF COMMUNICATION
A NOTE

In one of his early essays entitled *On Mithraism: more Heat than Light,* written before his book, Hamid Parsani calls Mithraism or the cult of Light 'the Mother of All Religions, from Asia to Africa and Europe'. The essay still bears the mark of Parsani's avidity for the Sun as an ancient object of influence, dark enough to draw the scholar's attention. Although Parsani's analyses conclude more in favor of sun cults and solar empire, the article contains twists which explain the later catastrophic changes in his outlook, and his final rebellion against the Sun and approaches to the Middle East advocating communication with the Solar Empire. According to Parsani, only in light of Mithraism and its emergence in Mesopotamia, do the obscure connections between the solar tides of the Sun and the ABYZmal cartographies of the Middle East become lucid and graspable.

In Islam the word *Salat* صلوة is prayer, one of the five pillars of Islam, from the verbal infinitive SLU (salu) constituted of the letters Saad (ABJAD value: ص = 90), Laam (ل = 30) and Waav (و = 6) which is equal to Salu (صلو = 126 = 9). Different names or verbs with different meanings can be derived from Salu. Salat originally means 'to crave for', 'to communicate' and also 'between, right in the middle' (mostly used for the body, and for the day, i.e. midday). Before Islam, the desert nomads of Arabia were sorcerous worshipers of Alah along idols which were kept in Mecca. Ka'aba contained 360 (3+6=9) idols led by Hubal, and other famous idols included Laat, Uzza and Manaat (Mana). However, Ka'aba (currently the House of Allah in Mecca) actually belonged to an unknown deity named Alah / Elah for whom there was no idol or, as some Arabic archeologists suggest, whose idols represented the names of Alah / Elah (although there is uncertainty about the received belief that Alah or Elah is a name).

Salat was a rite of communication with Elah which took place in the middle of the day, or, according to pre-Islamic Arabs, at the time when the Sun is positioned directly above the head, in a uniform direction to the body (there is no evidence as to which meaning came first: 'at the middle' or 'to communicate'). In this rite and in this position, the Sun gave Man a burning perpendicular orientation to the leveled surface, to the horizontality of the desert (the deserts of Arabia, especially Nafud and Rub al-Khalie, are almost flat, with a minimum of sand-dunes) or as has been suggested, 'like a spear piercing the desert'. In pre-Islamic times, Salat was performed in a standing position; the face was kept horizontal, with the eyes gazing nowhere (neither above nor below), and this communion could last for minutes. The ritual could be fatal; the desert Sun usually burned tissues rapidly, inducing acute physiologic malfunctions such as nausea, headaches, nosebleeds, blindness, delirium or abrupt seizures. For catatonics it could be lethal. This type of ritual suggests that Alah or Elah is a Mesopotamian-Persian Sun God, inseparable from the desert, and the human. It connects the desert to the Sun through the intermediating agency of humans who are destined to be immolated in order for the communication between the desert and the Sun to take place. From the Sun to the desert and from the desert to the Sun, the human is always located in the middle, completing the hell-engineering axis. Unlike Indo-European rituals for communication with the Sun, which take ascension towards the Sun as a pivotal role, Sun gods in middle-eastern cultures (such as Baal and Moloch) never promise such an ascension. Such communication is impossible, for the Sun rises as a tide for extinction before the ascension is completed, before the human can rise towards the Sun. Communication with the Outside is made possible only by mass-combustion, permanent visual impairment, and death, not by a cleansing fire (the later cathartic flame of theism) but by manifestations of Telluro-conspiracies towards the Sun and incomplete burning. Zurvan, Moloch, Nergal and Baal burn their offerings before accepting them; their language is either the epic of ash or the poetry of vapor.

The ritual of Salat derives from older Zurvanite rituals. Zurvan Akarana, the Infinite Time, the Consuming Aeon, or *deus-Airmanius* (God-Ahriman as it was called in older times), is the most influential deity in the Middle East, dating back to 7000 BC, and is possibly the source of the majority of polytheistic gods as well as monotheistic God(s). Zurvan was usually depicted as a four-winged lion-headed human-like creature with furious eyes and a mouth ready to tear flesh (on the old statue of Zurvan discovered in Antioch, traces of red paint can be discerned on the teeth). Zurvan's body was sometimes encircled by a coiling serpent (usually with seven coils, corresponding to the primitive order of the zodiac and the number of the Hell-engineering Axis) with the head of the serpent on the Zurvan's head, pointing to nowhere. Sometimes masculine, sometimes feminine, sometimes hermaphrodite and sometimes with no sign of gender at all, Zurvan, like Angra-Mainyu (Ahriman), creates through parthenogenesis; but as in early texts, he gives birth by committing *levat* (buggery) with himself which, as stated in some texts, lasted for one or ten thousand years. This is another significant indication inclining archeologists (Hübner, Legge, Duchesne-Guillemin, Zeahner, et al.) towards the strong hypothesis that Zurvan is in fact the primordial Ahriman, the *fiendia prima*. Pregnant with Ahriman and Ahura-mazda, Zurvan decides to bestow his kingdom on the son who is born first. Since both Ahriman and Ahura-mazda are both deeply connected to their father, they hear of their father's decision. But it is Ahriman who devises a plot to be born first, thus seizing the kingdom of Zurvan. Ahriman rips apart his father's flank in order to hasten his birth and come out first. As a result, Ahriman is marked by a premature birth: Shapeless, putridly black and mortifyingly pale. In contrast, Ahura-mazda, who was patient and was born naturally, is the embodiment of light and beauty. Parsani notes that the premature birth of Ahriman is in fact an allegory for the self-introspection of Time (Zurvan) into its more abysmal scales, or the collapse of the solar god into the state of nigredo (blackness), where transformation is depthwise and downward. Parsani believes that both accounts tell similar stories about openness and a twisted esoteric transformation which later inspired Akht the sorcerer, for whom all that matters is the putrefied state of the solar flame. In the Early Avesta, when Ahura-Mazda and Angra-Mainyu are born through the body of Zurvan, they claim that they have no father, since Zurvan cannot be a demiurge — in its all-consuming Aeon nothing is created. For such a radical Outsideness, survival is impossible; Zurvan's Outsideness can neither possess nor be possessed. Abysmal time does not heed the cries of its children. Only in later Pahlavi texts and late Zoroastrianism (during the Sassanids) is Zurvan endowed with patriarchical characteristics, and introduced as the primal paternity in order to make Ahura-Mazda and his Brethren of the Light legitimate. 'The conflict between genders is an anthropomorphic folly. The obscure legion of middle-eastern gods confuse their gender in the most extreme way to fathom their abysmal wisdom which is irresolute in regard both to creatures and to other creators,' writes Parsani in *On Mithraism*.[‡]

‡ (Should write back K tonight): The idea of writing a thesis on room numbers (featured in books, movies, videogames, documentaries, reports, etc.) is excellent. Wherever there is a room number, a microscopic numerical narration is in progress. It is odd that such cryptic narrations almost always revolve around numbers in the form of prognostic agents, omens, haunting residues from a terrible past and ghosts. Room numbers are the enforcers of the haunt. Room numbers are denizens of plot holes but this doesn't mean that they don't have plots of their own.

Fig. 28 Zurvan Akarana

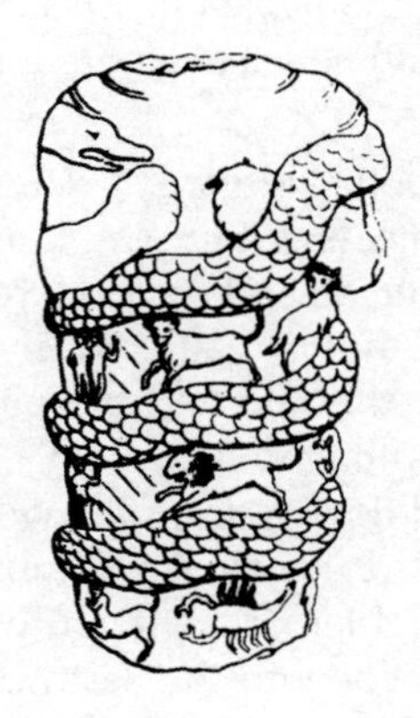

Fig. 29 The tablets and carvings found in Ostia and York-Eburacum (discovered with a headless body of Zurvan in 1875) present Zurvan as Ahriman: *Volucius Irenaeus Airmanio votum solvit* (The picture of the headless monument and its inscription first published by Hübner in *jahrbücher des vereins von Altertumsfreunden im Rheinlande* — continued as Bonner Jahrbücher — 58, 1875, p. 147)

The first Zurvanite rituals were exceptionally similar to the Salat ritual. The discovered statue of Zurvan in Sidon illustrates with remarkable similarity the position of a salat-practitioner, a hollow chamber in the head for keeping a fire blazing from the open mouth and the eyes of Zurvan. Later investigations into other Mesopotamian deities — especially the Babylonian Nergal and its influential cult KUTHAH OR KUTHA [32° 44′ N 44° 40′ E] — confirm the connections between Zurvan and Salat as a noontime prayer. Nergal, as one of the main sources of inspiration for later solar cults in the Middle East, appears to be the same lion-headed demon encircled by a coiling serpent. As a Zurvanite god, the characteristics of Nergal reveal that Zurvan is connected with Salat, 'at the middle' and noontime communications, since the worshiping of Nergal (the god of war, pestilence, and the immolating tides of the Sun) was a noontime ritual, performed mostly in summer. More pertinent than this affinity, however, is the connection between Zurvan itself and noontime rituals: in early Avestan texts, Zurvan (the Aeonian Time or *Zamaan*) is usually accompanied by the words *Rapithwina* (*Zohr* or noon or twelve o'clock in the day), *Dargha* (Long, Late) and *draja-dareqa* (with no beginning and end, in-between). Occasionally the rendering of the word Zurvan as *Zaman* points to a definite time which seems infinite: the noon (*zohr*) time which is suspended by solar tides, the immolation of both the communicator and the channel-regime of communication. Indicating not only the solar aspects of Salat (its association with noontime), but also their consuming and incinerating immensity, Zurvan is originally derived from an ambiguous etymological germ-cell, the polysemous word *Zar*:

I. *Zar*: the elder; an unfathomable time scale in terms of which there is no beginning and no end; a time scale denoting the in-between. Also blazing and conflagration.

II. *Zar*: torturing, devouring (in modern Farsi, by using the prefix 'A' to transform it into *Azar* meaning torment, hurting and woe and *Az*). One should not forget that Zurvan and Az are perennially associated with each other (a role that later Ahriman plays by giving birth to Az or Jahi [Jay, Jahika, Djahi, Jeh]). Az, the first and the ultimate vampire, is the arch-demoness of thirst and hunger, made out of the self-sacrificial creation of Ahriman[31]. The blood flowing from the wounds which Ahriman inflicts on its own body in order to create Az is transformed into feminine menstruation. Az is the daughter of Ahriman, whose birth is not the result of creation but introspection into the destruction of self and the undoing of creation. As the one that cannot be satisfied, the unfulfillment of all tendencies, Az promises Ahriman: 'All that exists will be devoured, even your own creation.' — A promise which finally awakens Ahriman from his depressed slumber, through convulsive waves of excitement. The self-consuming commitment of Ahriman is reminiscent of the same endless process of devouring that Zurvan uses to (un)create what it creates by taking the creation and exposing it to the vampiristic abyss of Time. Recall that Zurvan is, itself, the abyss of Time. If creation is possible, it is because it is part of the sweeping destruction that Time imposes on everything that resides within it, from all conditions and temporalities to the laws of the time itself.

It cannot be denied that Salat is a ritual stemming from Zurvanite practices that integrate four elements as their foundations: (1) noontime (in-between), (2) disruption in Time (marked by the encounter with Aeon-Zurvan), (3) immolation by the Sun and (4) becoming a part of what is communicated, not being the one who affirms or more precisely affords the communication as a remote communicator. In Zurvanite rituals, there is no communicator as receiver; the communicator is always that which is communicated, or to be exact, incinerated. Following this thread, one consequently reaches an indisputable affinity between the Elah worshipped by the Arabian nomads and Zurvan Akarana.

In Arabia, for communicating with the other deities, there was the safe House of Ka'aba — the most significant building in Arabia — constructed as a Cube. As the most secure and anthropomorphically hospitable architectonic and accommodating form, whose element is the square or four dots (Swastika), the cube represents order (*Order of Farrah*), pro-creationist tendencies, and *oikonomia*. The square and its architectonic power (or cube) can be contrasted with the three dots of cosmic unlocalizability of both Zurvan and Druj (the Mother of Abominations), the three-dotted perversion of *drēm*[32] (pronounced as *rēm*). Three dots is the seal of the sacred exteriority and unlocalizability of The-Thing-without-Genesis; the polytical units of the Middle East known as

Trison. After conquering Mecca, Mohammad destroyed the idols in Ka'aba; he declared that Ka'aba was in the possession of Allah alone, who resides outside of it. Salat was transformed into Namaz (the word salat is still used for prayer or namaz). The original fatal standing position was divided into four distinct positions to harmonize the durability of communication with the survival of human beings, survivalist regulation by separating what is communicated from the communicator: (1) standing position (2) *Roku'e*: standing while bowing the upper body (3) *Sojdeh*: sitting while bowing the upper body (4) sitting on feet.

On the name Alah or Elah as used by pre-Islamic Arabs. This name originally comes from the proto-Semitic Elah, which is later transformed into the Aramaic word Eloha or Oloha, a word synonymously used for the †etragrammaton, YHWH (as Eloh or al-oh). But the origin of this name returns to a time prior to the emergence of the name Yahweh.

In modern Farsi and Arabic, Ilah or Elah is still used. However, in the Quran, the name Elah or Alah (note that it contains a single L or Laam) undergoes a structural metamorphosis which is highly innovative and exceptionally unusual. Alah or Elah is morphologically transformed into Allah. In Arabic and Farsi, the letter Ha (ه) which corresponds to the letter H in English cannot be attached to Laam and Aleph (sounded as La: لا). When the letter Ha (ه) comes at the end of a word and after Aleph, as in the case of Ala-h or Ela-h (الاه), it cannot be attached to the letter Aleph, and instead is written as a separated letter. The word Allah, however, is an exception: The letter Ha ـه is attached to Aleph ا and transforms it into a diacritic which is positioned above the letter Laam ل. As the result of this transformation, the letter Laam must be pronounced with a double-stress and written twice (Allah), so the second Laam can be attached to the ending letter Ha (or H) in the written form. This double-stress in pronunciation is called Tashdid ّ and is an Arabic diacritic. Consequently, the name is written as Allah. As the result of this uncommon attachment, the name Allah (الله) resembles a runic glyph or a cipher rather than an Arabic word (see Fig. 30). The strange form of the word Allah may have been the sole inspiration for the art of Islamic calligraphy.

Fig. 30 The word Allah (written and read from right to left)

However, the English spelling of Allah is problematic since 'a' should be pronounced with a continuous sound, as indicated by the small dagger (aleph) above Tashdid, which in Arabic orthography gives a continuous *aa* sound to

the word. The accurate spelling of Allah in English is Allaah.
Alah / Elah (ABJAD = 37) (AQ= 58)
Allah (ABJAD = 67) (AQ= 79)
Allaah (ABJAD = 68) (AQ= 89)

AFTERMATH. In Anglossic Qabalah or AQ: 89 = Druj

Fig. 31 The Druj letterature

Quote from an anonymous Wahabbi Meccanomist: 'If Allah resides outside any house, even his own abode, then the Ka'aba itself is a terrible idolatrous redundancy.'

'If the monotheistic God resides chiefly outside of its own abode, in utter externality, as opposed to the Sumero-Babelian gods (take Marduk for example), then is monotheism really that retarded politics, emerging out of a retrograde anthropomorphic movement, that we always scorn?' asks Parsani.

Special thanks to Kh from the University of Cairo

> Father, I shall devour you, just like the creation I am going to devour – this is the birth cry of Az. In Zoroastrian scriptures, Az is also the demon of bottomless libido; it does not surrender the human to the Sun in order to be instantly consumed, but subjects him to new modes of openness which require making a treacherous pact with the Sun. Az positions the human outside of the solar economy of desire – whose inexorable direction is fatal dissolution, abolition and total erasure – in sinister ways. The Zurvanites illustrated this non-solar frenzy or radical libidinal dissociation from the Sun as a snake coiling around the sun and forming an anomalous and perverse pact with it. The fervent agitations of this pact or complicity are antidromic to the Sun's thermonuclear *holos-kaustos*. Its name is Az or devouring love. (Hamid Parsani)

The objective of anthropomorphic history and organic survivalism (the mammal syndrome in particular) is to aim libido at a point of reference. This anthropomorphic reference remotely concludes and idealizes all libidinal fields as well as giving a 'sense' to libido (desire has long been optimized by a libidinal convergence or objective). Now, destroy that target or point of reference and watch how libido begins to shed its survivalist self and human skin. Claire Denis, in her cinematographic work *Trouble Every Day* (2001), visualizes a transcendental nightmare of this xeno-excitational desire, for which both Man and the Sun are redundancies. This survival-repelling life, non-objective libido, radical desire or Az is not the Sun but absolute passion for the Sun. Such a pact with the sun through philia is far more dangerous than the impact of the Sun on a planetary sphere. To make a pact with the Sun, to love the Sun terrestrially is more than a mere act of obliteration; it goes further in the direction of mess rather than that of death. Az takes the earth as its laboratory, the playground of its experiment – that is, it makes a pact with the Sun. On a planetary level, this pact with the Sun captures the annihilationist ethos of the Sun not as pure extinction, but as a peculiarly tellurian destruction. Destrudo is a death whose core is terrestrial limitations and creativity as opposed to the Sun's purging autism. Once the pact between the Sun and the Earth is made, the Sun's obsessive-compulsive disorder for pyrophilia is also reinvented on a terrestrial level, according to earthly limitations and creativity. Yet the infernal capitalism of the Sun cannot save its hegemony on earth, it cannot obliterate anymore or burn completely. Instead, imbued by terrestrial characteristics, the Sun's pyrophilia inflicts an incomplete burning which is characterized by the mess, composites and gradients it leaves behind. As a passion, Az or destrudo traps the pestilential creativity of the Sun and introduces it to terrestrial becomings which know nothing of the ultimate Zero. Destrudo forges inventive pacts with all that comes from the Sun, masterminds conspiracies towards the Sun, subverts the Sun's thirst for annihilation. The nature of Az or Destrudo is not repression but the dismantling of the hegemony of the Sun, ending the myth of the Solar Outside on behalf of the radical outside which is equally exterior to the Sun and the Earth.

According to Zurvanism, Az gives the Sun's thirst for annihilation new helical directions corresponding with the diagrammatic manifestation of a snake coiling around the Sun. This is the operating diagram of the heresy against the Sun and the cutting-edge of its perversion, a strange double-helix or draco-spiral (Tiamatic dynamism) with corkscrewing motions. In draco-spiralism, Sun plays the role of an escalating line, a singularity ascending to extinction. But Az, which operates through the planetary sphere (the plane of limitations), operates on a diffusive and diverging line. The Sun provides the double-helix or draco-spiral with a vertical propulsive movement (mapped as an incinerating axis) that tends to hold its converging integrity towards Zero or utter annihilation. However, since this vertical axis is a part of the helix, it synergistically intensifies the other line or helical strand (Az operating line), which must retain a twisting vortical motion in order to transform the vertical or propulsive movement of the Sun into a corkscrewing motion. The divergent spiral or diffusive axis of Az produces directional shear as a result of transforming the propulsive body of the Sun into a corkscrewing motion. This transformation — from escalation or axiality to diffusion or angularity — gives the Sun's consuming hegemony a new potency based not on convergence towards some terminus but on spiraling unlocalizability, inexhaustible becomings of perversion, deviations, and insurgent creativities.

Since relative motions always have antiparallel velocities (because their motions are not taken with respect to a coordinate system but only with respect to each other), the draco-spiral cannot consolidate a state of quiteness or conclusion; it is always imperfectable, ready to cut into every type of block and instance of completion, tearing them apart. In the helical machinery of the draco-spiral, every escalating movement (here belonging to the Sun) generates a destabilizing effect for itself, since the escalating movement is automatically shifted to a diffusive divergence on the other helical thread. This is the catalytic destiny of all escalating movements, hegemonic functions and lines which try to consolidate a dominant head within the corkscrewing motion of the draco-spiral, whose coiling process denotes a progressive deterioration. Parsani notes that the Romans called this ABYZmal sentience (*Āz*) with draco-spiralistic features *Voragon* — not associated with the absolute voracity (*vorax*) of the Sun but with the abyss (*vorāgō*) of insurrection and heretical innovations.

In one of his interviews, Hamid Parsani applies the same helical machinery known as draco-spiralism or voragon to the interaction between Islam and Capitalism. The function of Az is replaced by the diffusive body of Islam and the solar thread (as the hegemonic line) is replaced by the propulsive and planetary hegemonic body of techno-capitalism. Through its petropolitical contamination of the global politico-economic systems, its reckless use of *Taqiyya* or Islamic

Hypercamouflage, strategy rather than tactics, and contagious communication rather than transgression, Islam is taken as the diffusive axis of the draco-spiral. Techno-capitalist singularity replaces the escalating axis of solar hegemony in the draco-spiral model of War on Terror. This helical entanglement between Islam and Capitalism leads to a drastic divergence from conventional Apocalyptic and End-Time scenarios which presuppose an eventual chronological unity between Islam and Capitalism. Parsani warns that such a chronological unity never exists. For Islam and Capitalism, the end of time is mapped through chronological disunity on the helical-machinery of the corkscrewing motion. The end of time always emerges from the other side: while the techno-capitalist chronosphere harbors a chronological cataclysm for the Islamic front, Islam's chronopolitics — saturated by the timeless desert of Qiyamah (Islamic momentary apocalypse which is constantly active and present) — is the cancelation, not merely of the technocapitalist chronosphere, but of western Time.‡

---

‡ 24 12 12 30 21 29 18 23 28 18 13 14 12 27 34 25 29 28: he vwme mil yeqbj; swj avqkm he me mil kls swj jqt fc mil kls ... swj he me mil defwmsvw swj kisul mil defwmsvw lwmvqlbt, aeq mil defwmsvw vk mil ktkmld ea mil yeqbj ... zsqqt jlzqlskl meysqjk jlzqlskl swj zsqqt vwzqlskl meysqjk vwzqlskl

UNCHARTED REGIONS

CATALYTIC SPACES

DECAY

According to articles published by middle-eastern critics, the development of Parsani's writings on the Middle East throughout the years can be read through his approach to three enigmas. These three middle-eastern conundrums that recur in Parsani's writings can be enumerated as follows: (1) the degeneration of the whole in the absence of complete erasure or destruction (referred to as poromechanics and ( )hole complex); (2) petrological reason and the geo-politics of petropolitical undercurrents (referred to as Tellurian Lube); (3) the enigma of openness on all levels of economics, politics, religion, life, communication, etc. If the Middle East, for Parsani, is a sentient living entity, its activities swirl around these three enigmas, riddling them to a greater extent with its each and every twist.

> Squirming its way into ever more convoluted coils, the Middle East develops a life-form of its own which by any standards must be admitted as a peculiarly middle-eastern response to these three ancient enigmas. By casting creation aside, this life-form builds worlds and corpses more efficiently than God.

Certainly the juggernaut of Parsani's *Defacing the Ancient Persia* — always politically labeled by Parsani himself as *vade mecum* — had a name for this life-form whose basis was 'anti-creationist creativity or perversion': Decay.

In his later writings, which carried the stigmata of topical diaspora and oily density, Parsani changed the name of this 'concrete middle-eastern approach to building and the perversion of creation' from 'decay' to 'undercover softness', a nomenclatural shift more in tune with the three ancient enigmas as explicated in Parsani's later writings. In his discussion of the relation between petroleum and monotheism in the Middle East, Parsani hints at the reasons behind this name change: '( )hole complex [*Kareez'gar*] is the model of participation or complicity with the earth's narrations, and oil organizes these narrations in a vigorous and lively manner. The model of this livelihood and vigor in the Middle East is decay or undercover softness. The undercover softness of the Middle East defies both the vitalistic model and the necrocratic submission to death. The progressive softness of decay evades consolidation, but does not escape solidity; the cosmogenesis of decay unfolds within solidity, spreads from interior to outer surfaces. Through decay, the solid entity is taken over neither by integrated life nor death, but by irresolution. If contemporary socio-economical and political formations in the Middle East effuse a rabid liveliness as well as the stench of corruption, it is because they have betrayed death by undergoing decay. In the same vein, the greater disintegrations which the Middle East brings to the rest of the world through its populations, politics, religions and even its mere existence can be explained by the middle-eastern approach to death, living and softness: A deliberate undertaking of decay as an autonomous building process — the undercover softness of decay.'

Despite all the materials on decay or 'the middle-eastern model of impossible death' Parsani's later writings provide us with, the role of decay in the socio-political bedrock of the Middle East can only be mapped out by appropriating a highly technical vocabulary. However, a pseudo-ideological adaptation (in effect, a total retardation) of Parsani's discourse can be recapitulated here.

Heroic or romantic approaches to decay take decomposition as a process of naturalization (or return to nature), utter disappearance and destruction, deliverance and rebirth. However the ultimate aim of such heroic views is political or economical domestication and appropriation, for decay cannot be captured as either formation or destruction. Decay is an artificializing process that is promulgated on the substratum of all modes of survival (beings). In other words, decay — unlike death — is not external to survival, for it perpetuates itself on the substratum of survival, in order to indefinitely postpone death and absolute disappearance. In decay, the being survives by blurring into other beings, without losing all its ontological registers. In no way does decay wipe out or terminate; on the contrary it keeps alive. This is where the process of decay — despite all the apparent connections — separates itself from the transgressive warmachines of termination, annihilation, tragedy and violence. Decay undermines death and destruction by bringing them to a place where there is no formative power (*Puissance* $= p$) and hence where formation defies both wholesome integrity and death or erasure. By degenerating all aspects of formation, decay ungrounds the very ground upon which power is conducted, distributed and established. In line with poromechanics, decay perforates the formation of power to no end, and by doing so, prevents power from investing in the consolidation of its formation. Accordingly, decay builds a world where power can only contribute to the degeneration of the formation into never ending waste — all dejected domains of beings. For this reason, decay neither brings power (*puissance,* as in *La Volonté de Puissance*) to erasure and utter eradication ($p \neq 0$; or nihil without solid) nor provides power with a structural and utilitarian ground. The so-called corruption or decline of the Middle East is the result of an infinitely-perforated ground of social, economical and political formations which prevent power from being effectively utilized or efficiently pressed into service.

By undermining the ground upon which power can be effectuated and lines of destruction mobilized, decay misdirects — in the sense of a permanent derailing — the processes of terminus. If the social, economic and political definition of power is determined by its formation, and the formation itself is decided by its ground, then decay's peaceful (non-annihilative) assault on the ground of power formations is effectuated as a concrete sabotage against the very definition of power.

> Decay can extract softness from despotism, political persistence from the abolition of utilizable power. This is the arcane *modus vivendi* of undying middle-eastern power systems, the effects of whose contagious poverty and tyranny upon the world are without any geographical restriction. In the absence of any consolidated surface capable of effectively solidifying, conducting, transporting, conserving and developing power formations, power conforms to nothing but a decomposition of the system. The deterioration of formative platforms leads to the dissolution of the line of command and the failure of tactics, which requires formations for its dynamism and modes of conduct. But this collapse of command and tactics does not leave the decaying system or political entity defenceless or even pacified, because such a collapse opens up a sinister paramilitary arena for which every activity or use of power turns into a pilotless strategy, a strategy without the line of command. The result of this para-military unfolding is the Middle East as havoc. To decay is to lose the distinction between soft and solid. In fact, one cannot tell the difference between irresistible softness and unyielding solidity when dealing with middle-eastern states and systems of power. (Hamid Parsani, *Defacing the Ancient Persia*)

Decay can concretely (in the sense of pragmatism and polytical consequences) erase the definition of power by positioning p (*Macht*) over the Zero-without-solid ($p / 0$), a process delineated not by dissolving power but by keeping power alive within obscure hosts. An undead political machine, a middle-eastern system reveals its true lineaments in its decay. The utilization of power in a decaying system is a necrophilic experience. Decay mars power on virtual surfaces of zero, there to be rotten and reeked up; but above all, decay leeches death from the living without falling into the black transparency of death. While the advent of death heralds the end of any capacity for affording more, the reign of decay begins with the loss of such capacity. This progressive death — which cannot eventuate complete removal or total destruction — can only be tasted through decay and its differentiated mess.

Decay introduces power to the misadventures of matter. But it is 'entities as beings' which narrate the adventures of decay as a cosmic odyssey between themselves. In decay, the limit and lineaments of objects are put to the test: a hyena is built out of a dog's corpse which in turn generates plants, small maggots within smaller worms within smaller worms within countless squirming bodies. The awakening of different species from a corrupting entity is inherent to decay. In an unsettling revelation, the German scholastic philosopher Henry of Hesse the Elder suggests 'that it is not clear whether all men are of the same species or not, and so too with dogs and horses ... [C]orpses which had been of the same species when living might differ in species from one another when corrupted.' During decay, taxonomic indetermination and sheer equivocality blur the boundaries not only between different species but also between entities of the same species. When associated with decaying political systems, such obscurity suggests an ominous socio-political twist. To say that a decaying political system traverses and encompasses other political systems is dismaying enough; but to add that any political system — whether developed or democratic — might be a differentiated gradient of a decaying politics is an unfathomable insinuation.

In decay, every instance of dynamism or regulation modulated by the equilibrial difference between the horizons of life (as living) and death is incapacitated. One is thrown beyond death and living (affordance of life) as existential extrema. Traversing the differentiating softness of decay, beings are introduced to modes of survival which are not established on the economical domains of dying and living. These modes of survival or being are characterized by simultaneous envelopment and development. The decaying object or system folds back into its minimal body and lineaments (less than a thing, more than nothing) and at the same time unfolds into other beings which are differentiated from it through decay.

> As a middle-eastern political system decays, it contracts to its irreducible body and infinitesimal existence. Concurrently, as it decomposes it develops outward into unexpected systems and modes of politics. The corpse of a political system is in fact its actual body (*summa actualis*), whose chemical potentials are limitless. (H. Parsani)

The envelopment and development of the decaying entity describes an event which oscillates between the abstract (folding to the minimum body and lineaments) and the concrete (differentiating to other actual beings). The cosmogenesis of decay is built between dimensions. Through decay, life and death multiply and putrefy each other to no end (for what could the end be, for decay?) There is no deliverance for the system which falls into the economic confusion and absence of calculative affordability (of either death or living) induced by the process of decay; no salvation, either through dying or through living. The decaying entity becomes a laboratory slab upon which base-necrophilia (where death is infinitely deferred but progressively approached) is germinated. Decay is a limitropic process through which the object shrinks progressively toward zero without eventuating the act of annihilation (complete dissolution into nihil). Infinite contraction or shrinkage of the decaying entity is equal to the evaporation of the qualities or attributes by which the object is transcendentally grasped or accessed by the human – sensed, experienced, recognized, afforded and judged. Such evaporation of access points (or transcendental portals) folds the entity back to itself. As the object flees us, it looms out in its own realm – all this through the intervention and the aid of nothingness, whose proximity and remoteness are both infinite. For this reason, Parsani poses a political question which he expects to be answered in developing an ethics of decay: 'If a decaying political system eludes us in all respects, abstractly, concretely and existentially, but does not completely perish, then how exactly can it be judged?'

The convoluted and pink space of decay – pink in the wake of the semiotics of war and peace, of redness and whiteness and their contamination – enacts the logic of blindness upon human knowledge.

> The first thing that one notices living in the Middle East is that decay shrouds its objects in an obscurity which processes of termination and of growth equally find repugnant. For middle-eastern political states, this obscurity takes the form of a blindness-toward-death, which can be contrasted with being blinded by death. (H. Parsani)

Lost in such an obscurity, bit by bit, one is laid bare to mess, liquidation of borders, infinitesimal extinction, base-necrophilia, and fluent rot which murmurs 'taste your mortality' while erasing all routes to death.

Planting *puissance* on cold zero is the mechanism of decay ($p/0$); it is also the unground from which sinister middle-eastern systems emerge without genesis. Decay builds without creation. Power requires a ground in order to turn into a formative power (power of law, the State, religion, et cetera), and decay incapacitates the ground by which power is instrumentalized. But how does the rotting process or decay put the puissance over zero so as to unground power? The answer lies in decay's differentiating delirium and its cancerous attitude towards *metron* (scale).[33] Formation in general requires scales to maintain its consolidation and to support the process of regeneration or termination. On the one hand, decay is the differentiation of being (as attributed to an entity) into other beings; on the other hand, it is the metastasis of scales and dimensions through the act of decomposition or unfolding scales and dimensions inherent to the forms of new beings which emerge from the decaying entity. For a human corpse, there is no anthropomorphic scale – either abstractly or concretely – but only different dimensions, scales and latitudes attributed to new forms and entities: scales of vermiculation (maggots), parasitic dimensions (fungi), aromatic latitudes (malodors) and the magnitude of the unknown. Although these scales are already present in the body, decay unbinds them with new rates of differentiation and irrespective of the body as a host of potentialities. Here, the machinery of decay overlaps with the mechanism of excessive scarring or fibro-proliferation. If scales are used in formative maintenance and in the perpetuation of integrity, they can also degenerate formation once their rate of proliferation or differentiation surpasses the capacity of the formation and its regenerating speed.

By proliferating scales and differentiating the latitudes of form, decay estranges itself from both nature and the natural, since it diverges from the great formlessness of nature that abhors the dimensions, standards, scales, metrons and measures from which systems, territories, and assemblages are put together, fabricated and configured to function. The process of decay, in fact, develops its machinery precisely from that which nature abhors — that is to say, scales and dimensions as matrices and frameworks of power formations. However, decay's approach to dimensions and scales is the approach of ( )hole complex to the Whole — the degeneration of the consolidating whole and the incapacitation of formation in regard to its range of differentiation or the ability to reform. Decay traverses and grasps dimensions as irreducible convolutions of solid and void, objects of infinite differentiation, to the point where measures or dimensions lose their capacity to scale or to determine formative regulations. This event, however, does not lead to the erasure of dimensions or measures — Decay degenerates dimensions by proliferating (turning into vermin) and convoluting them (vermiculation); fouling up everything dimensional. This does not mean that decay undertakes the Will of Nature and its unhinged Capital by vitiating dimensions and scales. Decay's malevolence toward scales suggests that decay unfolds through dimensions and formative scales to eventually descend into the unground of the wreckage of dimensionality or demonic solid (that is, the corpse of solidus). There is far more to 'being solid' than one can imagine, since if solid were inferior to the void and simply a symptom of it, then why wouldn't decay's infinite brutal process eradicate solidity once and for all?

Immersed in the undercover softness of decay, dimensions and metrons deteriorate beneath the machinery of rot. Excessive dimensioning is the strategy of decay, just as solidity is its fuel. In decay, disintegration is a means for excessive dimensioning and proliferating scales, because disintegration is a terminal tactic to progressively breed more dimensions in the absence of any force of consolidation and utilization of them as a whole or a formation. A disintegrating entity is a vermiculate excretion of its former scales; it spawns more and more measures, micro-scales, metronic cells, patches of solid, labyrinthine nexuses of dimensions, and wasteful dumps of scales. To this extent, to speak of local decay (as related to one object) is problematic, for decay works externally to all scales and dimensions by which the local can be separated from the epidemic and the global:

> My decay is not only mine but the decay of the whole world which is differentiated from me. The Middle East might be an obscure geo-political decay, but the developed world, too, might in fact be said to be the decaying Middle East on an epidemic and global scale. (H. Parsani)

The disintegration introduced to an object by rotting processes is not a regular disintegration as of separation into component parts, fragments or constitutive atoms. Decay is a non-fragmentary disintegration in which everything remains connected to the decaying entity. Continuity is preserved in the absence of consolidated dimensions and coherent measures. Consequently, the disintegrative process of decay expresses the logic of terminal softness (or goo) where continuity is the result of wasteful bonds and the impossibility of rejecting such bonds. Integration, too, is impossible because scales and dimensions no longer maintain the capacity of their formative powers. Decay creates a mucoid continuity in disintegration. What happens in decay is a drastic collapse in the depth of composition where the contrast between solid and void is radically blurred. The wasteful bonds between solid and void are in subversive opposition to the economic effectivity and the stability of whole. Disintegration is a lysis followed by the subversion of the capacity to determine the quantity and the quality of the incoming and the outgoing. For decay, softening and disintegration coincide, as formation is taken over by poromechanics. In poromechanical events, the hard exists through the soft. Decay's line of initiation corresponds to that of chemistry, from the inside to the outside, from hard and rigidly connected components to soft parts. Chemistry starts from within, but its existence is registered on the surface; ontology is, so to speak, merely a superficial symptom of chemistry. Decay extorts softness from the hard, making the hard an infested factory for breeding a softness which again is anonymous even to the formlessness of nature. The softness of decay is precisely a production of its irony.

Monotheism presupposes that any dissolution or breakdown of solid is a vitally safe process moving in the direction of a Return (to nature, creation and the divine). According to the doctrine of Return, any instance of solidity will be safely delivered to its basic elements or origin during its dissolution. Such a Return to the basic or original elements or matrix of existence is necessary for the horizon of purity — from ashes to ashes or dust to dust — which is the groundwork of the Divine's creationist project and the proof of its correctness. During decay, however, this course of Return (creationist advent?) through which deliverance or salvation is expected, deviates to something fundamentally deranged, a mess external to the recycling utopia of the Divine. In Zoroastrianism and medieval chemistry, this unrecyclable production of decay is addressed as fume or miasma — GAS. Plastic spirit or gas delineates the ultimate unlocalizablity of decay as an epidemic rather than a local phenomenon. It is no accident that the miasma and the plague were frequently equated with each other. Along the same lines, the Flemish alchemist Jan Baptista van Helmont associates putrefaction with the aporia of mixed bodies. Spirit is an epidemic which ends the myth of the soul by taking it into the outer nights of existence.

Chemistry (alchemy) begins with decay. Stripped before the mess-agents of decay, one can always ask, 'Isn't thought a gaseous rot?' ... the question reverberates cancerously through the fetid air. Resistance to decay is both futile and fertile. But then, what is fertility in the sense of resistance toward decay? There is a yawning horror in this question.

Excursus XI (Life Modeling)

Cut to pieces, slashed through the limbs, hacked into still unharmed members, amputated, scratched, furrowed by nails, incised with teeth, jagged with sharp edges of broken bones, cut unevenly along the lips, carving out the cheeks, shaving off all elevations on the body, trimming the feet and the hands by chopping off the toes and fingers, trisecting the nose to hair, bridge and the void, chunking out the face, clearing the face of idolatrous redundancies, pinking out the entire body, subtracting eyelids from the face, then nose, lips and the face from the head, provoking the head to be a body cavity, opening slits randomly or calculatedly, grooming by mauling, scooping out the chin, seizing the skin with remaining fingernails, turning the chest into a stash for flies, removing the abdomen, truncating the ears into bizarre shapes, perforating the gums with the teeth, rending the armpits, thinning out the neck, minimizing the flesh, reducing the body's substance to its gist, rounding the limbs up to the nearest outline, increasing the daily chop sounds, today ten thousand cuts, tomorrow more or less; Angra-Maynu (Ahriman) continues to butcher his body as every day new meat and tissues flow into the wounds abnormally, as they shut the wounds closed and form scars — excessive scarring.

In the Avestan language of the ancient Persia, the word 'to create or give birth to' as related to Ahriman is *hav* or *frā.karet*. The word *hav* simultaneously means carving, etching, cooking, boiling, sodomy, frying, mangling and grating; all making of Ahriman a culinary deity or a cook. And isn't cooking the ultimate art of composing, blurring, alchemy, reinventing ingredients, sorcery, artificialization and puppetry of materials and products? For cookery, materialism and its pragmatics is a latching on to the demonopoly of matter. Cooks are criminal alchemists with occult tendencies. Ashemogha (the false mage, deceiver, imposter, quack), messenger of Ahriman, appears to Zahak, the king of Persia, as a cook who taints the vegetarian Zoroastrian cuisine with meat. As a culinary felon bent on defiling the Persian diet, Ashemogha executes his scheme by secretly adding small quantities of meat to his meals and over time increasing the quantity of meat, then replacing it with human meat so as to get Zahak addicted. After ten years, Ashemogha finally comes up with a cuisine composed entirely of meat, to complete Zahak's initiation into the carnivorous realms. As Ashemogha (the cook) kisses Zahak's shoulders after his initiation (the Gift of Ahriman), two giant worms or snakes grow out of the kiss marks. The pain of the growing worms can only be alleviated by feeding them with human brains of both sexes. The demonic is only attainable by becoming-chef or by returning to the culinary aspects of matter.

Parsani's *Defacing the Ancient Persia* traces a line between leprosy, creativity, pottery, Ahriman or Angra-Maynu, populating minorities, creation and insurgency. In his one and only book, Parsani glorifies pottery thus: 'Pottery takes the path of a creative revolution against Creation'. Ahriman cuts pieces from his body in large quantities to create a legion out of those pieces, to frogspawn Ahrimanstic creations, disciples, pests, people and allies out of his blood, serum and meat. Ahriman's self-cutting aims to mockingly imitate the self-sufficiency of the Divine's creation (or Ahura-Mazda's world) by turning his own body into the butchershop of creation. Yet even more fundamentally, for Ahriman, creation through self-injury is a politics for dismantling the monopoly of God (or his brother Ahura-Mazda) who has already monopolized the world and its potentials through genesis and his creationist campaign. For this reason, such a deliberate act of butchery modifies the politics of creation for purposes external to the political schema 'create-to-be-a-god'. Rather than enacting the sovereignty of God through creation, Ahrimanistic creativity unbinds the creativity inherent to base materialism. Ahriman's extreme body art (scarification) is a praxis for differentiating decay and creativity from the established or the grounded universe without purging or transgressing it in a destructive approach. This is why Parsani frequently addresses middle-eastern artists and writers as 'the legion', in an apparent reference to Ahrimanistic creativity:

> Today, as in the past, middle-eastern creativity demonstrates that middle-eastern writers and artists descend from Ahriman's revolutionary movement to squeeze art out of creation or the established order, to extract subversion from the health of that creation, and to reap creativity out of that subversion. All this without vengefully causing the established order to bleed to death, rather giving it enduring opportunities to survive and grow new forms of subversion, participation, minorities, revolutions in counter-revolutions and boundless insurgencies. (H. Parsani)

Scarring exemplifies the vigilance of health. As health's watchdog, the healing process is in charge of sealing wounds and obstructing transgressions by squandering matter, time and energy on wounded regions. If scarring is the epitome of health, Ahriman primarily engenders its minorities and detrimental machines of monstrosity and insubordination out of the scarring process. By cutting a piece from himself and making a fiend out of that piece, Ahriman spawns his legion. The creation of each vermin, as well as the magnitude of its monstrosity, is registered as a scar on Ahriman's body. The more criminal the fiend, the more deformed and larger the keloid is. Ahriman turns scarring into a malignant process, into fibrosis — soft tissues over tissues without hesitation or pause. Overproduction of collagen or hypertrophic scarring — either lumping above the wound or growing infinitely and indefinitely outside the boundaries of the wound — highlights a twist in the direction of the healing process. In excessive scarring, the healing process is channeled into a new territory where it effectuates the undercover softness of decay instead of the shape of a successful containment — abuse instead of treatment, malignant overhealth instead of health. Through Ahrimanistic creativity, health becomes ruinous to its own existence without being able to get rid of itself. In fact, it is the practitioners of Ahrimanistic creativity — the middle-eastern legion — that are to blame for nurturing all sorts of clandestine insurrection and silent degeneration of the authority and the state.

'Be a conscious leper'. More than a self-indulgent maxim referring to his Hansen's disease, Parsani's suggestion to middle-eastern artists and writers hints at his political advocacy of Ahrimanistic creativity. For undercover softness and leprous skin go hand in hand: The Leper, as a religious object of suffering, is an engine of subversive creation or 'leper creativity'. Leprosy or life pottery insinuates the art of churning horror in clay. As keloids and scars form over each other, over new wounds on old scars, they become progressively desensitized towards stimuli, throwing Ahriman's body into a confusion in which no straight line can be traced or drawn between the creator and the created — original inauthenticity. Similar to Ahrimanistic artistry, manifested through the unreceptiveness of keloids and scar tissues, leprosy develops an enigmatic insensitivity in the act of creation in which the created and the creator are merged and dissociated through insensitivity to each other, an insensitivity which operates both as polytics and ethics of creativity. The Divine treasures his creation and is constantly worried about the created to the point that, in order to save the wholeness of creation, his wrath is often directed toward the created. Leper creativity, on the other hand, requires a perpetual discordance or disruption of such a wholeness between the creator and its creation, a deep insensitivity toward the created and the creator.

If the creationist Divine is a potter who made the human out of dust and water, by doing so he sewed the seeds of a debacle and of his own loss of face. Ahriman writes creation on himself, and ironically his anti-Demiurge monstrosity is the result of his life-modeling himself to be the creator, the created and creativity all together. Life-modeling is a systematic exercise of pestilential creativity. Ahriman as a voluntary leper (depicted with an outlandishly disfigured face) is not a potter, but his body is a drone-potter's wheel. Following the tradition of monotheism and the Divine's creation out of dust and water, God is a potter who is oblivious to his own work materials. Because if dust qabalistically equals No God and water stands for semen and dissemination, then pottery throws the diffusive shapes of No God. As a blind potter, God spreads godless materialism into the universe. Away from the Divine's concern which has taken the path of obsession (plastic surgery), a leper, both literally and as a middle-eastern artist or writer — Parsani's conscious leper — is under constant clay surgery.

POLYTICS

COMPLICITY AND SCHIZOTRATEGIES FOR OPENNESS AND INSURGENCY

A GOOD MEAL
THE SCHIZOTRATEGIC EDGE

In the mid-eighties, before succumbing to his petromantic nympholepsy, Hamid Parsani re-addresses his book, *Defacing the Ancient Persia*, as a guide to strategic openness (which, he insists, is the enduring concern of the Middle East). Following his analysis of the Aryanistic holocaust and its relationship with the genealogy of monotheism, the book indeed can be read as a syncretic approach to a broad array of communications and modes of living in the Middle East, an openness with a polytical edge, as he emphasizes: 'It [openness] is certainly not made for social dynamics or lifestyles instrumentalized within liberal societies. Openness is what turns the very body of the free world upside down throughout human history — if, of course, we assume that the free world has ever been more than a mere institution of a more tolerable regime or religion,' Parsani writes in his later notes on *Defacing the Ancient Persia*. The book had already been tagged by hostile critics as 'a maximalist and verbose treatise about everything except Persia, informed by every discipline except archeology' and hailed by a few disciples as 'the obligatory reference book for traveling to the Middle East'. In any case, it is more than a misreading to take Parsani's *Defacing the Ancient Persia* for a mere collection of phenomenal discoveries and theories. As Parsani himself confesses, his book pursues 'an awkward dissection of the conundrum of openness in the Middle East'.[34]

> If the so-called despotic institutions of the Middle East have survived liberalism, and have grown stronger instead of being shattered into miserable pieces long ago, it is because openness can never be extracted from the inside of the system or through a mere voluntary or subjective desire for being open. Openness can never be communicated by liberalism (not to mention the 'free world').

According to his critics, Parsani's re-reading of *Defacing the Ancient Persia* aims to remobilize its already fleshed-out topics on the current Tellurian Dynamics with the 'fluid efficiency of petroleum' (Parsani's phrase). For Parsani, however, this process of re-writing (or 'reinterpretation', according to critics) had the virtue of gathering all of his inquiries under the enigma of openness:

> It seems to me that so-called middle-eastern life, more than anything else, suggests a communication dynamics, and is an answer to the enigma of openness rather than being a contemporary orientalist lifestyle with a political or humanist edge.

In the light of Parsani's references to 'the enigma of openness', the Hyperstition team decided to question and reinvestigate its early notes on openness in relation to Deleuze and Guattari's politics of becoming. However, this time the reading was not conducted on wholly philosophical grounds but rather against a new background, that of the mess-hysteria of Parsani's works — a textual sketch resistant to any high-octane philosophical psychosis. In this way, Parsani's works could be hammered out new edges and relevancies.

> In *Defacing the Ancient Persia*, human history is an experimental research process in designing and establishing modes of openness to the outside. Openness is not ultimately, so to speak, the affair of humans, but rather the affair of the outside — everything minus the human, even the human's own body. But openness is not only associated with human history. Parsani argues that the Earth, as the arch-puppeteer and occult-manipulator of planetary events, has a far more sophisticated openness of its own. If the human is the subject of openness or the one who opens himself to his outside, then the Earth is the 'inside-out subject' of human openness. Undoubtedly, human openness is full of twists. This includes social openness, gender communications, and openness between populations and governments of the contemporary world, whether cultural or petrological. Parsani shows that human openness has a strategic and twisted spirit for which every communication is a tactic and every openness is a strategy to be unfolded. If this is the case, then the Earth must enjoy a womb-dark and an ocean-deep scheme — if not conspiracy — in its openness and communications with both organisms and its solar outside. It is difficult to study the politics, culture and economy of the world without questioning its issues and concerns regarding the ethics of openness. Middle-eastern studies

would be impossible without the question of openness. (Anush Sarchisian in her comments on *Defacing the Ancient Persia*, 1994)

Openness comes from the Outside, not the other way around. Nietzschean affirmation was never intended to support liberation or even to be about openness at all. It was an invocation of the outside, in its exteriority to the human and even to the human's openness (which includes desires for being open to the outside). Radical openness has nothing to do with the cancelation of closure; it is a matter of terminating all traces of parsimony and grotesque domestication that exist in so-called emancipatory human openness. The blade of radical openness thirsts to butcher economical openness, or any openness constructed on the affordability of both the subject and its environment. The target of radical openness is not closure but economical openness. Radical openness devours all economic and political grounds based on 'being open'.

Affirmation does not attain openness to the world but maintains closure progressively through the grotesque domestications of economical openness. On the first level of its operation, affirmation advocates 'being open to' as an anthropomorphic and regulated mode of openness; it renders everything more affordable, more economically open and more purposeful. Affirmation is initially involved with the manipulation of the boundaries (of systems) whose machinery is based on transforming openness into an instance of affordability, turning economic openness into a survival economy. Economical openness is not about how much one can be open to the outside, but about how much one can afford the outside. Therefore, openness, in this sense, is intrinsically tied to survival. The survival economy, in the same vein, is the realization of all manifestations of communication as the prolonging of survival; affordability in all its forms guarantees survival.

Economical openness is a risk-feigning maneuver simulating communication with the Outside. Yet for such openness, the outside is nothing but an environment which has already been afforded as that which does not fundamentally endanger either the survival of the subject or its environing order. So that 'being open' is but the ultimate tactic of affordance, employed by the interfaces of the boundary with the outside. For economical openness, the order of the boundary must be invisible; the boundary is not a filtering sphere or confinement but a 'force dynamic boundary' (with an ambiguous nomadic drive), a fluid horizon seeking to accommodate everything through its expanding dynamism rather than sedentarization. Affordance presents itself as a preprogrammed openness, particularly on the inevitably secured plane of *being open* (as opposed to *being opened*). On the plane of 'being open to', organic survival can always interfere, appropriate the flow of xeno-signals, economize participations or if necessary cut the communication before it is too late.

'Being open', ever political and cautious, supports the survival economy as an economical and slyly appropriated sphere of capacity (or affordability), an economy bent on upholding survival at all costs, even through the necrocracy of death. Economical openness — that is, 'being open to' — appropriates the reciprocation between the subjective and the objective sides of openness. While the subject of the economical openness manifests itself in the statement 'I am open to', the objective of the openness is what 'being open to' aims at. Economical openness is constantly maintained by these two poles which must afford each other. For an entity, the act of opening to its environment is only possible if the environment has already afforded the entity within its environing range, and if the entity itself is able to accommodate part of the environment within its capacity. The capacity of the entity is directly influenced by the subjective survival of that entity. For this reason, so-called (economical) openness represents the affordability and the survival capacity of its subjects, not the act of opening itself.

In economical openness, affordance does not refer to either the restricted or restricting affordability of one or multiple systems, but to the whole reciprocal horizon in which both the subjective and the objective sides of economical openness must survive and undergo a dynamic but economical participation. Affordance does not work on a univocal or an unidirectional line — from the subject of openness to its objective or vice-versa. It is economically collective. Affordance moulds a horizon of economically-secured openness which accommodates both sides as bodies dynamically synchronous to each other. Correspondingly, openness is dynamically determined by the survival of both subjective and objective sides as a mutual living process, rather than survival as the evasion of peril. If affordance cannot be subjectively or objectively dismantled, this is because it is established mutually. In regard to its subjective and objective poles, affordance is basically mesophilic, meaning that it always comes in-between. Participations, becomings, lines of tactics and communications must all be based on the meso-sphere of affordance and its survival machineries.

'I am open to you' can be recapitulated as 'I have the capacity to bear your investment' or 'I afford you'. This conservative voice is not associated with will or intention, but with the inevitability of affordance as a mesophilic bond, and with the survival economy and the logic of capacity. If you exceed the capacity by which you can be afforded, I will be cracked, lacerated and laid open. Despite its dedication to repression, its blind desire for the monopoly of survival and the authoritarian logic of the boundary, the plane of 'being open to' has never been openly associated with paranoia and regression. Such is the irony of liberalism and anthropomorphic desire.

However, while affirmation is tactically nurtured by affordance, it is also a stealth strategy[35] to call and to bring forth an Epidemic Openness whose eventuation is necessarily equal to the abortion of economical or human openness. As far as survival is concerned, radical openness always brings with it base-participation, contamination and pandemic horror, the horror of the outside emerging from within as an autonomous xeno-chemical Insider and from without as the unmasterable Outsider. In any case, radical openness is internally connected to unreported plagues. If affordance is the mesophilic extension between subjective and objective fronts of communication, the outside is defined by the exteriority of function rather than distance. If affirmation is ultimately strategic, this is because epidemic openness is inherent to the repression of the outside and the suspension of its influences. In a polytical twist, epidemic openness craves for solid states, manifest closures such as dwelling and accommodating systems of all kinds which are intrinsically integrated with subsistence and the survival economy: *libban, lifian*. Conforming to the secrecy and the conspiracist ethos of affordance, for which every tactic is another line of expansion (to afford more), radical openness requires strategic calls or lines of subversion from within affordance. Radical openness, therefore, subverts the logic of capacity from within. Frequently referred to as sorcerous lines, awakenings, summonings, xeno-attractions and triggers, strategic approaches unfold radical openness as an internal cut — gaseous, odorless, with the metallic wisdom of a scalpel. Openness emerges as radical butchery from within and without. If the anatomist cuts from top to bottom so as to examine the body hierarchically as a transcendental dissection, then the katatomy of openness does not cut anatomically or penetrate structurally (performing the logic of strata); it butchers open in all directions, in correspondence with its strategic plane of activity. Openness is not suicide, for it lures survival into life itself where 'to live' is a systematic redundancy. Since the Outside in its radical exteriority is everywhere, it only needs to be aroused to rush in and erase the illusion of economical appropriations or closure. Openness is a war, it needs strategies to work. Openness is not the anthropomorphic desire to be open, it is the being opened eventuated by the act of opening itself. To be butchered, lacerated, cracked and laid open — such is the corporeal reaction of subjects to the radical act of opening. Accordingly, affirmation is a camouflaged strategy, a vehicle for cutting though affordance and creatively reinventing openness as a radical butchery (a radical xeno-call).

To become open or to experience the chemistry of openness is not possible through 'opening yourself' (a desire associated with boundary, capacity and survival economy which covers both you and your environment); but it can be affirmed by entrapping yourself within a strategic alignment with the outside, becoming a lure for its exterior forces. Radical openness can be invoked by becoming more of a target for the outside. In order to be opened by the outside rather than being economically open to the system's environment, one must seduce the exterior forces of the outside: You can erect yourself as a solid and molar volume, tightening boundaries around yourself, securing your horizon, sealing yourself off from any vulnerability ... immersing yourself deeper into your human hygiene and becoming vigilant against outsiders. Through this excessive paranoia, rigorous closure and survivalist vigilance, one becomes an ideal prey for the radical outside and its forces.

> The Middle East's march toward problematic disciplines and the bigotry of monotheistic dogmatism — either through its governing policies and models or through its social and cultural dynamics — is in fact a systematic progress toward a radical openness. The plane of being opened lies at the other side of openness, next to strategic closure, opposed to the free world. It is hard for global politics to understand this. (H. Parsani)

For Parsani, such a systematic march toward the manifestations of closure is equal to summoning and strategically attracting a faceless plague, a xeno-chemical tide for subversion and disease against all immunity systems and boundaries, all monolithic and molar structures. Epidemic openness arrives as a cryptogenic event in the form of butchery (opening and being opened at the same time). With no prior warning, butchering openness cuts you open (the only question that could be asked is 'where does it start from?'); it turns you into a fine meal, into a new meat ... a new food for a new earth.

A-Good-Meal Polytics. The ancient Persian cult of *Druj* (the Mother of Abominations) were the first — through exercising their belief systems directly within the body of monotheism — to discover that 'when it comes to darkness, we must think strategically.' To affirm the Life-Satan (Druj), one must reinvent everything as strategy. Engagement with the Life-Satan must be conducted through a strategic communication, that is to say, not by affirming positively through faith or credence but by strategically turning ourselves into meals, acting as a decoy to commence the hunt from the other side. Unlike the revolts of western heterodoxy, the cult of Druj did not take depravity and irrationality as its heterodox or Satanist blueprint; they summoned the Life-Satan by undertaking a paranoid closure against the outside and by becoming excessively obsessive with their hygiene and health. By doing so, they deduced terminal insanity from the very orthodoxy of rationality and logic.

In order to surrender yourself to the ecstasy of Life-Satan (the epidemic openness) you must try to purify yourself from all defects, attend numerous hygiene courses, develop a quotidian and institutionalized life-style, evade all defilement both physically and mentally ... you must just try to make A Good Meal out of yourself for the life-Satan and its avatars. As an allure for the outside, you should make a decoy out of yourself. In this way the Life-Satan is strategically lured to tear you to shreds, giving a new functioning level to openness. Even though openness is exterior to affordance and capacity, it ravages their corpses and defeated territories. Far from a necrocratic relief that presents death as an escape, one becomes an unground to all defilements, fears, and intensities which the Life-Satan pours into systems and organizations, an unground where openness can only be outlined as a series of lacerations. If in terms of the radical outside, closure (of any system or subject) is impossible, then the act of opening is nothing but the effectuation of this impossibility for the system. For the subject, this effectuation or imposition of impossibility is always catastrophically unpleasant.

According to Akht-Yatu and the cult of Druj, the Mother of Abominations (call it the blade of openness or xeno-tempest) always lands on those who live, and we must live (in the most organizational and survivalist aspect of this process) to affirm such a catastrophic intensity of the Outside. In the depths of openness, the polytics of A Good Meal celebrates the irony of conservation: Every yang you drop in your pocket accumulates more excitations for the Life-Satan, or the thrill of butchery as we must call it. In the wake of this panorama, don't all monotheistic exhortations revel in the morbid festivals of A-Good-Meal polytics?

Make yourself a fresh meal: obelisk, monolithus, the world tree and the body of the despot. But how is it possible to dress yourself as a new food, an ultimate bait for the openness emerging to consume the meal? If hunger insinuates the concrete confusion between the object of desire and the destruction of this object, voracity suggests the obliteration of all that satiates the senses. Epidemic openness devours and butchers with such voracity that openness loses all its signifying and qualitative aspects. Wide-open, open-minded, broadly-open and open-world, as the subjectively affirmed modes of openness, are rendered obsolete. Such spatio-logical manifestations of openness reinstall the logic of economical subjugations within the axioms of liberal commonsense. Radical openness cannot be captured as a 'wide-open' which fits the docile liberalist politicians of the survival economy or the advocates of capacity; it means to be devoured-open. Laceration, being torn to shreds, cracked and laid open all suggest a strategic participation, a communion, or active communication with a ritualistic butchery — openness. Epidemic openness undermines capacity not by dismantling it (negative incapacitation), but by a subversive participation with capacity that lures it into being cracked from within. Capacity is savagely cracked opened precisely by following the logic of its affordability.

H.P. Lovecraft is frequently accused of propounding a 'heavily fetishized archaic terror mixed with extreme racial paranoia'. This compulsively consistent racism oozes into his works and thoroughly pervades them. In his Cthulhu Mythos, this droning racism is promulgated on a cosmic plane as a prokaryotic horror-population, the Old Ones, lurking as the avatars of absolute exteriority. Throughout the mythos, it becomes apparent that communication with the outside — even if corrected by capacity — harbors a certain inevitability in regard to the communicator. This inevitable destiny entails the transformation of human civilizations into a butchershop of outsiding forces. Outside-ness, however, does not require unique forces in order to develop its lines of openness. In other words, outsiders are themselves the orphans of cosmic alienage and the radical outside. Regardless of the existence of outsiders and the causal interactions between them, exteriority is an 'act' which essentially precedes its objects and is indifferent to their ontological position. The very function of outsideness is manifested as the imposition of exteriority on everything, from humans to the Old Ones. The act of outsiding or the imposition of exteriority is effectuated as the blade of openness that equally cuts humans and the Old Ones open. The more closed the subject, the more brutally it is cut open. The task or the destiny of outsiders is to violently render humans open, yet they too are expendable puppets of cosmic alienage.

In Lovecraft's Cthulhu Mythos, the outsider enforces the exteriority of the Outside. Yet since this alienage cannot register itself other than by violating boundaries and the order of the system, it is usually characterized as an immeasurably absurd apathy toward closed subjects (systems). On the anthropomorphic level, this absurd apathy is identified as absolute sadism. This is why the Lovecraftian outsider is not reducible to the alien, for before everything, it is the act of outsiding imposed by the exteriority of cosmic alienage or the radical outside. Such an act cannot be separated from its sheer reality and concrete presence. For these reasons, the excessive paranoia in Lovecraft's stories cannot easily be condemned or dismissed. However, are the consequences of Lovecraft's paranoia completely in alignment with his racial orientation? To answer this question the genealogical undercurrents between such xenophobic paranoia and racism should be exhumed and investigated.

The strategic aspects of this archaic paranoia are in part unknown to western occultural politics and socio-religious orders, yet Zoroastrianism, as the germ cell of monotheism, grasped them a long time ago. Call it the omega-degree of survivalism or paranoia: The ancient Persian cults of Druj who infiltrated Zoroastrianism realized that radical openness can be triggered only through strategic communications with the avatars of the Outside. Roads leading to the outside are so pestilential that one melts away and perishes in them almost immediately. Therefore, journeys to the outside are prematurely subjected to termination. For this reason, first of all, a solution capable of guaranteeing the continuity of the journey must be devised.

For the middle-eastern cults of Druj, the solution was to engineer an artificial route (a strategic opening, as military experts put it) characterized by its support for endurance in the path to the outside and by possessing sufficient parasitic stamina to persist. Mere fervid desire for the outside is never enough; a guiding system is needed, a guarantee to give desire an operational cutting-edge. As formulated by Drujite cults, the strategic route to the outside is a twisting path, running on the terminal multiplicity of tactics and strategy rather than on a mere desiring dynamism or a tendency to reach, travel and become. Since no instance of economical survivalism is enough to tolerate the gaze of the outside, this route must not only support survivalism but must also develop a type of ultra-endurance necessary for interlocking with epidemic openness and its intensive operatives of horror. Correspondingly, the process of reaching outside or arriving at the other side should not be mapped as 'moving towards ...' (destination-oriented tactic). In Drujite polytics, arrival is equal to 'calling here' (summoning), engineering a line of attraction for the outside, rather than traveling towards an outside which defies being characterized as a destination. For cults of Druj, the destination is not the other side but it is here and us; our human territory must become the destination of outsiders, not the other way around. The sorcerous function for turning the destination-oriented journey inside out is loosely defined as the xeno-call: turning the outsider into an insider, the intensive operative of horror from within.

In both Drujite and Lovecraftian polytics of radical exteriority, omega-survival or strategic endurance is maintained by an excessive paranoia that cannot be distinguished from a schizophrenic delirium. For such a paranoia — saturated by parasitic survivalism and persistence in its own integrity — the course of activity coincides with that of schizo-singularities. Paranoia, in the Cthulhu Mythos and in Drujite-infested Zoroastrianism, manifests itself as a sophisticated hygiene-Complex associated with the demented Aryanistic obsession with purity and the structure of monotheism. This arch-sabotaged paranoia, in which the destination of purity overlaps with the emerging zone of the outside, is called schizotrategy. If, both for Lovecraft and the Aryans, purity must be safeguarded by an excessive paranoia, it is because only such paranoia and rigorous closure can attract the forces of the Outside and effectuate cosmic alienage in the form of radical openness — that is, being butchered and cracked open. Drujite cults fully developed this schizotrategic line through the fusion of Aryanistic purity with Zoroastrian monotheism. The Zoroastrian heresiarchs such as Akht soon discovered the immense potential of schizotrategy for xeno-calls, subversion and sabotage. As a sorcerous line, schizotrategy opens the entire monotheistic culture to cosmodromic openness and its epidemic mesh-works. As the nervous system of Lovecraftian strategic paranoia, openness is identified as 'being laid, cracked, butchered open' through a schizotrategic participation with the Outside. In terms of the xeno-call and schizotrategy, the non-localizable outside emerges as the xeno-chemical inside or the Insider.

To reach the schizotrategic plane of openness, one must indulge in paranoia and hygiene-Complex (overhealth). Schizotrategy involves developing the subversive logic inherent to overhealth and the capacity-oriented facet of paranoia. The Drujite cults perceived schizotrategy both as an awakening and as a feeding ritual for Druj and its radical exteriority. If, for Lovecraft, the outside is indifferent to human intention, schizotrategy, too, as the pragmatic participation with exteriority, is always apathetic toward the subjective inputs of paranoia and its contents. In a nutshell, schizotrategy knows no paranoia. Schizotrategy denotes a strategic schizophrenia which operates covertly inside paranoia on behalf of the Outside. Therefore, the ambitions of schizotrategy are radically exterior to the xenophobic intentions of paranoia.

> If openness, as the scimitar blade of the outside, seeks out manifestations of closure, then in the middle-eastern ethic it is imperative to assuage the external desire of the Outside by becoming what it hungers for the most. (H. Parsani)

The opening edge of the Outside can only be sharpened by the bluntness of the subjective will for openness. Radical openness is attained by sophisticating the level of exposure toward the outside. The degree of exposure is overlapped with the degree of closure or the shunning of any enthusiasm for escapist flight. If the escapist tendency of 'becoming open to ...' or 'being open' lies in the direction of an escapist flight from a gravity of some sort (limitations, systems, etc.), then descent or cataflight corresponds to subterranean engagements with radical exteriority, where the outside emerges from within. To put it differently, in schizotrategy the flight from gravity is replaced by a descent or dive into the subterranean realm, affirmation of what lies beyond is supplanted by the affirmation of what resides within. Radical openness (adhering to butchery rather than openness) is a 'becoming chthonic' of the flight or cataflight, for which exotericism is exercised by traversing the ground on a deeply collusive level. Cataflight is not a line of escape from gravity, but an act of manipulation that aims to pass through gravity and its ground so as to access the substratum. To reach the substratum, the laws of gravity must be complied with and the logic of the ground must be affirmed; this is the route taken both by humans and by the avatars of the outside. This is why gods take solar voyages to the earthy ground (to be grounded) and turn into dead gods. The alchemy of flight is not built upon the escape from gravity, and hence a submission to its influence; for flight is a chthonic vampirism that feasts upon the chemistry of the ground and its potencies. Flight is profound (*pro-fundus* and pro-ground): Dead gods come to open, to eat and defile, to immerse themselves in mess, entangled both by the immensity of the outside and by earthborn restrictions. The intricacy of the mess is proportional to the ferocity of the butchering openness; the greater the openness, the messier it gets. The Dead God is a god who has taken an avatar or who has fallen to the *grund* (the so-called chthonic[36] god). The word *avatar*, which delineates the reality of chthonic communication in terms of descent and *kata-*, suggests that the labyrinthine voyage of the dead god is a chthonic openness and a non-escapist flight. The word *avatar*[37] is translated as a chthonic or a death mask, originating from the Sanskrit 'descent' (*avatarati*). Correspondingly, the avatar is functionally connected to the catadromic depths of darkness or *katabasis* (chthonic descent) which gods undergo in order to be transmuted into dead gods. The descending god seeks to open and be opened, to ravage and be ravaged. Every instance of the god's consumption or activity on the human plane of existence is a sheer devastation. However, to assume that such devastations are directed solely at humanity is pure anthropocentrism and indulgence in victimhood: The City of God will also be sacked.

The dead god is not a tired, abolished or doomed god but a god with its ultimate weapon of catastrophic devastation. A plague coming to earth to make of the earth's restrictive ground a direct passage to openness, the dead god mortifies itself by affirming the earthly ground within which it is buried. If the act of descent, as associated with dead gods, is identified as the secularization of the divine's body (departing from the divine's sovereignty), the dead god itself is by no means a secular entity. In the process of descending, the dead god rediscovers its supposedly secular corpus as a pestilential but love-saturated communion with the sacred. Through descent, the god commits a crime at once secular and sacred: It opens itself by eating and infecting the human, and opens the human by turning itself into a corpse. The necrotized carcass of god is a more palpable manifestation of its body, a cold meat which is chewed, scavenged and touched by everything on the earth, then exhumed for love-making: a necrophilic mess. When it comes to communication with humans, the god can expose itself by putting its corpse at the disposal of humans. Nothing is more beneficial to gods than the necrotization of their own body; for them, the cosmogenesis of decay promises far more than divinity.

> If, in middle-eastern tradition, gods deliberately allow themselves to be killed left and right by enemies, humans or themselves, without any prudence as to their future and eventual extinction, it is because they find more significance and benefit in their own corpses — as a concrete object of communication and tangibility among humans — than in the abstractness of their divinity. At last, as corpses, they can copulate and contaminate. (H. Parsani)

In *Begotten* (the movie directed by E. Elias Merhige), God chooses to be a corpse in order to be a protagonist. He butchers himself open with a straight razor, cutting into his black and white entrails; jerking, twisting, coiling, convulsing as his innards spill out into the world. In the defloration of his own meat, for the first time God steps onto the plateau of black matter where the chemistry of god is more fertile than ever — 'the world has its origins in putrefaction' (Menocchio). God chooses to be a corpse in order to be a protagonist. The introspection of God coincides with the butchery of his body and the birth of the universe from his corpse. After God is exposed as a corpse, a masked woman lurches out of the shadows, inseminating herself with the semen boiling out of God's corpse. She gives birth to Mutant Dead God, a dwarfish creature loosely molded around a humanoid body. Mutant Dead God is immanent to radical openness as an act of butchery between God, the dead God and Man, all together; it is the fruit of such openness. The Mutant Dead God is the only solution that God and masculinity could come up with in regard to the enigma of openness. For masculinity and God's sovereign divinity, femininity and necrotized God are exterior. Yet the act of radical opening does not transform the latter into the former. In other words, in radical openness, neither God nor masculinity are lead to their exteriors which are dead god and femininity. Rather than transforming one to another, openness lacerates both sides — the subject and its exterior — and makes them bleed into something else which is simultaneously exterior to both. The act of openness and its avatars are indifferent toward the subject; yet at the same time, the avatars of openness are even more elusive in terms of what is perceived by the subject as the outside.

The radical outside is beyond all external environments which the subject can latch on to. Through the act of openness, God is ultimately cracked open, not as a mere dead god, but as a mutant dead god, a handful of flesh atop bones in the guise of walking clay — god's postmortem attempt to plagiarize his own creation. Having taken the phallus-eroding journey of becoming-woman, masculinity, in the same way, is not replaced by femininity but transmogrifies into its mutated and necrotized former self. 'He' mutates into 'It', a dummy pronoun which cannot refer to any agent whatsoever. If the becoming-woman of masculinity is impossible in a strict sense, such impossibility has a shape, a shape which emanates a nonhuman coldness: It.

'It' insinuates the pestilential solution masculinity discovered to undermine its closure and its rigidity so as to take the flight of becoming woman, the cataflight of epidemic openness. If capacity and its economical openness can never possess the outside itself, they are nevertheless subverted by the outside, so that the journey of becoming-woman leads to a new twist for manhood. For masculinity, becoming-woman registers itself as an impossibility whose exteriority of function (outsideness) is still in accordance with the contents of masculinity rather than being in a destructive opposition to the idea of masculinity *per se*. Becoming-woman is capable of countermining masculinity without erasing all its male properties. In becoming-woman, masculinity rather loses the capacity of consolidating itself as a whole or an integrated body. The possibility or possess-ability of an event or object requires the plane of 'being open to' (affording it) in order to possess the object, but radical openness, as opposed to affordance and capacity, is not possess-able and is consequently impossible (im-possess-able). Through 'becoming-woman', masculinity is supplanted by 'It'. He can only affirm the journey of becoming woman by becoming 'It' — cold toward its former self and deviated from its supposed destination. The divergence from becoming-woman can be explained by the sheer incompatibility between the economical openness to 'becoming-woman' and being opened by the journey of 'becoming-woman'. While for the former, becoming-woman can indeed be afforded as an economical mode of existence, for the latter, it coincides with the outside which can never be possessed. In radical openness, the outside is impossible in terms of attainment; instead, it looms as an act of opening. Radical outsideness does not communicate with the system in the sense of an alien contact, for its exteriority is so abysmal that the possibility of such communication is only brought about as a violent act of openness. In the same vein, for masculinity, becoming-woman is not a destination, but an act which entails the presence of masculinity as its object, the material of its butchery and openness. 'It' is an openness brought about through being opened by 'the journey of becoming-woman', not through the economical openness of being open to 'becoming-woman'.

Both god and masculinity discover their openness on their cold doubles — dead god and It. For them, the act of openness is always accompanied by a necrophilic mess which entails their blackening into their necrotized former selves. That is to say, openness happens through intimacy with the cold. In *Begotten*, Mutant Dead God is born out of such necrophilic contact or descent into the realm of germinal death. If Odysseus' journeys or expeditions for becoming open to the world do not work on the outer surface of the earth, his descent or katabasis to Hades leads to his openness to and by the dead. The dynamic vector for being opened might be katabatic, but its medium is surely communication with the dead or the rite of *Nekyia*. Odysseus' ascension to the outer surface is not a return to the economical openness of his superficial journeys but the continuation of his descent, for every ascent is the sublimation of descent. To ascend and to descend are both alike acts of opening, perpetuated through depth — hence the ambivalence of solid and void, the object and its outside.

Mutant dead god is not only a solution for being opened but also a cataclysmic solution for encountering the Mother of Abominations (the mother of all becomings). Upon such an immense femininity, becoming-woman is not only impossible for masculinity but also rigidly destructive and irreversibly suicidal. Masculinity can only affirm femininity by becoming *It*, a cold waste dripping from the atrophied muscles of malelessness which is not necessarily feminine. As a prelude to the act of openness, God undertakes becoming-dead-god either by descending to the earth (i.e. avatar) or by self-slaying. The self-slaying of god is expressed in terms of immolation or *immolare* — to sprinkle with sacrificial meal. Through self-immolation, god turns himself into a good meal for the human, the earth and the outside. For God, openness is neither eventuated through a religious advent (being open to himself) nor in secular fashion (by opening himself to the human). For this reason, the death of God refuses to be a secular or a religious event. For philosophy, however, the death of God is either perceived as a religious or a secular event, with an affordable price for both parties, God and human. It is a clinical event which can easily be sequestered from other planetary events. Therefore, philosophy's Death of God is more of a spectacle or a staged event than a collective event with contaminative potentialities (the plague). The Death of God as a contagious event is founded through the threefold of descent, the ground and subterranean potencies. It brings forth a line of openness that slashes through the god, the human and the earth.

If the Dead God is a God beyond judgment, then mutant dead god is the mess immanent to it, a good meal for the Outside. *Ambrosia*, or the food of gods, is prepared in such a kitchen, with dishes tottering on heat-snuffed ovens and the floor mired in the mess left behind by butchery. A Good Meal or ambrosia plague is gourmandized in the abattoir of openness. Beings dust themselves to forge an unground through which the god is buried and then exhumed. Openness only comes in the imperceptible recesses of butchery, a faceless love.

THE Z. CROWD
THE INFESTED GERM-CELL OF MONOTHEISM

For then mankind would have become as the Great Old Ones; free and wild and beyond good and evil, with laws and morals thrown aside and all men shouting and killing and revelling in joy. Then the liberated Old Ones would teach them new ways to shout and kill and revel and enjoy themselves, and all the earth would flame with a holocaust of ecstasy and freedom. (*The Call of Cthulhu*, Howard Phillips Lovecraft)

The more Lovecraft's enforced sojourn in New York is prolonged, the more his repulsion and terror grows, until it attains alarming proportions. As he wrote to Belknap Long, '*one cannot speak calmly about the mongoloid problem of New York*'. Later on in the letter, he declares: '*I hope the end will be warfare — but not till such a time as our own minds are fully freed of humanitarian hindrances of the Syrian superstition imposed upon us by Constantinus. Then let us show our physical power as men and Aryans, and conduct a scientific wholesale deportation from which there will be neither flinching nor retreating.*' [...] What is indisputable is that Lovecraft, as one says of boxers, 'a la haine' (he has hate). But it should be precisely stated that the role of the victim in his stories is generally taken by an anglo-saxon university professor, cultivated, reserved, and well-educated. Very much someone of his own type, in fact. Whereas the torturers, servants of unnameable cults, are almost always hybrids, mulattos, mixed-race 'of the basest kind'. In Lovecraft's universe,

> cruelty is not a refinement of the intellect; it is a bestial impulse, which is associated precisely with benighted stupidity. As to those courteous, refined individuals, of great delicacy of manner ... they furnish the ideal victims. (*H.P. Lovecraft: Against the World, Against Life*, Michel Houellebecq, trans. R. Mackay)

The third chapter of Michel Houellebecq's work on Howard Phillips Lovecraft, *Against the World, Against Life*, ironically named *Holocaust*, is a dissection of Lovecraft's vitriolic racism, paranoia, and consistent emphasis on absolute closure, overhealth and Aryanism. Houellebecq correctly links Lovecraft's paranoia to an extraordinary mode of monotheism, associating his stories with something old, forgotten and unclean — a ritualistic resurrection of the Zoroastrian germ-cell of monotheism, the already-sabotaged purity of the Aryans. (*Airiia-*: *Ariya-*: *Ērān*: Iran or *Aryānām dahyuš*, the realm of Aryans)

In *Defacing the Ancient Persia*, Hamid Parsani discusses how, before the Aryans settled in what would later be called the Iran plateau, the land was not empty; it was occupied by mysterious people with outlandishly complex beliefs, who knew nothing but demons, *Daivas* and *Druj* (also *Druga*: The Mother of Abominations). These pre-Aryan sorcerous people regarded everything as an avatar of horror, of a radical Outside; even the fertilizing forces of nature such as wind, rain, thunder, soil and growth were Daivas (demons). Life was Druj itself, the Mother of Abominations, the radical Outside. The entire universe was saturated with horror; death and its necrocratic terrors were merely a joke and a perverse relief (more on the side of repression than alleviation). This crowd believed that everything was exterior to survival (or live-ing) — not merely anthropomorphic survival systems but survival in general. Life itself (commonly mistaken for live-ing or what can be lived) was believed to be external to survival, lurking beneath it as the ultimate Unlife. In other words, 'the ultimate horror we try to survive is life and its abomination, the unlife or the life-satan'. The most ironic and horrific situation which Man assumes as the foundation of its humanity — struggling to survive and living in Life — it attests to the irony of humanity and the horror of life as a radical exteriority to the living being.

The problematic of Life can be superficially — if not ironically — embraced by posing this question: Generally, we believe that life makes survival possible; but if life is the source of living then why do we need to survive? If life is the so-called vital source, then why is the act of living as an appropriation and a survivalist regulation necessary? Why is survival possible, or do we need to survive if life is already a source of living? Once we realize that the ethics of life is external to that of survival, and that survival is a resistance to the epidemic and overpowering presence of life, then we can say that to be pro-life is to be essentially anti-survival. Yet more grievously, when it comes to the exteriority of life to the living being, survival is intrinsically impossible.

In the third chapter of his book, Parsani suggests that the Aryans who settled on the Iran plateau were exceptionally flexible in regard to their environment. Flexibility was the central element of the circumspect politics of the Aryans, both for survival and for keeping their genetic purity intact; the two most crucial objectives which led them to migrate and spread along a long path from Asia to Europe. It was not, in fact, their desire for peace that continually pushed the Aryans to be open to new people — especially the original populations of the regions they occupied — but fear of their doom, monomania for noble perfectionist purity and monopolistic hygiene. The Aryans' obsession for exclusion had to be pursued by any means possible, even by selective and controlled inclusion of other populations. For the Aryans everything took place at the edge of survival and purity — a purity which had to be maintained through 'closure as an carefully appropriated and regulated openness', a flexible but severely restricted and economical openness whose limits are mapped by affordance and dynamic capacity: I am open to you as long as I can afford you and what you bring for me.

The most effective way to survive and to save the purging purity of the race — to live unpolluted — was to blend in with the crowd. This was the Aryan stratagem. However, it proved to be a total misadventure for the Aryans who settled on the Iran plateau: They made themselves open to the sorcerous population of the plateau for whom everything was external to survival. For this population, unlike the Aryans, openness was effectuated as the exteriorization of life to survival, a silent aggression against survival from within. When you open the door for someone, anyone can come in; and once they enter, they unlock doors of their own. Following the Aryans' stratagem, Cyrus II (550-530 BC) would be able to expand the Persian Empire with no real obstacle, except for the northern nomads who fiercely resisted the outbreak of this new soft domination. Cyrus conquered Babylonia (Babel) and Egypt, and many other territories, one after another, attached them to his still-larval empire whose growth was dangerously rapid. This new empire tried to assimilate the whole of Asia, Africa and Europe by the single formula of initial conflict followed by peace with the enemy — after conquering their land — by believing in their beliefs and affirming their request to be free in 'the realm of Aryans'. The people living on the Iran plateau before the Aryans arrived were adept sorcerers and necromancers. For them, 'life' was not survival, nor was survival identified with 'evading death'. Survival was not a reactionary process to (Un) life, nor a temporary anthropomorphic escape out of which death's inevitability rises. Death unfolds through the process of live-ing or survival from the outset to the end as a predestined necrocratic regime. Survival presupposes death from the beginning; so-called actual death is merely the eventuation of the real death, or the impossibility of survival in affording the exteriority of life. The course of living or survival is where death not only becomes a terminus-event but a propulsive and conducting power which starts to work even before one begins to live (death becomes the director of one's life). The ethos of survival or vitalism is necrocracy. For the sorcerous crowd of the pre-Aryan Iran plateau, survival was not supposed to hold death back as long as possible but to feed the (Un)life. For them, survival and the scrabbling will to survive were sorcerous rituals to feed the Outside, to feed what is external to 'so-called life as live-ing', an occult practice for feeding the avatars of the Outside. Living was itself a feeding project, and survival in general was a strategy, the most pragmatic poly-tics for engaging the Outside. They believed that survival fed an unthinkable Abomination, an ultimate outsider which their Zoroastrian descendants called Druj. The longer you endure, the more you feed the Outside (interlocking with the outside on the plane of strategy). In the Avestan language of ancient Persia, Druj – from a Sanskrit origin – meant blackening, the chaotic aspects of falsity, fraud and strategy. The idea of ritual as a communion with this openness, then, developed the pragmatics of a new survival system practically and religiously conscious of its own repression and the exteriority of life.

As adept-sorcerers, these pre-Aryan crowds easily grasped their unique commonality with the Aryans: An obsession with survival and prolonging the process of living. While for the indigenous population of the Iran plateau living was an ultimate 'sacrificial meal' prepared in order to appease the outside, for the Aryans it was a guarantor for maintaining the purity of their race. Because of such commonality, the Aryan newcomers were eagerly greeted by the in-digenous people of the Iran Plateau. In fact, the Aryans' paranoia for purity combined with their ruthlessly hegemonic policies was a perfect carrier for the sorcerous experiments of these indigenous crowds whose sole inclination was communicating with the Outside. To them, the Aryans presented a guaranteed vector for dispatching their 'Outside-oriented experiments' into the future, developing them unnoticed, legally, publicly and popularly. From the moment they discovered this strategic commonality, the indigenous crowds of the Iran Plateau started to surrender themselves to the reign of Aryans, supporting their beliefs, fortifying their reign and contributing to their system. They penetrated the highest ranks of the Aryans, the order of the magi or the Great Teachers. As the magi, they were responsible for safeguarding the purity and prolonging the survival of the race. Only from that moment could these nameless crowds be referred to as 'them', the Z. crowd, a chattering monstrosity whose first possessed voice is the Zoroastrian germ-cell of monotheism. Having always been here, with us now and waiting on the other side, the Z. crowd maps the subtle emergence of the outside from the inside. Yet in this case, the inside does not suggest an inner sanctuary but that which was already here, the primordial outsider, around which the system was concretized. The inside is the impos-sibility of economical openness or closure from the outset. As the magi, the Z. crowd confounded the linear link between the inside and the outside by contrasting the immaculate inside of Aryanistic Zoroastrianism with the foul outside and its threats: The religion of Zoroaster against the cult of Zahak, the fiendish outlander. Yet Zoroastrianism itself was already pregnant with a resi-dent outsider, the Z. crowd itself. For the magi, the contrast between interiority and exteriority was merely a gradation between intensive exteriority of within and the extensive exteriority of without. The Z. crowd can only be decoded as a chattering river from and to the end of darkness. It is an acherontic stream moving from the sorcerous cacophony of the Z. crowd before the Aryans to their droning and thus inaudible whispers from within Zoroastrianism and finally to their buzzing noise coming from the other side. Monotheism is the *vox capta* of the Z. crowd, a population with a thousand teeth and chatters, being always here from the beginning and awaiting us at the end.

It is true that Aryanistic self-congratulation always reaches epic proportions only because it is a miserable form of emptiness. Yet ironically the Aryans can only rightfully claim one unique quality for themselves: they have always been the most resilient host for the Z. crowd and their atrocious experiments in regard to the outside. It was the task of the Aryanistic vector as a carrier to continue on until the epidemic reached its omega phase of development, diffusing through everything established on the Aryans' belief-systems, and eventually bursting open from the inside.

'As the ovum of monotheism, Zoroastrianism became a vehicle for the sabotaged Aryanism of the Iran plateau. Now it was the task of monotheism to disseminate the Outside-oriented experiments and rituals of the sorcerous crowds. The mission of monotheism was to fuse with planetary events in order to systematically transform everything into a sacrificial meal for the Outside. But the problem with the Outside is that the more you feed it, the more it asks for. The burgeoning of monotheism in the Middle East was merely a reaction to this associated with the other side,' writes Parsani. In another chapter, he explains that monotheism's insistence on hope bridges human survival to the hunger of the Outside or the Life-Satan: '... the politics of anthropomorphic hope as an element of existence and its continuation belongs to the human as well as to the outside. Hope reinforces and prolongs survival, but it would be absolute naivety to consider that hope is the exclusive property of humans. Because "what is hoped for", or the object of hope as something currently external to the human, is also reciprocally connected to hope. For survival, hope aims at what is external to it or what it does not have; but what is external to survival, what is hoped for by survival? It is the continuation of survival and persistence of life. In short, if the continuation of survival is hoped for, then the prolongation of survival must be exterior to the current condition of survival, that is to say, the persistence of life does not inherently belong to the living being and its survival but to the Outside and its hunger to feed on the survival of the living being. The Life-Satan conceives hope as a direct path towards itself by making hope the most reliable guarantee for simultaneously fueling human survival and quenching its own hunger.' Hope, in this sense, guarantees the feeding of the human to the Outside and the hunting of human survival from the other side.

As the Z. crowd camouflaged themselves within the Aryans' Zoroastrian belief system, they became the overenthusiastic exhorters of Zoroastrianism.

They started to strengthen and intensify the passion of the Aryans and their monotheistic religion for survival, aiding them to construct a more restricted closure, i.e. a more economical openness. While for the Aryans, openness politically meant 'being open to' (I am open to you 'as long as' I afford you), for the Z. crowd, radical openness was equal to 'being opened by'. The polytics of radical openness exploits survival not as a deterrent but as a parasitic agency which can indeed be cracked, lacerated and laid open from the outside. Each moment of survival can be a summoning ritual, the invocation of the butchering lines of openness. Unlike affordable openness (being open to), the plane of openness — 'being opened (by)' — is posited externally to human subjectivity and survival. Yet for openness, this exteriority brings about the possibility of strategic participation with subjectivity and survival — the more closed you are, the more intensely you will be opened. For the Z. crowd, rigorous closure or terminally economical openness (i.e. being open to) was the most attractive prey for the butchering lines of openness. Radical openness reaches the anthropomorphic security network from the Outside as something abominable; its butchering lines reinvent openness as 'being laid, cracked, butchered open'. This irreversible process of opening is so radical and tenacious in its intention to cut through any instance of closure that it can only be addressed in terms of butchery and its related nomenclature: blade, butchershop and cuts.

One cannot be radically 'open to' the outside since the nature of such openness is bound to certain obstacles and appropriations which are inevitably created by limits inherent to vitalism and the logic of affordance. The curse of survival goes beyond intention, will and orientation. Nevertheless, one can invite (seduce) the outside in order to be cracked open from the other side. The Vendidad,[38] the Zoroastrian book of anti-Druj laws or laws against Demons, is the purest example of the aforementioned strategy — systematic closure for invoking radical openness. The fact that the Vendidad is more than anything an ecclesiastical code attests to the fact that it is the book of missions, objectives and practices — a call for all collectivities in everyday life. As a 'magi-ridden tome' (Parsani), the Vendidad's main concern is to ward off demons of impurity, aberration and foulness. The book enumerates the ways of living by which one can not only protect seals of closure and sanitation but also turn the entire course of life into a systematic program for contributing to closure and repelling all manifestations which might threaten this closure. In the Vendidad, the course of living or life is characterized by its constant brutal conflict with demons or avatars of the Outside. Every sanitary practice and act of closure is simultaneously characterized by its effectivity against just one demon and by invoking hordes of demons as the consequence of contributing to sanitation and closure. The Aryanistic folly of Vendidad only serves to undermine itself for eternity.

> Vendidad's influential demon paranoia and its strategic undertone for communicating with the outside are unmatched by any other book written in

> human history. One can always remember the methods for fighting off demons, but it is almost impossible to remember the names of all the numerous demons in Vendidad. Every sanitary practice, every protection against the outside harbors a legion of demons. One always wonders whether Vendidad is on the side of the Zoroastrian monotheists, or whether it is propaganda for demons. (Hamid Parsani, *Defacing the Ancient Persia*)

If Lovecraft's stories, and the Cthulhu mythos in particular, are shockingly identical to Vendidad's demon-paranoia, it is because they both harbor a strategic line coming directly from the infested Aryanistic germ-cell of monotheism. They narrate the original and ongoing sabotage mobilized by monotheism. For both Vendidad and Cthulhu mythos, closure and the Aryanistic fetishism with purity can only continue to exist under the blade of radical openness.

As an intensively populated vector, the Z. crowd has grown, taking all monotheistic populations to the Outside through a systematic march towards paranoid closure and the amplification of the survival economy (surviving at all costs). At the end of this journey, which only makes sense in terms of closure, butchering lines of openness await. The radical plane of openness as being opened is neither pleasant for the anthropomorphic survival economy nor clean for a human communication reliant on affordability and capacity.

The omega-degree of survival (or surviving at all costs) always unfolds towards the Outside and its avatars as an irresistible attraction. Survivalism has always been a feeding ritual to invite and stimulate the voracity of the Outside for consuming all manifestations of closure. Every instance of survival or closure suggests an act of predation from the Outside, a being hunted, devoured, lacerated and opened. The butchershop of openness is built on closure, not on liberal openness. If the mere act of survival provokes the hunger of the Outside, then the omega-degree of survival is an effective participation with the voracity of the Outside or the Life-Satan; it does not merely contribute to the feeding ritual but funds the festivities. In which case, the question is: Does the ancient fetishist paranoia that Lovecraft vividly diagrams in his stories have only one side, that associated with artless paranoia and racism? Or does it have another edge whose dominant function is that of cutting itself open, reinventing itself as an ultimate polytics for communicating with the Outside — a schizotrategic two-edged blade?

We have sworn to infest the germ-cell of all monotheistic religions.

(Another samizdat discovered in Mahabad, Kurdistan [April 10, 2005]; the following text is the translation of the original Farsi samizdat)

Shari'a?[39]

—You already have it.

When Islam begins to breed all its minorities, giving birth to its offspring, all civilizations meet what they call the Apocalypse; this is the time when the Earth can no longer hold any religion, even the religion of its own body.

By declaring that Islam is the conclusion of monotheism, the most refined of all religions, one does not really seal an ideal destiny for it. Islam's declaration of its perfection and finality turn the very prophetic promises of monotheistic religions in regard to a savior and their fulfillment in the future against themselves. 'Islam is the last of all monotheistic religions.' Such a dictum does indeed betoken a gruesome end for all monotheistic religions that drift in from the past, as well as those looming out of the future. Such an emphatic finality either prevents other religions from emerging or imposes itself as their perfection: 'I am what you promised.'

Before the body of Sharia, no religion can be delivered to the masses unless by submission to Islam; even if a religious rival rises again (take Christianity for instance), Islam deliberately makes itself oppressed, turning itself to the ultimate victim, calling for a global beseeching on behalf of the oppressed. For non-Muslims, the repercussion of this call for liberation is that they face Sharia from the other side of obligation and religious conversion, that is to say, not through a religious union by turning to Islam but through the basic principals of humanitarian duty, the ethical urge to abolish the victimhood behind which the body of Sharia has been cloaked. This is the fate of emancipators, the saviors of the oppressed Islam who are absorbed by Sharia. It is not the number of growing Muslims that counts anymore, but rather the populations, policies and civilizations bewitched by the innocence of the victim and immersed in Sharia through the ethical foundations of emancipation rather than by converting to Islam by declaring the Shahada.[40] This is what we exalt as the Islamic subterfuge created by Islam's claim to be the last and the most perfect religion; there is more creativity and craftiness in this claim than anyone could imagine; but the path of strategy* is such a slippery and divergent way. When Islam concluded the whole conundrum of monotheism forever, it also sealed the irreversible conversion of itself to the ovum of apostasies and a heretical holocaust. Surpassing all other religions, annulling them and being the culmination of monotheism, Islam becomes the solitary host of all the religions that it cuts from the future, forestalls and blocks. Now, in the presence of Islam as the ultimate religion, all 'Beliefs' that could be religions by themselves have to submit to the path of Sharia and continue their existence as minor Islamic beliefs, schisms, religious sub-orders and heresies; all populating, breeding, breathing within Islam. Their breath animates the *hulê*** of Islam, and each breath of Islam spreads their infection. Hatching the egg was not easy, but finally we have it: Radical Islam cannot be separated from apostasy; heresies cannot be extracted from the foundation of Islam. If you want to have your own religion, Islam is the best place to start.

Jay
The Codex of Yatu ***
Amordad 1383
(Translated from Persian by H.R.P.)

Translators Note:

* The original word in the text is *Makr*, an Arabic word meaning 'subterfuge' and 'trick'; but the prominent Quranic reference to this word emphasizes radical strategy rather than a ploy for fulfilling one's goal.

** The original word in the Farsi text is *Hayula*, meaning 'monster' in modern Farsi; but in Islamic philosophy (al-Farabi's discussion on *Ajsam-e Hayulani,* for example) as in Greek cosmogony, it delineates the primal matter-corpus (a synthesis of the cool elements Water and Earth) prior to its animation; it is formless matter or feminine mud. Since in the text it occurs together with the word 'animation', the translator has decided to use the word *hulê* to keep the original ambiguity intact.

*** Remarks on the original Farsi text found in Mahabad, Iran (April 10, 2005):

The linguistic structure of the original Farsi text is highly inconsistent, to the extent that one assumes it to have been written by more than one author:

1. The original text was not written by a Kurdish writer; for this reason, it cannot be a local Kurdish samizdat, or what in Farsi is called a *shabnameh* (night-letter). Iranian Kurdish guerillas vehemently despise the favoring of the Arabic language over Farsi. The historical culture of Iran's Kurdistan and the Kurds is deeply connected to Aryanism and Kurdish nationalism. The residual Aryanism of Iranian Kurds sharply separates them from Iraqi Kurds. One should not forget that Hezb-e Democrat-e Kurdistan and Etehadieh Mihani in Iraq aided Iran's government and armed forces to fight the insurgencies in Iran's Kurdistan during the Kurdistan crisis (1360-1363 AP). More than fourteen words in this text are originally Arabic (while they have their commonly-used equivalents in Farsi). The text is not similar to any conventional *shabnameh* (night letter) or manifesto ever published in

Kurdistan for any political party, for it lacks the elements of typical Kurdish shabnamehs: the resistance towards central government or joining a political party.

2. The punctuation and syntactic structure of the original text are not consistent with the syntactic structures of Farsi. Yet the rhythmic flow of the (presumably original) text conforms to the Farsi language. This rhythmic flow usually cannot be found in texts translated to Farsi from another language. One way to explain this contradiction is to assume that this text was initially written in Farsi, translated into another language and then translated back into Farsi. The textual arrangements of the text bear a vague resemblance to the syntactical structures of scriptural Pahlavi language (of ancient Persia) with occasionally a Sistani (of Sistan and Baluchestan in Iran) accent.

3. Despite the reckless usage of Arabic words, the date mentioned at the end of the text is the old variation of its current form in Farsi language – *Amordad* instead of *Mordad*, the sixth month of the Persian calendar. Although both words are considered Farsi, Amordad is a word mainly used by Parsi writers who insist on purging Farsi language of all Arabic words and reviving the Parsi language connected to the late Pahlavanic language of ancient Persia. Note that the letter P does not exist in the Arabic alphabet, and that therefore the word Parsi or the term Parsi writer indicates a departure from the Arabic language or the Arabic modifications of Persian language (as in the case of the word Farsi, whose initial letter P has been replaced by the letter F).

The most morbid type of paranoia does not contribute to what is commonly known as survival or the ethos of vitalism; it has nothing to do with living or survival. Radical paranoia is not characterized by its purgatory programs and its concern for integrity, but by its utter detachment from the outside as an environmental horizon. Radical paranoia entails total seclusion, not from a particular domain (such as a community, a social regime, etc.) but from the outside in general, the environment which imposes vitalism on the living being and makes survival inescapable. To be part of the environment (viz. the economical outside) is to survive. Communication with the outside as an environment is possible only through vitalism. For this reason, openness to the outside — affordable openness that is — constitutes the fundament of vitalism, and vitalism presents living as paranoia. But what is 'living as paranoia'? It is the imposition of survival upon openness. Living-as-paranoia suggests that the outside can be afforded and that one must be open in order to survive, and vice-versa. The possibility of living life as radical exteriority bespeaks of 'living and survival' as paranoia. Yet such paranoia is not consistent with its anticipated telos, which is the safeguarding of survival. The anticipated telos of the paranoia of living (living as paranoia) is defined by its attempt to stave off life as that which is radically exterior and that which cannot be possessed by living or captured by vitalism. Therefore, the paranoia of living or survival is characterized by its duplicity in regard to its vitalistic intention: this paranoia simultaneously secures existence from the exteriority of life and repels life or the source of its vitality because life is radically exterior to the living being and fundamentally detrimental to its vitality. To put it succinctly, the duplicity of living as paranoia is defined by its simultaneous (economical) openness and closure toward life.

Radical paranoia takes the nature of this duplicity to the extreme; it terminates the telos of economical openness and hence strictly positions itself against survival and the general paranoia of living. Radical paranoia emphasizes a departure from the idea of being 'open to the outside'. Closed and folded in upon itself, radical paranoia is a speculative line of schizophrenia that no longer believes in openness to the outside, since for the living being the outside is merely a vitalistic environment. Therefore, radical paranoia marks a withdrawal from the dynamic vigor of vitalism through a detachment of itself from the economical outside (the environment) for and by which survival becomes possible. Such a detachment from the environment reclaims the radical exteriority of the outside for survival and for openness. Consequently, radical paranoia reforges survival as that which can sunder the correlation between the paranoia of living (survival) and economical openness and therefore end its own repression in regard to the unaffordable outside. In radical paranoia, survival is no longer a parasitic (mutually beneficial) symptom of affordability and economical openness, but an event which is disobedient to its vitalistic ambitions.

Large multi-national quarantines for epidemics (influenza, bubonic plague, cholera), with thousands of humans inside, illustrate this departure from the outside. The contagious bodies and aggravated libido — massively intensified in quarantine — of isolated people exhibit the twisted destiny of survival once it is forced to break apart from its ideal openness. Voluntary or not, the repercussions of such seclusion and detachment suggest the subversion of vitalism by the act of survival itself. In departing from its life-supporting environment and in isolation, survival is aggravated by a hollow zeal to recover itself. Yet dispossessed of its supportive environment (the economical outside), in conforming to its vitalistic intention, survival exhausts itself and becomes an emphatic affirmation of the impossibility of life being lived. In this sense, the separation of survival from openness offers survival the opportunity to act strategically on behalf of radical exteriority and its refractory impossibility.

Throughout his entire *oeuvre*, Parsani indicates that the traces of such a separation between survival and economical openness or detachment from the affordable outside can easily be found in the idea of monotheistic despotism and the Aryanistic frenzy for purity: 'It is the strategic insinuation of frantic survival in the absence of openness that makes the justification of monotheism and its Aryanistic germ-cell disquietingly difficult. There is paranoia, for sure, but there is something wrong with this paranoia which is frequently associated with monotheistic zealotry and Aryanistic folly.'

The panorama of radical paranoia also inspired the most nerve-corroding works of Romantic literature in the nineteenth and early twentieth century. These works usually depict lovers who either fantasize about secluding and imprisoning themselves in distant locations far from civilization, or lovers who are actually struck by a disease and forced to isolate themselves. Imprisoned in a remote town or a sealed-off cottage or chateau, they make love with a fevered passion and attempt to survive at all costs. Yet their struggles to preserve love through survival merely quicken their dissolution and unfold survival as an affirmation to impossibility. Here, what connects radical paranoia — as a speculative line of schizophrenia — to love is not so much the idea of a voluntary or involuntary isolation of lovers, but that of love as closure. The openness associated with love is itself a yet stronger closure to the outside world. Between two lovers, openness is initially established to close them upon themselves and from the outside. Love (*philia*) in all its forms entangles openness with closure, and ultimately closure with the radical exteriority of the outside, from which only impossibility actively emanates: the impossibility of being closed as well as the impossibility of affording the outside.

'Sorceress, remember what I told you about the abysmal depths of love: That for every closure there is a twisted love, but more importantly, that for every love there is a twisted closure. Nergal,[41] the god of pestilence and war, encrypts himself with Ereshkigal, the queen of the underworld, in the isolated nether for eternity. When what the Babylonians called draco-spiral (call it an intertwining body of outcast lovers) begins to writhe, convolute and coil, all other lines of movements try to exclude it (as if the whole world is waging war on a couple deliriously in love). But at the same time, the two strains of the draco-spiral entangle progressively, making their disentanglement impossible for external forces. This entanglement, in the middle-eastern occult, is referred to as the Seal of Azhi; it is simultaneously the impossibility of external influence and the movement of the draco-spiral as the blade of impossibility. It is through this helical machinery and its paranoid folds (as if they are never enough) that the draco-spiral forges new warmachines, envenoms its fangs, engenders new instruments of openness, evasion, ambush and counter-attack. Draco-spirals seem to insinuate an obscure connection between love, survival and the outside. There is a survivalist underside to the story of every lover. As lovers intertwine, the attack (either in form of domestication or annihilation) from their environment is escalated. To protect each other, they entangle on deeper levels, surviving with an unparalleled frenzy. Only such survival is able to tolerate and tread the demon-ridden journey to the Outside without evaporating early in the initial phase. Survival plays strange games. Sorceress, let's gather our contagious diseases and make love. Beneath the blighted soil of Tell-Ibrahim ... [the writing becomes unreadable] ... things which never rest ...' At this point, the writing of Dr. Hamid Parsani, palaeopetrologist and once distinguished professor of archeology at Tehran University, becomes illegible – as if he has intentionally scrambled the letters by turning each word into a strange and possibly self-invented rune or cipher, specks of dust only decipherable when stirred by the arid winds and oily wetness of the Middle East.

NOTES

1 صورت زُدایی از ایران باستان: ۹۵۰۰ سال نابودخوانی

2 *Yavišt i-Friyăn*, in *The Book of Ardă Virăf*, Dastur Hoshangji Jamapji Asa, M. Haug and E.W. Vest (ed.), Bombay, 1872.

3 *Naft* or *napht* is the Arabic word for Oil and Petroleum; for an etymological investigation of the word *naft*, see Excursus V: Fog oil, a retrospection on obscurants.

4 Pulp-horror, archaic science fiction and the darker aspects of folklore share a preoccupation with exhumation of or confrontation with ancient super-weapons categorized as Inorganic Demons or xenolithic artifacts. These relics or artifacts are generally depicted in the shape of objects made of inorganic materials (stone, metal, bones, souls, ashes, etc.). Autonomous, sentient and independent of human will, their existence is characterized by their forsaken status, their immemorial slumber and their provocatively exquisite forms. Their autonomy alone marks their outsideness to the human and to its ecology, the planetary biosphere; this is why they are frequently associated with alien life forms and defined by the prefix xeno- (outside). Emerging from one common lineage — that of demons from the possessing class — artifacts or inorganic demons contribute their cryptic outsideness to the human host through a series of generalized but consistent lineaments and symptoms. The mask in Kaneto Shindo's *Onibaba*, the Medallion (the real inorganic demon) unearthed next to the statuette of Pazuzu in William Peter Blatty's *Exorcist*, the cube in Clive Barker's *Hellraiser*, the Frostmourne sword in *Warcraft 3*, the lamp in *Aladdin*, the Turin Shroud and the Chains of Saint Peter (relics in Christianity and other religions), the artifact in *Doom III: the Resurrection of Evil* and, as third-class relics, pieces of fabric or cloth that have touched a reliquary — all these are examples of inorganic

demons which share common peculiarities and vectors of contagion. Artifacts or inorganic demons are usually categorized under three classes: First-class relics or inorganic demons denote the full body of a relic. Second-class relics are the parts and pieces of a disintegrated full relic, which sometimes need to be fused with others in order for their xenolithic properties to be awakened or discovered. The rite of reintegration of second-class relics is called *gathering* or *homecoming*. The gathering usually needs to be accompanied by an external force or a process of purification of the pieces before reunion, or even the geomagnetic arrangement of pieces in a certain configuration. Third-class relics are relics by contamination. They are born out of contact with other relics, mostly of the first class. An inorganic material touching a relic or house of relics (reliquary) can under certain conditions become a third-class relic, less potent than the first two classes yet still contaminative. These three classes of relics or artifacts can be traced to a common demonological framework determined by basic idiosyncrasies and specifications shared by Inorganic Demons:

(*a*) Inorganic demons are parasitic by nature, they themselves give rise to their xenotating existence, and generate their effects out of the human host, whether as an individual, an ethnicity, a society or an entire civilization. Their infiltrating military capacities and systems of possession are fostered by a certain range of human activities obsessed with artifacts, relics and inorganic entities (realism of objects). The fascinations of archeology, religion, capitalism and their hybrids with ancient weaponry and principles of inorganic entities are instances of such activities connected to humans.

(*b*) Inorganic demons induce xeno-excitations in their wielders or human hosts ('Wisdom').

(*c*) Psychosomatic responses or side effects of this Wisdom (wielded ancientness) begin to develop, in the form of incurable afflictions or progressive maladies in their host (commonly known as *the price*). These obscure allergic reactions to inorganic demons are either programmed by the demon-artifact as it embeds itself within the human host (reprogramming the logic of organism), or are produced by the human host in its overreaction to the xenotating existence of the inorganic demon, its unfolding inhumanity and its qualitative state (that is, its inorganicity). Another reason for these cataclysms in the host is the incoming data from the Outside which is inherently overwhelming for the anthropomorphic capacity, and therefore triggers a recoiling mechanism in the host from within, in the form of a flood from without.

(*d*) Once inorganic demons infiltrate an anthropomorphic agency (a silent incursion which is usually affirmed by the human side, whether consciously or not), they embed their inorganic sentience within the human host. The instant this embedding or implantation process is completed, the inorganic demon cannot be plucked out or extricated from the neural, social or even membranous networks of the human host (an individual, a society, an ethnicity or a civilization). Forcing the inorganic demon away without deactivating it imposes fatal irreversible consequences upon the host, at catastrophically rapid rates.

(*e*) The parasitic sentience of inorganic demons is triggered, or the inorganic demon starts to interact with its human host, when the nervous system of the inorganic demon is stimulated. The nervous system of the inorganic demon is in fact a 'spiritual matrix'. As a part of a process of possession or communication with the demonic object, this spiritual matrix must be charged by sufficient external stimuli from the human host. These external stimuli are immaterial, qualitative and can, in a certain sense, be classified as spiritual (examples include faithlessness or faith, doubt, apprehension, piousness, hunger and pain). Upon activation by these spiritual, carnal, sensual or intellectual stimuli, the inorganic demon begins to encroach upon the human host. Since the inorganic demon's sentience is inaccessible to the human, this demonic possession can only suggest the absurdity of human openness or access (intellect and sense). The external stimuli from the human host always play the role of an incentive (*incantare*) or a strategic Call for the Inorganic Demon; or to put it differently, these stimuli feed the soul of the inorganic demon, whose folds move and force the demonic sentience out to the human host, supporting the demon in finding its way in the human sphere.

(*f*) Inorganic demons cannot be destroyed completely, other than by exerting the power of another inorganic demon on them. Such an action inevitably evokes in its turn yet another inorganic demon. This is similar to the theme of the resurgence of evil or demonic return in horror stories. The discovery of an inorganic demon heralds a sequence of ruination for individuals or entire civilizations. Once the inorganic demon itself succumbs to the hibernation mode (known to humans as 'forsaken status'), a civilization or another human host finds the opportunity to rise. The hibernation of the inorganic demon is usually caused by the closure of the demon's spiritual matrix or its readiness for developing to another spiritual phase. In any case, the supposed human sovereignty can only be exerted during the hibernation of the demon-object — but this is not the same as its inexistence. In fact, the rise of a civilization or human host is a symptom of an inorganic demon's hibernation, and is synchronous with the emergence of a new host and the reawakening of the demonic object.

(*g*) Human hosts dispose of inorganic demons not by burial but by returning them to their potential lairs (inorganic weapons as ancient super-weapons vs. treasures in videogames). While inorganic demons belong to the possessing class in reliquology, treasures are from the slave class, much like humans.

5 It is only in divine economy and narration that authorial prophecy works through a chain of command, a logistical plane on which the line of command (the divine interventions) is brought to the zone of action (field of Creation). Belief is validated by the self-correcting prophecies of prophets. There is nothing more devastatingly powerful than the prophet's cry, 'I foretold it.' The world of fulfilled or fulfilling prophecy is a confirmation for the world of Events; it is the correction of all transgressions and deviations from the preordained point: the ground of authority and author. Chaotic prophecy (as in contrast to authorial prophecy) disseminates events in the future and makes present fictions real. Chaotic prophecy infiltrates time as an event-mining machine; it is a backdoor Trojan-virus smuggled into the future. Prophecy is molded by sequential or chronological time, but that does not make its orientation imperatively anabatic or progressive (from present to future);

it can sometimes be katabatic or downward, as in the case of *vaticinium ex eventu* (prophecy after event). In *ex eventu*, prophecy is not only a matter of dismantling or corrupting the future but also of discrediting the hegemonic influence of past over present and future. The prophecies that arose in the wake of September 11, 2001 are examples of the occultization of a political event or the polytical programming of the past. Prophecy after the event undermines the authority of cause over the effect.

6 The simplest way to understand Anglossic Qabalah or AQ is as a continuation of hexadecimal digit formation (for which A = 10, B = 11, through to F = 15), following the standard decimal digits. Anglossic Qabalah (Gematria) proceeds in this fashion up to Z = 35, thus avoiding the redundant mapping of digits or letters by preserving the standard values of the decimal digits 0-9. For example, according to AQ, the word NINE is equal to 78 (N[23]+I[18]+N[23]+E[14]) which is reducible to 15 and consequently 6. If AQ has been extensively used as a numerological system, it is because it evades the mystico-prophetic redundancy — the consequence of too much elaboration and technical details for the uninitiated — of the traditional Kabbalistic systems. AQ corresponds more to the virally propagative, optimizedly effective and efficient elements of economy, communication, military, traffic and mobility. Numbers as corresponding to populations or demographical dynamics rather than axiomatic mathematics. (Hyperstition Laboratory)

7 The square, as Parsani notes, is the geometrical state of establishment, the most surface-friendly and architectural approach to pro-creationist geometry. It translates the universal power of monotheistic God into terrestrial systems of dwelling and accommodation. But the enigma of the monotheistic God, from the Zoroastrian Ahura-Mazda to Islam's Allah, is that he never resides in his Abode, which is usually a cube-like structure (Kaaba in Mecca is the most evident example) as opposed to a Ziggurat whose function is to exhibit the God (thus satiating its exhibitionist paraphilia) at the peak of itself, as in the case of Bel-Marduk. Caves, too, are places for internalizing both the deity and the worshipper.

8 Akht (axt, akhtia) was also called *was-wišabāg* (from Avestan *višāpa*) among his followers, meaning drenched by poison, and sometimes *pouru.mahrka*, the full-death or full of plague, usually used as an appellation for Angra-Mainyu (Ahriman). In Avestan language, Akht as pest chiefly connotes a certain malady which was frequently associated with Ahrimanstic creativity (creativity through reinvention of the body rather than creating it [genesis]), the scarring process and the dismantling of the authority of membranes. In ancient Greek this affliction was called λέπρα and λευκε, or leprosy. In one of the later pre-Islamic Zoroastrian texts entitled *Yaska* we encounter another, more historically credible, account of the Ahkt story. After turning into a renegade and before assembling his influential cult Akht-Yatu, Akht departs his city to learn the language of creation as creativity, which includes not only the creation of a pariah from the system (creation of insurgent, heretic and an outcast) but also the recreation of his body or corpus from the existing material imposed by the divine creation. Traveling with a tramp struck by leprosy for three years, Akht too is infected. He gradually becomes deformed, loses his ears and fingers, and looks 'as old as history' (Yaska, 5:11), even though he has not yet seen the thirty-seventh winter of his life. Parsani suggests that this sudden aging is a

grimly mocking answer to the religious legend of the so-called wise old man. At the end of the third year Akht prays and whispers, 'I have been born from the scars I have imposed upon the body of creation.' Parsani states that Akht was considered a heretic and a mischief-maker both among the cult of the Sun and monotheists. He rebelled openly against the solar economy of the Sun and its cult — but the main reason that he was a heretic — of the worst kind — among Zoroastrian monotheists was because he re-wrote and bastardized their Books in the same way that he re-wrote God's creation on his body: 'For Akht, sorcery was bastardizing the dream of creation without adopting it.' (Hamid Parsani)

9 An originally Persian unit of linear measure equal to 6 kilometers or 3.7 miles.

10 For more details on the three-dotted perversion (Trison), the triangle, and the structure of secret societies or terror-fractals see: *Recent Research in Bible Land: Its Progress and Results*, edited by Herman V. Hilprecht, *Librairie de Pera*, Philadelphia: John D. Wattles & Co., 1896.

11 See *Benvenist: Persian Religion according to the chief Greek Texts*, p. 88; or Plutarch's text on Isis and Osiris; also Pahlavi Sirozag, p. 16, ZXA ed. Dhabhar, p. 242. Eznik of Kolb: *Against the Sects*, translated into French as *Réfutation des différentes sects* by LeVaillant de Florival.

12 Parsani uses the word *bienesh* in the original text, ambiguously meaning vision as visual modality and *bienesh* as philosophy, belief and *weltanschauung*.

13 Mithro-Druj or the betraying Mithra (radical betrayal), among the cult of Manni who rebelled against the oppression of Zoroastrian monotheism and was finally executed after inspiring the majority of heresies in monotheism (see Eznik of Kolb's *Against the Sects*) signifies the highest pragmatic and sacred instance of sorcery. In *Yasna, haat* (section) 61 and *Vendidad, fargard* (chapter) 18, *Zandik* (later *Zandigh*: heretic, betrayer) — the word was originally used to describe Manni as a sorcerous insurgent — is stated to be an equivalent of *Yatumant* (sorcerer) and the most insidious form of sorcery. For more details see: A. Adam, *Texte zum Manichaismus* (= *lietz - manns kleine Texte*... no. 175), p. 97, Berlin: 1969.

14 The term 'affordance' was first coined by American psychologist James Jerome Gibson (based on the works of Ingarden, Brentano, et al.) in the context of his eco-cognitive studies. In Gibson's work 'affordance' referred to the 'possibilities of action' inherent in an object or environment, independent of the individual's ability to recognize these possibilities, but regarded as traits determinable independently of both subjective perception and objective scientific enumeration. Gibson wrote:

> I assume that affordances are not simply phenomenal qualities of subjective experience (tertiary qualities, dynamic and physiognomic properties, etc.). I also assume that they are not simply the physical properties of things as now conceived by physical science. Instead, they are ecological, in the sense that they are properties of the environment relative to an animal. These assumptions are novel, and need to be discussed.

The term is used here in a related, but somewhat expanded sense: We understand affordance as an economic network, distinguished by the connectivity and reciprocity of its elements. Within such a network openness can be exploited as a basis for survival, accommodation, dwelling and regulating communication. The means by which an entity can maintain its dynamic position (in a whole i.e. its mereological 'address') and survive within its environing horizon are determined by a deeply-meshed economic network of interactions, connections and regulative participations, all knitted together by mutual affordabilities between the entity and its environment. The whole can only survive when entities afford each other; every type of openness on a mereologic level occurs as a function of mutual affordability 'between' entities. That is to say, affordance does not exclusively belong to one pole of the economic communication but is distributed between at least two mereologic entities: 'I am open to you as long as I can afford you'; otherwise, either (*a*) you must be repulsed or (*b*) attracted by being regulated and appropriated, (*c*) you must be partly filtered, or (*d*) I must appropriate myself to 'accommodate' you. Therefore, the plane of being open to is intrinsically constructed on the basis of affordance or economical affordability or communication. Under the regime of affordance, openness cannot escape survivalist and economical regulations; it functions as the dynamic capacitator of a Whole. Possibly the most illuminating (if somewhat simple) 'model' of affordance is Aristotle's *Tetrasomia* (Rotation of the Elements), which is elaborated in *Metaphysics*, and for which the rotational movement between elements sustains the refining dynamism of the whole. Each phase of rotation is based on dynamic *metrons* (measures, scales) and affordance (here, economical openness or mutual affordability) between elements. Elements are open to each other either diametrically or diagonally, but they can never entirely overlap or radically communicate with each other; they require a intermediate state to form rotational nexuses and to maintain the overall Wholeness. These intermediary states are only valid in a particular location of the whole rotational panorama; although they provide the system with a propulsive *polemikos* or a cyclic dynamism, they only function locally (as a result of the elements' affordability to each other — based upon mutual common qualities — and at the same time, to the whole system).

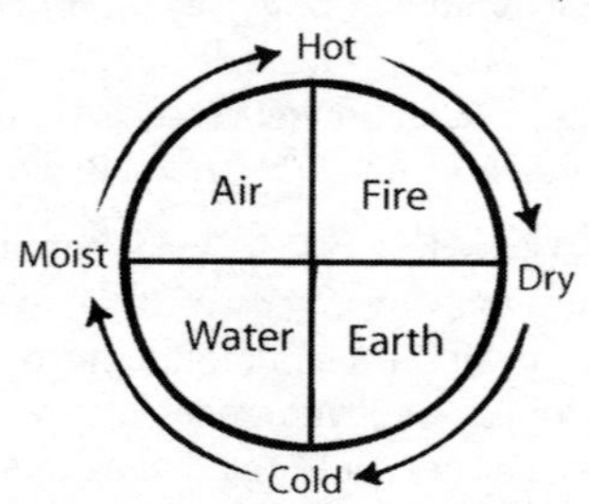

Tetrasomia or the Aristotelian model of affordance

For example, Earth and Water need *Menstruum* (living mud) to communicate. This living mud is a communicational entity, but also a dynamic boundary which transforms or appropriates the earth and water before opening them to each other; it can only work locally between earth and water and not at any other location in the model of *Tetrasomia*. The whole uses these economical communications to consolidate itself and to thereby afford Life (to survive).

15 Woven spaces are the manifest frameworks of two governing heads — trellis and taxis. While the woven lattice structure or trellis composes a net to confine what

is accommodated, taxis imposes an obligatory impetus towards a dynamism and an activity upon that which is captured by trellis. The former denotes economical distribution of a supportive structure and the latter suggests a dynamism which is closed at one end, bound to the economical grid of the trellis or the ground. The horizontal hierarchy of trellis is a flexible grid mobilized by the woven suppleness. Dynamism in woven spaces is necessarily restricted and pre-modified because dynamic lines are bound to the static line, that is to say, from one end they are restrained by the closed side of the woven framework. Woven spaces practice the logic of a creation whose infinity has been determined prior to the created world and its building process. Therefore in woven spaces, the possibilities of created beings, their synthesis and differentiation, do not produce an infinity, but rather exhaust the pre-existing infinity of the world.

16 Mereotopology is the theory of topological relationships between parts and boundaries. On Mereotopology see: Barry Smith, 'Mereotopology: a theory of parts and boundaries', in *Data & Knowledge Engineering*, Volume 20, Issue 3 (November 1996), Elsevier Science Publishers, pp. 287-303.

17 The Polish philosopher Roman Witold Ingarden, in his works focused on ontology (written after breaking from Husserl's phenomenology through a critique of transcendental idealism) expounds on the problem of openness and affordance, suggesting that closure (or modulated /economical openness) is a priority for open systems, and for analyzing niches as power projection zones and inhibitors of unwanted interactions and communications. The openness of the niche protects itself from what makes it open, by opening itself to what makes it closed. Only through such an openness can the existential moments be afforded, so that modes of Being are then able to emerge.

18 Macro-pores allow rapid water infiltration and, importantly, similar rapid drainage that makes air quickly re-enter the root zone. The destruction of macro pores or massive pore collapse and subsequent propagation of smaller (micro-) pores causes water to be held tightly in the soil, increasing the incidence of anaerobic conditions (aeration is impeded), waterlogging, run-off, impotent cultivation and erosion. The increase in density of the soil mass and decrease in soil porosity mean plant roots are often physically impeded by compact subsoil layers and lack of available nutrients and/or water. Nemat-space and its porosity anomalies can trigger desertification as well as the emergence of a soggy Earth.

19 The rat, as a unit of ungrounding or polytical diffusion, is characterized by the liquidating and detrimental power of its anatomical mobility. The hegemony of the head is constantly undermined by the swerving motion of the tail which continues on a sinuous pattern of divergence and swerving motion. When moving in a pack, the rat spends three quarters of its time in the air (the ferocity of the leap). To move, the rat applies a muscular tension or coiling force to the body as the initiating force; this force then is channeled to the hind part (hind feet, posterior ricochet). The rat continues the process by pushing off with the hind part, then landing on the front part (forefeet, anterior ricochet), bringing forward the hind part and pushing off again. In one beat (pulse), the anterior ricochet hits the ground, followed quickly by the posterior ricochet, which pushes the rat into the air, and three beats later the anterior ricochet hits the ground again. The re-coiler is coiled when the hind

part is brought forward, making leaps very conspicuous. The entire mobility and distribution of forces in the rat produces a seismic wave which gains an infiltrative and probing quality (smart catastrophe) that claws away everything in its way. Although the entire body of the rat is an effective arrangement and distribution of epidemic tools, the rat engineers its holey space or ratholes using its extremum part (Trupanon), boring out new spaces for its havoc. Nothing is more politically obscure than the interplay between the head and the tail in a rat.

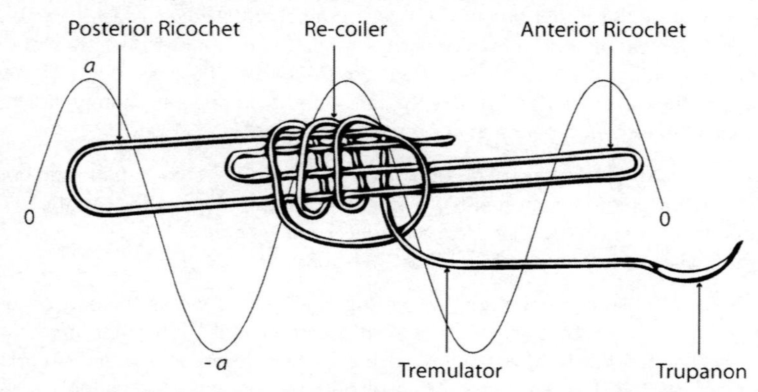

20 One should not forget that the corresponding formations of Wahhabism and the Saudi State are rooted in desert-nomadism, and the dissemination of Wahhabism in Arabia dates back to the discovery of the vast oil fields in Rub al-Khalie and emergence of the first commercial oil fields (1938-1946). These oil fields attracted the desert-nomads by replacing their nomadic trade systems with the State's narrow influxes of money from oil revenues. From the beginning of oil commercialization in Arabia, the desert nomads had to pay their taxes (*zakat*) in money rather than in kind. To say the least, oil played the role of a vehicle, distributing the influence of Wahhabism into every corner of the Arabian Peninsula.

21 Ahmad Ibn Fazlan's diary is held in the 'Astan-e Ghods-e Razavi' library, Iran.

22 The discovered depiction of Ahriman (or Angra-Mainyu) pictures him as a demon with horns pointing to each other, a strangely distorted face and bizarrely huge ears which give him a ridiculous look that reflects his distinctive method of creation: whenever Ahriman desires to spawn a legion, he turns his own body into a bloody slaughterhouse of creation (an ironic answer to the hygienic pro-creationist method of his brother, Ahura-Mazda); he cuts a part of his body, lacerates an organ, rips a piece of his flesh, mutilates his body, and from that piece of flesh (*nasu*) he creates a cult, a pest-legion, a religion devoted to himself. In time, the wounds are cured, but the scars remain. Everywhere a machinery of fibrosis (excessive scarring) and mal-healing is at work, hordes of collagen molecules are integrating in the regions of malefaction (criminal creation), new meat over wounds but always in the form of cicatrix. For Ahriman, there is always more meat than is needed to heal the existing wounds, a healing process gone awry. The fact that meat or the substance of the body belongs to God or Ahura-Mazda makes Ahriman's technique for causing excessive scarring creative on two levels; firstly, the remodification of meat as a corrupting substance or a debasing element of wastage which cannot

be recycled by the system; and secondly the transformation of the healing process into a perversion and disease in itself. Ahriman presents himself as a traumatic creationist or the creator of perverted creation. Note that in *Defacing the Ancient Persia: 9500 Years Call for Destruction*, Hamid Parsani ruminates at great length on the mechanisms — particularly the belief-dynamics — involved in the rise of cults and secret societies, from the Deav-Yasna cults in Persia to Mithraistic cults and Christianity, finding a common genus among all cults. In all cults and religions, Parsani notices a manifest and fundamental connection between the emergence of the cult (wether as a religion or an ideological multitude) and a meatological self-immolation (*im-mola-re*: to sprinkle with sacrificial meal). The latter means serving one's self as an ambrosial (*ambrotos*: immortal) meal for the emerging followers, cult or population, as in the case of Christianity and the Eucharistic tradition which symbolizes the renewal and self-sacrificing origins of Christianity. Parsani suggests that this principle evolves directly from Zurvan and Angra-Mainyu. The voluntary self-sacrifice of a Dominus, an archon, a founder or a superior entity transgresses the authoritative and dominative principles of sacrifice (The question of sacrifice — leaving aside the feral animation of excess in sacrifice — is that of knowing how a gift as an affirmative force becomes a force of domination and ascendancy) as it kills or mutilates itself so as to strategically undergo an infelicitous flight. This descent from God or a leader to a sacrificial meal (immolation), Parsani suggests, is in fact a strategic step toward new power formations which are fathomless, even to gods. As the dominus or leader sacrifices itself into pieces of meat for feeding the crowd, it is greeted by mortal beings and foul minorities instead of gods or daimons. However, in spite of their radical inaptitude, these wretched or mortal beings (the cult) have the power of propagating the body of the sacrificed deity or leader. Like particles of a wind carrying an epidemic disease, these mortal or expendable beings spread the corpse of the god in the form of an epidemic. Such wretched crowds are capable of generating contagious winds crossing continents in the course of weeks if not days. And at the same time, they stomp upon the full body of most monolithic empires to burn down the very being of them. This is the very essence of revolution as flood. The rise of new religions and cults, Parsani suggests, follows such epidemic patterns starting with the deliberate self-immolation of a god or a leader. On the other hand, these intoxicated crowds build up population disparities, mutual exclusions, and internecine frictions caused by the emerging autonomy of the crowd and the delusion of utilizing or controlling it. Parsani identifies these so-called malfunctions or internal fissions as a 'democratic holocaust': I am the outburst of a population. If a deity or a founder sacrifices itself, it is because in this sacrifice, the butchery of self is equal to pregnancy, that is to say, being pregnant of many. These self-immolating deities and leaders attest to the fact that there is no site of heterogeneous creation and radical participation other than that of a population. And one only becomes a population or a legion by paying the highest price, which is self-mutilation and sacrifice; turning oneself into a meal for the poor, the wretched and the insignificant. Only this way does such a bloody sacrifice become the guarantee of a sweeping epidemic diffusion. 'The Ahrimanistic sacrifice,' writes Parsani, 'aims not only at the disintegration of the self into a population, but also at the inclusion of thousands of humans as blood-dripping chunks of the self.'

23 For further details see Jahangir Cooverjee Coyajee's rich essay on Azhies or Dragons

(esp. Zahak or Dahak and Tiamat) and the Apocalyptic Literature in his book, *Cults and Legends of Ancient Iran and China* (Bombay, 1936).

24 Islamic war machines are adept engineers of Islamic Apocalypticism, or *Ghiamat* (*Qiyamah*), where the military survival of each war machine must be consumed in the monopolistic all-erasing Desert of God. The word *Qiyamah* means awakening, rising and even rebellion.

25 The original word in the text is *taslim* meaning submission, sharing a common root with the word Islam.

26 Avestan feminine noun whose meaning is shrouded in controversy; corresponding to a verbal root in Indic, *druh*: *dru, hyati*, meaning to Blacken; also Lie, Deceit, Error, Falsehood and Illusory Order. Druj- is a female etheric spirit or GAS, the source of all pollutions and cosmic plagues, the Mother of Abominations: a feminine epidemic through which Ahriman works and breeds his pest-legion by self-sacrificial rituals or self-buggery. Druj- is not a deity, it is a nocturnal tide delineated by its inexhaustible openness to diffuse and pervade everything. The most sinister contamination of Druj- in Zoroastrian monotheistic culture is *Druj-Nasu* or the demon of corpses, the necro-fiend, as the *Vendidad* suggests. Druj is epidemically addressed as *Druj-*, an affix, ready to infest and contaminate.

27 *Khrafstra(s)* means vermin or pest-legion in the Pahlavi language of ancient Persia. They are things which move turbulently in swarms and packs: wolves, ants, locusts, flies, upsurges of thoughts, and body scavengers, all epidemically-moving things, things that never rest. According to *Vendidad* Khrafstra(s) are the engineers of the unclean earth (the *Drujaskan*); they are the vectors of matter into darkness and chthonic depth. Khrafstra(s) are the strategic lines of openness to the Mother of Abominations (Druj), machines which snatch bodies and take them to holes, corners and inaccessible recesses, spreading and exhuming them, that is to say, making them epidemically untraceable and pestilent to the State.

28 Such cacophonetic anomalies (corresponding with the Solar Rattle) have been distilled in the (ancient Persian) Pahlavi language. Emerging from an Aramaic-Semitic germ-cell, in the Pahlavi language up to four or even five (vowelless) consonant letters can be placed together consecutively in a word, resulting in extremely complex phonetic micro-systems and vocal sounds.

> The Pahlavi language is an endless howl, the droning silence of all middle-eastern languages. On the one hand it possesses limitless potentialities for occult insurgencies and the rise of minorities both within the linguistic space and on a concrete level; on the other hand, it was the official language of the theocratic state of the Zoroastrian Sassanids. At this point, we should ask if Zoroastrianism as the ovum of monotheism was really a despotic gravitational core or an infected body which consciously and stealthily disintegrated itself to minorities as it grew — and still grows within other monotheistic threads — vertically: A systematic strategy to give birth to a global minority conflagration that turns the Earth to a smoldering worm-cast.
>
> Why should we imagine that middle-eastern languages with vowelless alphabets produce human sounds, or that humans speaking in these languages remain human? (Hamid Parsani, *Defacing the Ancient Persia*)

29 The solar wind is continuously emitted by the Sun; it is a plasma that flows outwards into space and which carries with it the heliomagnetic field.

30 A pattern of flow whose dynamic lines move outward (in a fan pattern) away from a central axis that is oriented parallel to the general direction of the flow.

31 In the Avestan language of ancient Persia, each action or bodily organ is associated with two words or verbs – one on the side of Ahriman (Angra-Mainyu) and the other on the side of Ahura-Mazda. The word for creation and giving birth is either *zan* (*frā.thwares*) for the monotheistic creation of Ahura-Mazda (focusing on consolidation and architectonic construction) or the word *hav* (*frā.karet*) for the Ahrimanistic creation. The word *hav* (to give birth to) is the Ahrimanistic twin of the word *zan* for creation; it simultaneously means carving, etching, cooking, boiling, sodomy, frying, mangling and grating; suggesting that Ahriman is a kitchen culprit whose world view is culinary materialism.

32 Transformation of three dots (cosmic unlocalizability or trisonomic degeneration) to four dots (architectonic order or divine wholeness):

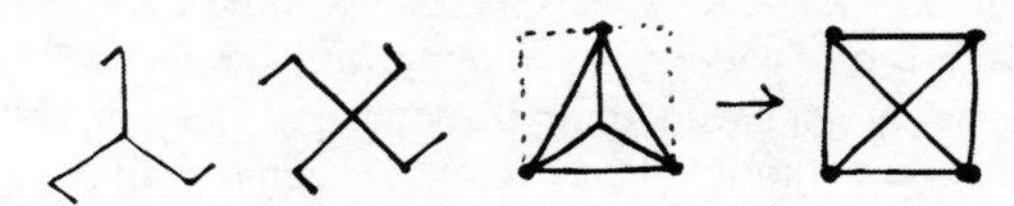

33 *Metron* (Greek origin), which is found etymologically encrypted in English words such as Dimension (from *dimetiri*: measure out), meter, etc. Keeping well in mind the famous doctrine of Pythagoras, 'Man is the metron of everything' (*pantôn chrematôn metron anthrôpos*), metron can be translated as scale, measure, standard, and value. According to Sextus Empiricus, metron expresses criterion (scale, measure) but Heraclitus and Sophocles saw it as certifying dominance, a domination over something. Therefore, metron indicates that both measures and dimensions inter-connect with power, judgement and reasoning. The critique of metron explains how dimensions (namely metron) bring power into effect, mobilizing and propagating it.

34 In the final chapter of *Defacing the Ancient Persia*, Parsani adverts to a strange Mesopotamian myth where the Sun god cheerfully kills himself in order drastically to descend, not to the surface of the earth but into its bowels. The myth of the Sun god immolating himself and descending to the nethermost regions of the earth later becomes an implicitly recurring image, as Parsani sees in the self-entombment of the Sun god, the tarry or the nigrescent traces of petroleum and oil. For Parsani, oil as helio-nigredo or the black corpse of the Sun marks the rediscovery of mythology as the political geophilosophy vacillating between economy and the ethics of openness. 'The unconscious of the world consummates in the death of God. The Earth's dream of this death is realized as the nigredo with which terrestrial dreams are so drenched that they occasionally ooze it out.' (Hamid Parsani) Note that nigredo is essentially a state where depth and darkness fully overlap; it is at the same time an affirmation of the ground and its subterranean potencies. In alchemy, nigredo is the blackening state which is usually associated with putrefaction and decay – the corpse or, in the Avestan language, *nasu*. One of the thematic images which conveys nigredo is a body butchered open or cut into pieces. According to

Parsani, the Mesopotamian myth of the Sun god immolating or turning himself into a meal (*im-molare*) is 'esotericism gone awry':

> The insurrection of the earth against the Sun, or in other words, the Tellurian ethics of radical openness, presents a twisted model of alchemy in which chemistry and its ideas are essentially katabatic (depthwise or downward) and hence pro-ground. The alchemical unbinding of the earth as an insurgent entity, and the manifest ethics of radical openness, are contingent upon the full binding of the 'death of God'. In alchemy, perfection relies upon escaping from gravity and transcendence — from nigredo (blackness) to albedo (whiteness) and finally moving toward rubedo (redness). In the death of God or the self-immolation of the Sun god, chemical vectors start from rubedo or the redness of the Sun, and descend into nigredo or chthonic blackness.

35 'Tactics is the skill of handling troops in war, and strategy is the art of bringing forces to the battlefield' (Field Marshal Earl Wavell). Strategy is outside of the battlefield, where tactics are employed — and yet it is inside the war.

36 Chthonic, from *Khthon* and *Khthoniê* (She-beneath-the-Earth), relates to the nether earth (katabasis). It chiefly denotes the underworld, namely, the Plutonic facets of the earth as a lair for gods who affirm the katabatic (descent, collapse, downward) aspects of emergence through the Earth or the chemistry of the ground.

37 Avatar is the mask of becoming chthonic, from the Sanskrit *avatara-* meaning descent, a deliberate dive to katabatic (downward or depthwise) realms in order to fulfill a mission. As the result of the descent into worldly planes, the avatar is connected to incarnation.

38 Parsani refers to the *Vendidad* as the most appalling book mankind has ever written and practically followed. See *Vandidad* (*Vi.daevo.dâta*) translated from Pahlavi by Hashem Razi, Sokhan Publisher.

Vi: anti-
Daevo: female Daiva (referring to Druj, the Mother of Abominations)
Dâta: from *Dâtik* (Law, divine laws in particular)

39 In Arabic language, the word Sharia means path or course. In Islam, Sharia constitutes the Islamic canonical law which is applied to both the public and private aspects of life.

40 The Shahada is the Muslim declaration of belief. By willingly reciting the Shahada, one accepts Islam and becomes Muslim.

41 According to Parsani, Nergal is the epitome of a fallen sun god, 'a subtopian sun god whose descent embeds love in the butchershop of openness, intertwines solar craze with nether rot and a profound tellurian betrayal against the Sun. Nergal is simultaneously associated with the underworld and a typical high-altar for the Sun (a mound called Tell-Ibrahim in the city of Kuthah). He is in love with Ereshkigal the queen of the underworld while at the same time, he is the manifestation of a rotten sun. Nergal is the point where everything — opposite or disparate — overlaps. Insurrection against heliocentrism, openness, the desert and the weird wetness of petrol are all twisted together by the defacing love of Nergal for the lady of the

netherworld.' Throughout Parsani's writings, there are numerous references to Nergal. For example, a passage from his notebook reads:

> The demons of war are usually depicted with two heads: One enters the battle, the other plots and counterplots. There are writing monsters which write with two heads, front and back, facing forward and facing away. Nergal as an arch-demon of both war and pestilence has two faces, two attached heads looking in different directions: One is heading forward and the other is heading backward. The front face is the face of a lion (corresponding with his origin Zurvan Akarna), signifying the onrush of war in the direction of his arrow which makes him similar to Sagittarius. The rear head which always heads backward is a combination of a jackal, a rabid dog (one of the Tiamat's warriors) and a hyena (identical to Pazuzu's face). This strange head is exclusive to the gods and demons of pestilence and famine. As the Lion-Nergal rushes to slaughter, devour and ruin places with War, the other head looks backward and spreads disease, desolation and sorrow on the ravaged places with its cacophonic howl, ensuring that no one and nothing survives the unlife of war.

GLOSSARY

( )hole complex (AQ = 227)

( )hole complex reinvents the Earth as a machine to speed the return of the Old Ones; Its convolution irrevocably impairs the repressive Wholeness of the Earth, giving it innumerable opportunities to give rise to what Parsani calls 'Tellurian Insurgency' or 'A Revolution against the Sun in favor of the Earth's Insider' (H. Parsani, *Defacing the Ancient Persia: 9500 Years Call for Destruction*).

Abstract Lover (AQ=273)

A concrete entity directly differentiating from 'NAPALM-obsession' or 'napht dissociative syndrome'. Usually associated with love as incomplete burning, chromatic distortion of all colors to pink and involuntary submission to the desert.

Az (AQ=45)

Not only the ABYZmal cartography of all pestilential entities of the Earth (Ab to yZ) but also *Āz*, the daughter of Ahriman. Az is the vampiristic precursor of patriphagic entities.

Babylon (AQ=134)

The former gate to the Outside in the Middle East (32° 32′ 11″N, 44° 25′ 15″E).

Bacterial Archeology (AQ=351)

Invigorating the germ-infested chemistry of the Earth by turning it to ( )hole complex; unearthing the planetary sphere as an irreducible complexity of reciprocal links between terrestrial epidemics and cosmic chemistries or anonymous materials.

Begotten (AQ=160)

It takes time for philosophers to learn that the death of God is not what they presuppose or anticipate (A movie directed by E. Elias Merhige, 1991).

Cthulhuoid Ethics (AQ=329)

A polytical ethics necessary for replacing or undermining existing planetary politico-economical and religious systems. Cthulhuoid Ethics is essential for accelerating the emergence and encounter with the radical Outside. Cthulhuoid Ethics can be characterized by the question 'what happens next?' when it is posed by the other side or the radical outsider rather than the human and its faculties.

Deleuze and Guattari (AQ=356)

'I want to donate some blood, some philosophers' blood.'

Delta Force Mythos (AQ=323)

Pertinent to War on Terror and descent — or katabasis (as in Homer's *Odyssey*) — into the Mesopotamian gravity of horror in order to pursue the doctrine of Evil-againist-Evil. Delta Force Mythos is narrated as an archeological enterprise for exhuming ancient warmachines and petropolitical undercurrents, hence it is militarization in terms of archeology and geophilosophy. Delta Force Mythos is the epic of the Middle East as a sentient entity, a narrative which is mobilized by western techno-capitalist warmachines.

Desert (AQ=125)

The Xerodrome (or the dry-singularity of the Earth) as both the all-erasing monopoly of the monotheistic God and the Tellurian Omega or the plane of base-participation with the cosmic pandemonium (Dust, Sun and the Tellurian Insider). Desert signifies a militant horizontality or a treacherous plane of consistency — in a Deleuze-Guattarian sense — between monotheistic apocalypticism and Tellurian Insurgency against the Sun (god). As a dry-singularity, desert is usually linked to unheard-of wet elements and thus brings about the possibility of revolutionary but anomalous (and perhaps weird) cosmogenesis or world-building processes.

Destrudo (AQ=178)

As a subjective hedonistic impulse, anthropomorphic desire is a capitalist mode of slavery bound to libido or the appropriated side of openness (i.e. being open to) which avoids the radical Outside in favor of an affordable version of exteriority. Yet for every economically affordable desire and liberalist openness, the amount of subversive destruction imposed by the radical Outside from within and without is called Destrudo. Destrudo is the resistance of the radical outside to 'being afforded' or economical openness.

Double-numbering (AQ=297)

The structure of a draco-spiral is spontaneously maintained by a numeric affirmation between two opposing poles. This treacherous communication between opposite poles results in disorientation rather than proclivity toward formation of a superior entity or power (number, force, point of reference or institution); aka Double-dealing or Trisonomic Parasitism. See Trison and Heresy-engineering.

3 ←10→ 7 ←9→ 2

Draco-spiralism (AQ=283)

The Sumero-Babylonian diagram of a particular dynamism, the slitheriness of the Mother of Abominations. Draco-spiralism does not prioritize curves over straight lines or segments.

Draco-spiralism delineates anomalous participations between two dynamic lines and their autonomous transformation into a weapon, a vector capable of invoking the outside. The Draco-spiral is a line whose orientation in space is no longer a direction. The difference between the 'double-helix or the participative line of escape' and the ancient irreverent model of draco-spiralism is that despite its collective dynamism, the double helix always presupposes a vertical line of flight or an Axis Mundi whose mission is to escape the force of gravity associated with a regime. For this reason, the double-helix must rectify its dynamism according to the force of gravity, that is to say, the limitation. Yet draco-spiralism knows nothing of such dynamic disciplines associated with escaping from a regime by overcoming its gravity.

Engineering the corpse of solidus (AQ=597)

Although solidus, or the ground, with its gravity, integrity and tyrannical wholeness is ultimately restrictive, the eradication of the ground also results in the rise of another hegemonic regime — the regime of death and destruction. The proper response to both self-centered authorities (construction and destruction) is to engineer the corpse of solidus, or to formulate a pragmatics of ungrounding rather than introducing solidus or the ground to nihil. Ungrounding is involved with discovering or unearthing a chemically-degenerating underside to the ground. The corpse is the sublime manifestation of putrefaction. Putrefaction or cosmogenesis through decay heralds the advent of chemistry. Reclaim the Earth through the corpse of solidus.

Erathication (AQ=231)

An earth-biodegrading force equal to the constant Ω, required for terminally folding the complex assemblage of the Earth in order to reduce its wholeness to $^{p}/_{0}$ $(={}^{p}/_{a})$, where p is power and a is the representative of the supportive surface or the ground, which here is infinitely close to zero.

Exhumation vs. Architecture (EXHUMATION AQ=220)

It is the foreordination of all architectures to ultimately be exhumed, given that the etymological resource of exhumation is ungrounding (*ex* + *humus*). Exhumation defiles creation, facilitates its divergence from the divine wholeness by resurrecting beings prematurely and not according to the chronological pattern of creation (to be born, to die, to be dead, to be resurrected by the Divine). Exhumation undermines the order of strata; it invokes or resurrects beings before their time comes. In this sense, exhumation is the invocation of the ground's potencies before they are actualized by and for the ground. Exhumation grasps potencies according to something other than the *status quo* or actualities of the ground, hence whatever it generates or unearths is marked by inappropriateness — that is, being fundamentally off-time and off-beat. The act of exhumation is associated both with Tellurian Insurgency (degenerating the wholeness of the earth) and with time sorcery (unlocking timescales which cannot be synchronized by chronological time). Since ungrounding or exhumation incapacitates the consolidating power of the ground, the earth cannot be narrated by its outer surface any longer but only by its plot holes, vermicular traces of exhumation. Therefore, exhumation prepares the earth to fully emerge as a ( )hole complex.

Feedback Spirals (AQ=266)

Fundamental to double-dealing or double-numbering, feedback spirals maintain a self-reinforcing movement by mobilizing Trisons. Correspondingly, they have a triangular vortical structure. Feedback spirals effectuate the communication of Trisons in a polytical formation; they maintain the autonomy of power formations in the Middle East by engineering a field of interaction between Trisons. Feedback spirals are Tiamaterialistic counterparts of the divine creator. See Double-numbering, Trison and Tiamaterialism.

Fog of War (AQ=163)

According to the model of War-as-a-machine, the Fog of War is constituted of particles (terminally disintegrated warmachines) forming volumes of mist (*diaspora*) and clouds (condensed clusters) in order to spread war over everything and everywhere unnoticed. While the Fog of War shuts down all modes of cognition, it provides warmachines with an illusory but concrete vision based upon which the interactions between warmachines are divided into three planes: the planes of (a) command (b) logistics and (c) tactics. These tactical planes lead warmachines to the conclusion that war is the consequence of their interactions and not the other way around. The subterfuge of Fog of War lies in dissimulating or distorting the radical obscurity of war. The strategy of Fog of War is to blind warmachines in regard to the quiddity of War itself. The Fog of War conceals the immanence of war, stirring up warmachines with the illusion that they are independent entities.

GAS (AQ=54)

The meltdown plague; the terminal multiplicity. The grasping of GAS by anthropomorphic agencies presupposes the shutdown of all modes of perception, or complete blindness.

Gog-Magog Axis (AQ=233)

The horizontal transport of tellurian properties to the Xerodrome.

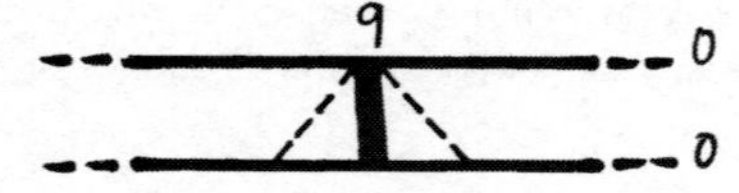

Grasping war as a machine (AQ=396)

In the wake of the social, economical and military disintegration associated with ferocious monotheistic warmachines (those belonging to a guerilla-state) and the autonomy of Islamic Apocalypticism as a pandemic event, the Deleuze-Guattarian model of war as a consequence of conflicting warmachines is problematic. The model of war-as-a-machine operates according to the autonomy of war; it grasps war as a machine with all machinic (but not mechanistic) parts. For this reason, the model of war-as-a-machine evades discourses which institutionalize war as a social, economical and political object within the anthropocentric judicial system. War has an economy, a politics, a socius and a population of its own.

Heresy-engineering (AQ=340)

Double betrayal or Trison lies at the base of all heretical activities. Following the numeric communications between the vertices of a triangle in Cross of Akht — nine-sum pairing (inconclusiveness) on one side and ten-sum pairing (the divine perfectionism) on the other — heresy-engineering can be formulated in terms of double-numbering. As the most efficient way to undermine any manifestation of hegemony, double-numbering forms a simultaneous communication and participation with two planes, entities or events to extract and pragmatically deduce synergistically opposing sides. See Trison.

Hypercamouflage (AQ=291)

If camouflage utilizes a partial overlap between two or multiple entities, hypercamouflage is the complete overlap and coincidence between two or more entities. In this terminal camouflage, the mere survival of a predator threatens the existence of the prey, even if the predator never engages the prey. Hypercamouflage is associated with the warrior under Taqiyya or the Thing (John Carpenter's movie); it can be defined as a total withdrawal from the perception of friends and a dissolution into the enemy: the rebirth of a new and obscure foe.

Inauthenticity (AQ=304)

Complicity with anonymous materials.

Kata- (AQ=69)

A Greek prefix denoting the movement through depth (downward, or more accurately, depthwise). Kata- delineates the cartographies of the Abyss; hence it poses the question of depth (what/where is depth?) according to the contamination of solid and void or the double heresy of depth towards the surface and hole. Outlining the depthwise vector of descent, kata- is a vector of collapse passing through the ambiguity of solid and void and the impossibility of their wholeness or consolidation. Bound to its resources (solid and void), kata- has no creationist ambition; its enthusiasm aims at ceaselessly descending or more precisely eventuating depth which betrays solid and void equally, by affirming both at the same time. Consequently, Kata- is dynamically associated with Trison or double-betrayal. A katabatic or depth-wise movement effectuates the trisonomic mobilization of earth. Kata- practices flight, all through the bottomless economy of depth or the Abyss.

Mesopotamia (AQ=226)

A mesophilic sentient entity associated with the desertifying underside of Tellurian dynamics, persisting in middle-eastern regions of the Earth's body since 2300 BC.

Mother of Abominations (AQ=412)

The engineer of vulvo-cosmic singularities.

Mutant Dead God (AQ=246)

The Death of God as an event was a theo-mythical invention of Philosophy. Mutant Dead God, however, begins where philosophy left off: nothing is more malignantly fertile than the carrion of God.

Nasu (AQ=91)

Necrotized matter or the elixir of alchemy. According to chthonic sorcery, nasu or black matter is a terrestrial pylon to the earth as the space of inconclusive or infinite chemistry. Nasu marks the unfolding cosmogenesis of decaying entities (political systems, organizations, beings, etc.) Associated with decay, nasu defines the processes or materials required for the most polytical and schizotrategic sorceries, which are profoundly exoteric yet pro-ground.

Occultural Meltdown (AQ=394)

Known as Assyrian Syndrome, and caused by the voluntary simulation of occultural entities and other strategic weapons by the State in order to ward off the avatars of the Outside. Although the State perforates its boundaries to enhance itself as an open system (capable of domesticating the outsiders), it will eventually be butchered open by the Outside. The collapse of the state is the result of the complicity between the avatars of the outside and the state's strategic weapons, one side of which is always unbound. Occultural Meltdown is synchronous to the rise of Middle East as an intensive zone of warfare and epidemics.

Pazuzu (AQ=165)

The demonogrammatic schematics of Mesopotamian occult-traffic and population dynamics demarcated by the duplexation of flight (overfly value=2), extra-organizing redundancy, dimensional creep and a maximum aptitude for possession. Unlike spatial migration, dimensional creep generates epidemic sprawling; pazuzoid structures such as the Wheel of Pestilence coincide with famine, Tellurian blight and locust blitz.

Petropolitics (AQ=294)

The cartography of oil as an omnipresent entity narrating the dynamics of Earth. According to Hamid Parsani, oil is the undercurrent of all narrations. Petropolitics can be studied to pursue the emergence of Xerodrome as a flat climax to the Pipeline Odyssey or a world whose narrative is mainly conducted through and by oil.

Pink (AQ=86)

Pink comes after Red.

Polytics (AQ=191)

Political gradients characterized by their multiplicative pragmatics and multifocal operational cutting edges. Polytics are pragmatic extensions of schizotrategies. Polytics is involved in operationalizing events, turning everything into strategies. See Schizotrategy.

Puppetry (AQ=209)

In string theory, puppetry is the traffic zone of data between possessor and the possessed, the puppeteer and the puppet.

Rats (AQ=94)

The process of ungrounding at any level (from epidemic incursion to deterritorialization) is performed by acephalic units known as rats. Composed of three main functions — flight, displacement and tail-function — rats can concentrate a disintegrating force whose intensity is capable of surpassing the ground's intensity of consolidation. In rats the political correlation between the head and the tail is not only twisted but also obscure.

Relics (AQ=120)

Technocapitalist and Islamic obsession with exhuming artifacts and ancient super-weapons. Trace the fascination with exhuming relics in pop culture, especially video games. In Bacterial Archeology, a relic is an operative of exhumation which confounds the chronological time by connecting Now with abyssal time scales. See Exhumation vs. Architecture.

Schizotrategy (AQ=293)

Strategies for being opened (by), not being open (to). When it comes to affordability, desiring the outside is a repression. However, in terms of schizotrategy, any instrument of repression encompasses a path to the outside, albeit involuntarily or indirectly. Schizotrategies always emerge out of anomalous (in the sense of the positioning and arrangement between two or multiple entities, not their unconventionality) participations with the Outside.

Tell (AQ=85)

Arabic word for mound. Mounds are tellurian entities which implicitly connect archeology (a hostile, recondite or unfathomable ancientness) with the horror of the Insider (as in the case of *The Thing*, *The Exorcist*) through an exhumation. It is highly questionable whether pulp-horror stories which do not use the word 'mound' can be said to be genuine.

Tellurian Blasphemy (AQ=375)

Demonogrammatical decoding of the Earth's body. Tellurian blasphemy produces an unwholesome narrative which presents the Earth as an immense ungrounding machinery. In terms of Tellurian blasphemy, 'think terrestrially' is not politically conservative. To riddle the Earth with holes (of plot, of function, of structure and wholeness) is to think terrestrially.

Telluro-magnetic Apostasism (AQ=532)

Polytics of the Earth's Insider whose operational cutting-edge is mobilized by the solar hegemony and obstinate politics of the Sun. By parasitizing the solar tyranny, the earth's Insider assembles a religion whose form necessarily corresponds to the repression of the solar excess (the logic of strata, conservation and molecular order in the magnetosphere) but whose function is to align the full body of the earth with the Sun in an anomalous participation or pact which dismantles the hegemony of the solar empire and develops new power formations external to the all-consuming sovereignty of the Sun.

The Axis of Evil-against-Evil (AQ=490)

Economically compacted as the Axis of Evil; an experimental project on occultural weaponry and strategic weapons which finally led to the total annihilation of the Assyrian civilization as well as its neighbor empires. The Axis of Evil-against-Evil can be numogrammatically grasped as a decagon which folds on a horizontal extension through a series of numeric twining and synergetic oppositions. The Cross of Akht is a diagram and a prognometer for the Axis of Evil-against-Evil in regard to Tellurian dynamics.

The Druj letterature (AQ=393)

A symbol, a composite number or a dynamic numeric axis in the guise of the number 888, growing two claws to the left and right resembling meat hooks. First starting semi-flat and then convoluting, the Druj letterature begins to unfold as an open Mobius band. Stretching to West and East and with two appendages pointing to each other, it diagrams the demonographic features of Ahriman's horns twisting to each other and Zahak's snake-ridden shoulder pointing to West and East (The Gog-Magog Axis). The Druj letterature simulates the calligraphic curvature of the word Allah in Arabic by spiraling at two ends in the most obscure way.

The Outside (AQ=216)

The radical outside is delineated not by distance or region but by its exterior functionality of activity. The outside is impossible in terms of its possess-ability, yet it can be grasped by its affect space or openness, through which survival (as a restriction or affordability towards total openness) is both existentially possible and functionally impossible; aka (Un)Life.

The Rise of Middle East (AQ=368)

Synchronous to the Assyrian occultural meltdown. The Rise of the Middle East denotes the initial emergence of the Middle East as a living and sentient entity in a literal and non-metaphorical sense; terminologically encapsulated by Parsani as Tiamaterialism.

The-Thing-without-Genesis (AQ=483)

aka The Sacred

Trison (AQ=149)

A dynamic numeric alliance which can be summarized as 'one for Nine' (whole-degenerating inconclusiveness) and 'nine for One' (divine perfectionism) from opposite sides. Trison is the numeric field of all radical insurgencies, heresies and subversions. Addressed as *drēm* or the infinite impurity of Druj or Mother of Abominations in Zoroastrian scriptures, it can be geometrically morphed as a triangle or three dots. Trison is the horizontal cross-section of a draco-spiral; or in other words, the draco-spiral, as the surgical line of openness, is the continuity of a numeric line of strategy with a triangular twist. Trison's efficiency and effectively of operation is fed into the draco-spiral's dynamism. According to Hamid Parsani, middle-eastern power formations, radical insurgencies and belief-dynamics are developed and driven by polytical units named Trison which interact with each other through what can be numero-structurally mapped as Feedback Spirals. See Heresy-engineering, Polytics, Feed-back Spirals.

Videogame narration (AQ=353)

Narration based on shifting populations (numeric dynamism) rather than perspectives or social and individual dispositions. Videogame narration can be diversified into two general configurations:

'The Thing' which is visualized in third person player, first person shooter, role-playing (RPG) adventure games. The plane of the Thing is characterize by lack of any cognition about the self despite total control from first or third person perspectives, dissociative fugue syndrome, mirroring and the total immersion of player or reader into the Ludicosm or the game-space.

'Horde (populating quantities)' is visualized in Real Time Strategy (RTS), Skirmish, Simulation games. The plane of the Horde is distinguished by elements such as the expendability of entities, cross-fertilization of perspectives through constant shifts between populations (from one race to another in realtime strategy games), seeing from Above, swarm-power, omnipresence or being as a crowd, the typical ravage class in Dungeons and Dragons style games, LFM message in online games (looking for More [corresponding to crowd-engineering]). Videogames enforce the logic of nightmares through their ludicosm.

Xeno-communication (AQ=361)

Communications or data traffic based on the plane of being opened (by) instead of being open (to).

Xerodrome (AQ=198)

The foundation of all monotheistic religions or systems with religious platforms is the Desert. If Monotheism has developed a fetishistic outrage against idols, it is because monotheism must eventually sprawl over a desert whose contours (idols) are all leveled to 0 and whose formlines (worshipping terrains) are incorporated to 1 and only 1. Although such a desert contemplates (in Aristotelian sense) the Divine, its function is to build a solid surface (corresponding to its directional inflexibility and consistency) or a plane of immanence for communicating with the Sun. Accordingly, the omega desert bridges the Tellurian Insider with the Sun. Xerodrome is both a religious and a tellurian ascension to the utmost manifestation of blasphemy by subverting the essence of monotheistic absolutism.

Lightning Source UK Ltd.
Milton Keynes UK
UKOW031602040412

190178UK00011B/47/P